Managerial
Analysis

IRWIN SERIES IN QUANTITATIVE ANALYSIS FOR BUSINESS

CONSULTING EDITOR   ROBERT B. FETTER   *Yale University*

Managerial
Analysis

ROBERT E. SCHELLENBERGER
Chairman, Department of Management
Southern Illinois University

1969

 Richard D. Irwin, Inc., Homewood, Illinois
Irwin-Dorsey Limited, Georgetown, Ontario

First Printing, April, 1969

Second Printing, August, 1970

Library of Congress Catalog Card No. 69–17165

Printed in the United States of America

Dedicated to those whose inspiration, service, and assistance made this book possible, and especially to the University of Maryland, Department of Business Administration (Dr. C. A. Taff, Chairman), which, through a reduced teaching load and other assistance, made its completion possible.

Preface

This text is intended to describe and explain the process, tools, models, and evaluation of *managerial analysis*. Managerial analysis is a process which uses any tools, models, and evaluation techniques appropriate to assist the manager to make decisions. Many friends and readers have suggested that management science or operations research, or possibly systems analysis, or even systems engineering could have been substituted for managerial analysis. The reason such suggestions have been made is that each of these fields, although identified by separate professional associations, subscribe to a similar underlying analytical process which is very frequently aimed at managerial considerations. This book has no desire to coin a new phrase or begin a new professional association but merely recognizes what appears to be a convergence toward a widely accepted underlying process. It is true that the examples and models presented are more closely allied with those frequently used by practitioneers in management science/operations research.

This book is intended as an introductory text for either advanced undergraduates or first-year graduate students. While it assumes only two years of high school algebra or one semester of college algebra, obviously, the stronger the mathematics preparation, the easier to concentrate on the heart of the subject. This author finds that it is not formal mathematics which make the better student but the ability to visualize mathematical functions and see them in more than an abstract light. This text has been classroom tested at the University of Maryland in both a graduate and undergraduate introductory course in quantitative analysis.

The book is divided into six sections. Section One explains what managerial analysis is, how it is conducted, what analytical approaches are used in its conduct, and a historical perspective. Section Two discusses the process of managerial analysis in detail. Since Sections One, Two, and Six are the sections which emphasize analysis for management as a meaningful process, they are essential to the book.

Section Three includes a discussion of mathematical and statistical tools used in managerial analysis. The author normally assigns part of this material as outside reading because it is a review of material covered in other courses. All of the author's students (both graduate and undergraduate) have had topics covered in the two chapters on statistics (8 and 9). However, the author may lecture the undergraduate students on the concepts of regression analysis. The author's graduate students have had at least mathematics through differential calculus; thus, Chapters 10 and

11 are used for review. Often the author's undergraduate students have had only one year of finite mathematics. Consequently, the author assigns only sections 1–10 and 13 of Chapter 10 as a normal part of the course. Since part of Chapter 12 requires differential calculus, those sections of Chapter 12 are omitted for the undergraduate students.

Section Four presents a fairly thorough introduction to models of common processes. These are the models and solution methods of frequently found situations in the business environment. The models include: classical economic optimization models, inventory models, queuing and other probabilistic models, models of linear systems (linear programming), network models (including PERT), and decision theory (payoff matrix) models. Section Five presents an introduction to models of complex systems. This section deals with approaches to modeling complex systems which may not be amenable to models of common processes. This section covers systems analysis and simulations.

Since the book covers a great deal of material, most instructors will omit some chapters or sections of chapters from Chapters 12 through 20, depending upon the desires of the instructor. However, Chapters 13, 15, and 18 are essential to the book and should always be covered.

Section Six covers the topic of validity. It attempts to give the prospective user of the tools and models a basis upon which to evaluate either his own analysis or someone else's analysis. This section is essential to the book and should always be covered.

The author is grateful to all of the individuals who played a part in the development of this text. The students who endured the preliminary drafts and made many helpful suggestions are due a special note of thanks. I would like to acknowledge my friends and associates whose reviews and suggestions also added materially to whatever merit the text deserves. These associates include William Bassin, Kirby Madden, and Stanley Hilley. A special thanks to Rudolph Lamone who has taught three different classes using preliminary versions of the text and offered unmeasurable assistance in its development. Thanks are also due to my typist, Mrs. Margaret Warren, who has endured patiently the many revisions. A very special thanks to Dr. Charles Taff, chairman of the Department of Business Administration of the University of Maryland, who has provided reduced teaching loads, and secretarial and editorial assistance without which this manuscript would have been impossible. Further thanks are due my graduate students and graduate assistants who made direct contributions. These include Frank Budnick, Richard O'Niell, Ronald Lessing, and A. K. Sherman. Thanks are also due Mrs. Barney, Mrs. Dillard, and Lynda Weber, secretaries.

Thanks are also due those authors from whose books I have taught. These books have had a significant impact on the development of my approach to presenting certain materials. Those books which have had the greatest impact on my approach are R. C. Meier and S. H. Archer, *An Introduction to Mathematics for Business Analysis* (New York: McGraw-Hill Book Co., Inc., 1960); R. I. Levin and C. A. Kirkpatrick, *Quantitative Approaches to Management* (New York: McGraw-Hill Book Co., Inc., 1965); and N. S. Loomba, *Linear Programming: An Introductory Analysis* (New York: McGraw-Hill Book Co., Inc., 1964).

Thanks are also due Professor Robert Fetter, editor of this series, whose editorial assistance has also contributed greatly. Finally the patient understanding of my wife Linda must be recognized as essential to the successful completion of this manuscript.

February, 1969   ROBERT E. SCHELLENBERGER

Table of contents

or difference of functions. Rule 5: Derivative of a power of a function. Rule 5(a): Derivative of independent variable to a power. Rule 6: Derivative of the quotient of two functions. Rule 6(a): Derivative of a constant divided by the independent variable to a power. XVI. Equation forms: *Second-degree equations. Third-degree equations. Other common forms.*

SECTION FOUR: Models of common processes

additional considerations: *Alternate optima. Optimum solution with unused capacity.* IV. Assumptions of the linear program model: *Linearity in the objective function. Products are identified by processing and raw material requirements. Linearity in the constraints. Assumption of static time period. Assumptions of certainty. Requirements of the linear programming model.* V. The value of added capacity. VI. The case with more than two constraints. VII. A minimization problem. VIII. Other graphical interpretations.

ities planning model: *The existing facility. The alternatives. Calculations for an additional employee. Calculations in using overtime. Using the driver to help unload. Improving unloading methods. Expansion of facilities. Summary of findings. Accuracy of findings. Mixed alternatives. Additional considerations.*

SECTION SIX: Validity

Epilogue

Index

Prologue

The subject of this book is a process which aids the decision maker to make decisions. As with any process, it becomes operational when the activities which allow it to function are specified. Thus the book must deal with a description of the process as well as the ingredients which make it operational. It is to be expected that readers have differing interests in managerial analysis. Some students (probably most) will be interested in using the analysis conducted by others or in applying only a very elementary form of analysis. This group must develop an ability to evaluate the work of others. A thorough understanding of the underlying process is the first requisite to judging and using analysis. A brilliant and sophisticated analysis which maximizes the wrong objective is worse than an elementary analysis which promotes the fulfillment of the right objective.

The student who aspires to be an analyst must, more than the manager, understand both the process of analysis and guidelines for evaluating any analysis. He cannot rely upon the manager as the final judge of his work. The analyst should be judged on how close the actual results come to the predicted results. The models presented here are in a form which is elementary enough that the student can stand back and separate the mechanics from the purpose. The author hopes this introduction will serve continually to remind the student to separate the mechanics from the purpose.

As managers in all forms of organization rely more and more upon analysis conducted by highly specialized analysts, the decision maker needs to be assured that the correct analytical process was used. The author frequently lectures to top and middle management about the models used in managerial analysis. Often the mathematical and symbolic complexities serve to distract attention from evaluating the application in managerial terms. This text prepares the present or future manager to use managerial analysis in two ways: (1) It provides a thorough discussion of the underlying process and guidelines for evaluating any analysis, and (2) it provides an elementary discussion of many of the models which have found wide applicability. If at least the elementary form of a number of models is understood, the mathematical and symbolic complexities are less apt to distract the manager. At the same time, such an understanding provides a basis for conducting elementary analysis.

1

With this discussion in mind, let us briefly outline the structure of the book. Managerial analysis can be a very extensive and elaborate undertaking. The Department of Defense has spent millions of dollars on a single analysis. On the other hand, a few minutes with pencil and paper may constitute managerial analysis. Regardless of this diversity, the underlying process is the same. There are numerous steps and substeps which must be understood. Thus, Section One (Chapters 1–3) provides a general overview and brief explanation of the steps and tools used in managerial analysis. Then in Section Two (Chapters 4–7) the steps in the process are presented in more detail. In these chapters, essential terminology and more operational considerations are presented. This book distinguishes between tools and models of common processes.

Sections Three, Four, and Five are divided according to this distinction. This can be illustrated by the situation facing a salesman who must decide which route to take to service a particular customer. The following table shows a sample of times it has taken him to travel the distance to the customer ($\overline{X}$ is the arithmetic mean, and R is the range):

Day of week	Route	Time (in minutes)	Statistical summary
Monday through Friday	A	62, 55, 60, 65, 58, 60	$\overline{X} = 60$ $R = 10$
Monday through Friday	B	53, 59, 54, 57, 51, 56	$\overline{X} = 55$ $R = 8$
Saturday and Sunday	A	58, 66, 72, 64	$\overline{X} = 65$ $R = 14$
Saturday and Sunday	B	72, 80, 60, 68	$\overline{X} = 70$ $R = 20$

The purpose of the analysis is to give the salesman a basis for deciding which route to take. The choice is obvious, but this example provides an excellent vehicle for distinguishing between tools and models. The tool of statistics has been used to gather the data and prepare the statistical summary. The situation for Monday through Friday is represented by the following symbolic model:

If route A is taken, $\overline{X} = 60, R = 10$.
If route B is taken, $\overline{X} = 55, R = 8$.

Given this model, we use mathematical tools to assure that the objective is fulfilled. Thus the salesman should take route B on Monday through Friday. The model represents the situation. However, the tool of statistics has been used to provide quantified values so that the representation is concrete, not abstract. Furthermore, the tool of mathematics is used to provide a solution to the model. Fortunately, some models recur frequently, and we may study a group of models called models of common processes.

Section Three presents mathematical and statistical tools. Section Four introduces models of common processes. Section Five discusses methods of modeling complex processes. Section Six presents a scheme for evaluating any analysis.

Many students will find the material covered in this book difficult. A recognition that mathematics is not abstract but a means of representing real and interesting phenomena is the first step to reducing the difficulty of this book. Mathematical representation is an efficient and exact way of aiding in the solution of very real and interesting managerial problems. Mathematics itself is not difficult if you follow its logic. When it becomes an exercise in rote memorization, it loses its meaning.

A second step to reducing the difficulty is to remember that many chapters use the same basic problem as a reference point throughout. This is especially true in Chapters 13, 15, and 16 and for sections of Chapter 18. Thus the reader is urged to have a pencil and paper at his side on which the basic problem data is written. When a calculation is made or a result is shown, the reader is urged to verify it by conducting the calculation. Generally, it is wise first to read the entire chapter rapidly to identify the chapter plan. Then the reader should try to follow the calculations on the second reading. Finally, the reader should review the chapter in order to see it as a whole.

A third step is to remember that you may wish to refer to other sources. Other sources may approach the matter in a slightly different fashion and complement the text. The author recommends group study sessions, but *only* after a thorough preparation on the part of all participants.

The final step in reducing the difficulty is to remember that much of the material is cumulative. Background deficiencies require individual effort. The student who has forgotten algebra is at an initial disadvantage. For those who have been away from mathematics for some time, an excellent review is provided by the following paperback: Clifford H. Springer, Robert E. Herlihy, and Robert I. Beggs, *Basic Mathematics.*[1]

---

[1] Homewood, Ill.: Richard D. Irwin, Inc., 1965.

SECTION ONE

An overview

1

What is managerial analysis?

Managerial analysis is an analytical process which aids or assists the manager to make decisions. In order to understand what it is, one must first discuss its relationship to the manager and then its basic characteristics.

I. MANAGERIAL ANALYSIS AND MANAGEMENT

All management activity falls under four prime activities: (1) setting organizational goals and objectives, (2) developing plans to fulfill these objectives, (3) combining the human and physical resources so that the objectives are met, and (4) monitoring the results to see that the desired objectives are met. These activities can only be effectively carried out with the aid of objective analysis. The analytical approaches used to aid management in the conduct of these activities are extensive and varied. Since each of these activities of management is carried out by making decisions, the supporting analytical tools are oriented toward decision making.

Since managerial analysis is an analytical process which aids the manager to make decisions, one must always remember that it is undertaken for the manager. Consequently, it must be carried out with the proper interplay between manager and analyst.

II. THE CHARACTERISTICS OF MANAGERIAL ANALYSIS

Managerial analysis includes all analysis designed to aid managerial decisions as long as the following conditions are met: (1) the analysis recognizes organizational goals; (2) the analysis explicitly recognizes

7

relationships between relevant variables (sometimes called a model); (3) the recommended course of action is explicit, verifiable, and independently reproducible; and (4) the analysis uses an adaptation of the scientific method.

It may be said that managerial analysis is the systematic investigation, compilation, manipulation, and presentation of information to a decision maker in order to aid the decision-making process.

It can be seen that managerial analysis is basically a *process* rather than a specific tool or model. It may be accomplished using specific analytical tools and models, but the end product is more than the analytical tools and models which have been used in its conduct.

The process must recognize organizational goals because it exists to aid managerial decisions. Further, one cannot demonstrate the superiority of any course of action without such information. Recognition of organization goals requires the ability to empathize with the managerial viewpoint.

The analysis must explicitly recognize relationships between relevant variables in order to arrive at a verifiable rationale for recommending one course of action instead of another. Consequently, one must have an understanding of the process of evolving a model to represent the environment. Then one must be equipped to take the model and evolve the best solution in light of the objectives. Since the environment of concern to the manager is viewed as a system, the analyst must have the ability to view the organization as a system. Further, one must have an understanding of the objectives of the organization before the information is gathered or structured.

The process uses an adaptation of the scientific method in order to avoid bias and make complete disclosure in the final recommendations. A significant contribution to decision making can be made only if the analyst looks objectively at the validity of his recommended course of action in light of the many possibilities for error. This includes evaluating the validity of the model, the data that went into the model, and the conclusions drawn. Later, it will be pointed out that quantitative analysis (which requires an optimal solution) and systems analysis (which requires the best solution among a set of alternative solutions) are both valid subjects of managerial analysis. The adaptation of the scientific method requires *systematic investigation* of the totality or system with which the analyst is concerned. This systematic approach allows the analyst to be sure that he has considered all of the factors necessary to make the ultimate decision. When some factors are ignored, they must be clearly identified, and the conclusions drawn must clearly state that those factors have been ignored.

Finally, the necessity for explicitness, verifiability, and independent reproduction requires that the recommended course of action be verifiable and reproducible; i.e., given a knowledge of the inputs, assumptions, and analytical technique, any managerial analyst should be independently able to reach the same conclusion.

III. OBJECTIVITY AND QUANTIFICATION IN MANAGERIAL ANALYSIS

Managerial analysis reduces the possibility of contamination of the final conclusion because of inherent or subjective bias. This reduction occurs because of the adaptation of the scientific method and because the individual responsible for the conduct of managerial analysis is not acting in the role of the decision maker. If he is the decision maker, he is wearing a different hat. He should be capable of having a complete and clear understanding of the assumptions, the data, and the investigation that went into the making of the conclusions drawn by the managerial analyst.

Managerial analysis also requires quantification. One cannot proceed from the knowledge of relationships to managerial action via a demonstrable and systematic method without at least an elementary form of quantification. Elementary quantification may take the form of recognizing the presence or absence of an attribute.

IV. THREE PHASES IN THE PROCESS OF MANAGERIAL ANALYSIS

Managerial analysis can be divided into three distinct phases. The first phase lays the groundwork for the actual analysis. As with any building activity, a weak foundation cannot be compensated for by any amount of frills. The second phase is the action phase, which results in a suggested decision. Most introductory texts concentrate on this phase. The final phase is the evaluation phase, which investigates the validity of the recommended course of action. The following pages will discuss the general components of each phase.

Phase 1: Establishing objectives of the organization, purpose of the analysis, and a general understanding of the environment

The process of managerial analysis begins with an overall look at the organization and the subunit for which the manager is responsible. This step requires the establishment of the complete set of objectives of the organization and the subunit. The process of establishing these objectives is one that need not be repeated for every analysis that is conducted. Later the problems of identifying *measurable* objectives that contribute to nonquantitative objectives will be discussed. One should now merely understand that there is a hierarchy of objectives. Thus a firm that has established an objective of a quality product has established this objective as a means of fulfilling its other more basic objectives, such as profit maximization.

The second step involves investigating the environment, identifying the problem, and determining the general nature of the environment. This begins with background preparation in order to identify and understand the major elements in the environment. Some aspects of this basic awareness will carry over from one analysis to another. At this point the analyst establishes an *exact* statement of the purpose of the analysis. In some instances, it will become evident that the preliminary statement of purpose, whatever its source, will be in error.

Any manager operates in the real world, but the decision he makes must be from an abstraction of that real world. The real world of the manager can be described as a complex of interrelated components, i.e., a system. In referring to business firms, one commonly uses the terms *inventory system, distribution system, production system*, etc. Also, one often speaks of the *economic system*, of which each industry is a subsystem. The exact systems to be identified and the relevant components depend upon the purpose of the analysis and the familiarity of the analyst with the environment. Since the analyst is studying the general characteristics of the environment in order to develop an abstract representation of the system called a *model*, it is useful to identify the system and subsystems at this point.

After investigating the environment and identifying the objectives, the analyst must establish the specific criteria to be used to measure the extent to which the objective is fulfilled. If he finds a number of objectives that may be measured, he must establish some basis of measurement that will make them comparable. If, for example, he has an objective of minimizing costs, the opportunity costs should be reduced to dollar terms so that they can also be included with direct or operating costs.

Phase 2:   Developing relationships, the model, and a solution

The analyst must now depict the system he is dealing with and identify the possible course of action that might be taken. This phase may be approached in two fashions, each of a different degree of sophistication. Consequently, it becomes somewhat difficult specifically to identify and recognize the steps in this segment of the process of managerial analysis. All of the tools, methodologies, or techniques that may be applied to managerial analysis portray the environment as a model; consequently, before proceeding further, one must understand the meaning of the term *model*.

A model is a physical or symbolic representation of the relevant aspects of the reality or system with which one is concerned. Implied in the concept of a model is a series of connected and identifiable relationships that essentially demonstrate the following proposition: If this action, then this result.

A model is a means of portraying the system or reality of concern to the decision maker. Models may be quite different in the way in which they describe things and in their sophistication.

Quantitative analysis. A term to describe one methodology used to conduct this phase of managerial analysis is *quantitative analysis*. According to Ira Horowitz:

> The quantitative analyst is a problem solver who attempts to formulate the decision problem in mathematical terms. This mathematical formulation or model is particularly useful in that it explicitly requires (1) specification of a comprehensive list of the variables that are considered relevant to the problem at hand and (2) specific hypotheses concerning the interrelationships of these variables. The model then can be used to help the decision maker make the choice that is most compatible with his goals as well as to determine which of these variables are the most important ones to consider in arriving at an appropriate decision.[1]

The term *quantitative analysis* will serve to identify one approach to developing the model and a solution (i.e., phase 2). This approach relies upon the concept of a mathematical model, whereas the alternative approach is consistent with a looser description of the system and is consequently called *systems analysis*. The basic methodology for quantitative analysis involves, first, the development of a pure or complete model in symbolic terms. This begins with an identification of or hypothesis about all of the relevant variables that exist within the environment. This involves identifying the dependent and independent variables in the environment and then hypothesizing the specific nature of those relationships. Note that one of the prime reasons for identifying all of the relevant variables is that some information may be nonexistent; consequently, the analyst may later ignore or make assumptions about those relationships. This step then publicizes the fact that the analyst has ignored or made assumptions about potentially relevant relationships.

Having developed a pure model, the analyst gathers all relevant data and develops the interrelationships by mathematical or statistical methods of inference. The next step is to develop the final or modified model in mathematical terms.

Systems analysis. Another approach used to develop a model and a solution is systems analysis. In systems analysis the method of representation may be looser than in quantitative analysis. The representation is still symbolic, although the explicitness and the demonstrability of the relationships need not be as evident or explicit as they are for quantitative

---

[1] Ira Horowitz, *Quantitative Business Analysis* (New York: McGraw-Hill Book Co., Inc., 1965), p. 3.

analysis. A *mathematical* model may or may not be used in systems analysis, although some form of model must be used. The central requirement of systems analysis is the identification of the alternative means by which the objectives of the organization may be accomplished. According to Hitch, systems analysis focuses upon (1) the objectives, (2) the set of relationships between objectives, (3) the alternative means of accomplishing the objective, (4) the environment, and (5) the resources required by each of the alternatives, including their costs.[2] Once the relevant courses of actions are identified, the costs attached to each must be netted against the benefits to determine the best of the investigated courses of action. Identification of costs and benefits requires only the ability to determine such costs and benefits, and does not require a knowledge of the variables which cause a given outcome. However, a knowledge of the causal variables is desirable. Systems analysis bases its approach in part on the principle of bounded rationality. The principle of bounded rationality recognizes that one can deal only with those factors he can comprehend at one time. Consequently, bounds are placed on the environment with which one deals. Systems analysis via the principle of bounded rationality recognizes that there is a limitation on what one can do via the explicit process of mathematical modeling.

One element that distinguishes quantitative analysis from systems analysis relates to the concern with the alternative means by which the objective may be accomplished. In quantitative analysis the identification of the alternative courses of action is implicit because construction of the mathematical model results in the number of alternatives being very large or infinite, whereas in systems analysis there is a limited number of alternative courses of action. Thus, via the systems analysis approach, one says: What is the contribution toward the objective of taking this alternative? Via the quantitative analysis approach, you say: Out of all the range of possible alternatives, what is the alternative which optimally fulfills the objective? A description of this type may impute a great deal of desirability to quantitative analysis and less desirability to systems analysis. However, this is not necessarily the case. Quantitative analysis requires an explicit mathematical model; and as such, it may demand a greater degree of abstraction from reality than systems analysis.

Systems analysis may be applied on a very local (limited) scale or on a global (extensive) scale. A lease-or-buy decision is an example of a local systems analysis. In military parlance, one may equate the distinction between global and local systems analysis with the difference between tactics and strategy. Finding the best method of capturing the hill to the front is a tactical maneuver, whereas an overall plan of action which

---

[2] J. Hitch, "Analysis for Air Force Decisions," in E. S. Quade (ed.), *Analysis for Military Decisions* (Chicago: Rand McNally & Co., 1964), pp. 13–14.

requires a series of tactical maneuvers for its fulfillment is a strategy. If a production engineer is planning a completely new production plant, the scope of the analysis must be much more extensive than when he is planning how to use an existing plant most effectively. Given the expected use of the plant, systems analysis will allow him to choose between the limited number of machines he can purchase for each phase of the production cycle. Then, given the machines, he may use quantitative analysis (via an economic order quantity model) to decide upon inventories. Because some of the stages in designing the production plant do not encompass an explicit mathematical model, this total approach is systems analysis despite the fact that quantitative analysis was used in the intermediate stages.

At this point a recommended course of action must be chosen. The solution procedure which yields a recommended course of action depends upon the approach used, i.e., quantitative analysis or systems analysis. It is necessary that the analysis explicitly include a statement of the assumptions of the analysis.

Phase 3: Evaluation and implementation considerations

Having recommended a solution, the analyst must attempt to prepare information on the validity of the recommended solution, i.e., the degree of confidence a manager may have in the recommended solution. This involves determination of the validity of the data inputs which are the basis for specifying the relationships between variables. The extent to which the data are valid or invalid is dependent upon the accuracy of the information, which is in turn dependent upon the ability to measure and record the data properly. This text includes a chapter (Chapter 6) on data collection and measurement that attempts to explore further questions essential to data validity. One must look extensively at the validity of the model by observing the extent to which the model portrays all of the relevant events within the environment and the extent to which the assumptions have glossed over relevant considerations in the environment. A technique called *sensitivity analysis* may be used to investigate the sensitivity of the solution to potential errors in the data or model. In short, one must present to the decision maker extensive information for judging the validity of the recommended course of action.

Also, managerial analysis must be concerned with how the recommendations resulting from the analysis may be implemented, the effect implementation may have on the organization, and the extent to which the analyst has reflected the (potential) effect of implementation within the system. Further, the managerial analyst should present the decision maker with a procedure which can compensate for changes in the environment that may affect the recommended solution.

Following is a summary of the steps in the process of managerial analysis:

STEPS IN THE PROCESS OF MANAGERIAL ANALYSIS

Phase 1: *Establish objectives of the organization, purpose of the analysis, and general characterization of the environment.*
   a) Establish organizational objectives.
   b) Obtain a general understanding of the environment.
   c) Identify measurable criteria to be fulfilled.

Phase 2: *Develop the model and a solution.*

Systems analysis	*Quantitative analysis*
a) Identify alternative courses of action.	a) Develop pure or complete model.
b) Identify costs of each relevant alternative.	b) Measure interrelationships between variables (includes data gathering).
c) Identify benefits of each relevant alternative	c) Develop final model.
d) Derive a solution.	d) Derive a solution.

Phase 3: *Determine and maintain validity.*
   a) Ascertain data validity.
   b) Ascertain model validity.
   c) Ascertain dynamic effects of implementation.

V. MAJOR ANALYTICAL APPROACHES USED FOR MANAGERIAL ANALYSIS

Certain general analytical tools such as operations research, management science, statistical analysis, economic analysis, econometrics, systems analysis, and others are used as approaches to managerial analysis.

None of these approaches are necessarily managerial analysis. For example, the scientist is validly concerned with the nature of relationships in the environment as an end in itself. The use of hypothesis testing in statistical analysis is simply a means of establishing the nature of relationships in the environment. So, for that particular purpose, statistical analysis is not a part of managerial analysis. The second chapter will explain these approaches and their use in managerial analysis.

VI. AN EXAMPLE OF MANAGERIAL ANALYSIS

Let us assume that the Asphalt Paving Company, a road construction company, has requested assistance in improving its operations. The president has attended a conference which discussed some of the possible applications of managerial analysis to road construction companies. One such application dealt with minimizing the costs of delivering asphalt to the construction site. Asphalt is mixed at a semipermanent site and delivered to the construction site. The company has two mixing plants and is currently working at three construction sites. Table 1–1 shows the capacity (in truckloads) of each mixing plant and the number of truckloads required at each site.

Table 1–1

Sites	Mixing plant A	Mixing plant B	Needs for asphalt (in truckloads)
1			15
2			20
3			15
Capacity (in truckloads)	30	20	

Given this information, the analyst must probe deeper to find out what further information is necessary. He must first establish the primary objectives of the organization. Assume that the objectives of the Asphalt Paving Company are purely economic, i.e., to maximize long-run profits.

Objectives may be much more complex, involving all manner of psychologically laden ingredients such as maintaining the present ownership and/or management. However, the knowledge or tool necessary to maximize long-run profits does not exist, let alone maximizing added objectives; consequently, this single objective is complicated enough to merit further attention. An example of the difficulty of maximizing long-run profits is the fact that one does not know the impact on future sales of a given price; accordingly, one frequently ignores the impact of any given price on future sales, thus maximizing short-run profits.

Since the objective of long-run profit maximization cannot be measured, the analyst must identify a measurable objective which the manager agrees will lead to fulfillment of the basic objective. Let us assume that the overall company objective will be met by the measurable criterion of minimizing costs of delivering asphalt to the construction site. It is important to recognize that minimizing cost of delivering asphalt is the basis on which we are going to judge the final solution, and it is used because it can be measured. The point is that the analysis will minimize short-run dollar costs, on the assumption that this will yield long-run maximum profits. Thus the step of establishing the criterion translates the broad objectives into something measurable. The result of specifying this criterion is that all variables must now be expressed in this common form, i.e., dollars.

The step of obtaining a general understanding of the environment has been partially fulfilled by the information previously provided. The analyst then must ask the question: What factors affect costs of delivering asphalt to the construction site? Obviously, the number of trucks going from plant *A* to sites 1, 2, and 3, as well as the number of trucks going from plant *B* to sites 1, 2, and 3, will affect the cost. Further, the cost of going from any plant to any site is dependent upon such things as (1) miles from plant to site, (2) traffic density or congestion, (3) number of traffic lights, (4) frequency of accidents, (5) cost of the truck and driver, and (6) other items which each reader may add. The analyst must sort out this confusing array of information.

Figure 1–1

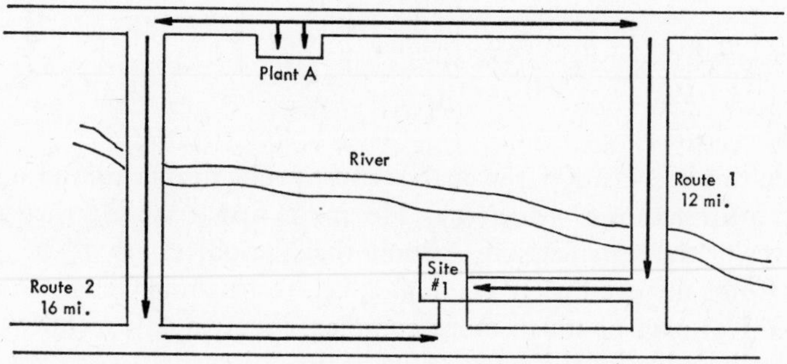

Although not necessarily obvious, this problem can be broken into two distinct parts. This is true because if we know the route which results in the least delivery cost from each plant to each site, we may use a separate analysis to find how many truckloads should be taken from each plant to each site. Let us first develop the analysis to find the route which minimizes the cost to deliver one truck from an imaginary plant to an imaginary site. Since there are three sites and two plants, six separate analyses are necessary for the first part.

The situation is shown in Figure 1–1. The reader will note that route 1 is the shorter of the two alternative routes. We could assume that the greater the distance traveled, the greater the total costs. However, choosing route 1 does not assure minimum delivery expense, because this assumption may not be true.

Let us begin phase 2 by now postulating that costs are composed of the following four elements:

1. Vehicle operating costs (including such things as gas and vehicular repair).
2. Accident or safety costs (i.e., on one route the probability and cost of an accident may be higher than on another).
3. Direct driver costs (the cost of the driver's time).
4. Indirect costs (the impact of each route on future efficiency). If the driver works less efficiently unloading the truck because of the trauma of one route versus another, then all savings may be illusory.

Now the analyst must ascertain the nature of the above-postulated relationships. Assume that the investigation shows that the following formula predicts vehicle operating costs:

(1)   Vehicle operating costs $= 0.05M + 0.02T + 0.005S$

where:

M = Distance traveled (in miles)
T = Travel time (in minutes)
S = Number of stops for stoplights, etc.

Further, assume as given the data shown in Table 1–2. Therefore, operating costs for route 1 are calculated by finding the travel time, total number of stops, and distance traveled for each route (see Figure 1–2). These are now presented:

	Route 1	Route 2
Total travel time (in minutes)	50.4	48.0
Distance (in miles)	12.0	16.0
Stops	45.8	46.8

Substituting in formula 1 gives:

Vehicle operating costs $= 0.05(12) + 0.02(50.4) + 0.005(45.8) = 1.862$
Vehicle operating costs $= 0.05(16) + 0.02(48) + 0.005(46.8) = 1.994$

Further, assume that the truck driver's time and other direct expenses are 5 cents per minute and that indirect costs cannot be calculated. Thus, direct driver costs are $50.4(0.05)$, or \$2.52, for route 1; and $48(0.05)$, or \$2.40, for route 2.

Safety costs are $7.2(0.02) + 4.8(0.01)$, or 19.2 cents, for route 1; and $16(0.01)$, or 16 cents, for route 2.

Table 1–2

Street	Frequency of stops per mile	Accident costs per 100 miles	Travel time (in minutes per mile)
First street	6	\$2	5
Second street	1	1	3
Fourth street	3	1	3
A street	2	1	3
B street	1	1	3
C street	4	1	3

Figure 1–2

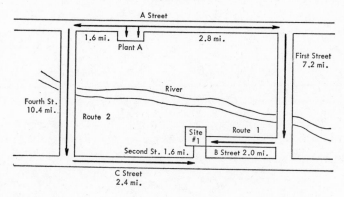

$$\text{Total costs for route } 1 = 1.862 + 0.192 + 2.52 = \$4.574$$
$$\text{Total costs for route } 2 = 1.994 + 0.16 + 2.40 = \$4.554$$

Thus, route 2 should be taken instead of route 1.

Although the analyst now has an answer to the first part of the analysis (i.e., what is the best route), it is not complete until he determines the validity of the findings. Here, he is asking the question: What faith can he place in his solution?

He begins by questioning the validity of the data: Are the data accurate? Have the data been properly gathered? Have they been properly used? For example, are the expected costs of accidents truly reflected in the historical costs, or did abnormal conditions cause First Street to have high accident costs? If some of the data are in question, the findings can be further checked by sensitivity analysis. For example, if the final decision is not affected whether accident costs on First Street are $1, $2, or $3, one need not worry about the validity of that piece of data.

After questioning the validity of the data, the analyst questions the validity of the model. In this connection the analyst has assumed that the time required to travel any fraction of a street is proportional to the fraction of the street traveled. Thus, if one travels 20 percent of the street, it takes 20 percent of the time required to travel the entire street.

If the data and model are valid now, will the decision be valid in the future? This requires a provision to modify the solution if conditions change. Also, the analysis should consider the impact of implementation on the system. If the company's trucks increase congestion on Fourth Street, that alone may increase the travel time and negate the benefits.

The second half of the problem may now be considered. Assume that the matrix of costs shown in Table 1–3 reflects the findings. Thus, one load going from plant *A* to site 1 costs $12.

On the basis of this information, let us proceed to minimize the cost in order to fulfill the needs for asphalt. Let us solve this relatively easy problem by systems analysis, recognizing that it could be solved by quantitative analysis. This approach requires the enumeration of all relevant alternative courses of action.[3] It so happens that the five courses of action indicated in Table 1–4 are the only relevant courses of action. Let us demonstrate why this is true.

Table 1–3

PLANT

		A	B
	1	12	22
SITE	2	20	15
	3	18	16

Table 1–4

MATRIX 1

To:	Trucks from plant A	Trucks from plant B	Trucks needed
Site 1	10	5	15
Site 2	20		20
Site 3		15	15
Trucks available	30	20	

MATRIX 2

To:	Trucks from plant A	Trucks from plant B	Trucks needed
Site 1		15	15
Site 2	20		20
Site 3	10	5	15
Trucks available	30	20	

---

[3] Relevancy has both a practical and an analytical element. Here the objective which dictates only five alternatives determines relevancy. However, judgment often plays a role in keeping the number of alternatives down to manageable proportions.

TABLE 1–4 (*Continued*)

MATRIX 3

To:	Trucks from plant A	Trucks from plant B	Trucks needed
Site 1	15		15
Site 2		20	20
Site 3	15		15
Trucks available	30	20	

MATRIX 4

To:	Trucks from plant A	Trucks from plant B	Trucks needed
Site 1		15	15
Site 2	15	5	20
Site 3	15		15
Trucks available	30	20	

MATRIX 5

To:	Trucks from plant A	Trucks from plant B	Trucks needed
Site 1	15		15
Site 2	15	5	20
Site 3		15	15
Trucks available	30	20	

Matrix 1 is obtained by saying: "Let us use the output of plant A to fill completely the needs of site 2."[4] When this has been accomplished, we have 10 loads from plant A which have not been assigned to any site. If we now assign all of them to site 1, we *must* assign 5 loads from plant B to site 1 in order to have the needed 15 loads delivered to site 1. At the same time, we must assign the remaining 15 loads from plant B to site 3 in order to fill the needs at site 3. The result of this assignment method is matrix 1. Matrix 2 begins with the same statement. However, instead of assigning

[4] A matrix is a rectangular array of numbers with m rows and n columns.

the remaining 10 loads from plant *A* to site 1, we assign them all to site 3. Thus, five loads from plant *B* *must* be assigned to site 3 in order to fill the needs of site 3. Further, the remaining 15 loads from plant *B* must be assigned to site 1 in order to fill the needs at site 1. These are the only two relevant alternatives if we begin by filling the needs of site 2 from plant *A*. This is true because any other combination is a mixed strategy and does not take advantage of the best strategy. For example, if we begin, as earlier, by assigning 20 loads from plant *A* to site 2, we may assign 5 of the remaining 10 loads to site 1 and 5 to site 3. This results in a mixed

Table 1–5

To:	Trucks from plant *A*	Trucks from plant *B*	Trucks needed
Site 1	5	10	15
Site 2	20		20
Site 3	5	10	15
Trucks available	30	20	

Table 1–6

To:	Trucks from plant *A*	Trucks from plant *B*	Trucks needed
Site 1			15
Site 3			15
Trucks available	10	20	

strategy because each assignment was not exhaustive. Thus, when it came to assigning the 10 remaining loads, they were split between two sites, but exhausted the needs of neither site. The real test of the mixed strategy is that more than one site have partial fulfillment of its needs.

For example, Table 1–5 shows a mixed strategy. The undesirability of a mixed strategy can best be illustrated by assuming that it is desirable to fill the needs of site 2 from plant *A*.

This then reduces the problem to the situation shown in Table 1–6. The reader will recall the delivery cost matrix presented in Table 1–3 (page 19). Some of the needs of site 1 may be filled either from plant *A* or from plant *B*. It costs $12 to deliver from plant *A* to site 1, but $22 to deliver from plant *B* to site 1. The difference is $10. It costs $18 to deliver from plant *A* to site 3, and $16 to deliver from plant *B* to site 3. It is very important to deliver as much as possible to site 1 from plant *A* because each shift from delivering one truck from plant *A* to site 1 requires $10 more, but reduces delivery costs to site 3 by only $2. This concept becomes confusing unless we can see the nature of the internal shifting. Assume that we shift the assignment so that six trucks deliver from plant *A* to site 1. This results in the necessity of only nine trucks from plant *B* to site 1 in order to fill the needs of site 1. This is shown in Table 1–7.

Table 1–7

To:	Trucks from plant *A*	Trucks from plant *B*	Trucks needed
Site 1	6	9	15
Site 2	20		20
Site 3	4	11	15
Trucks available	30	20	

Thus the shift of one truck from plant *A* to site 1 instead of site 3 means that one less truck from plant *B* must go to site 1 and one more truck from plant *B* must go to site 3. Since the total delivery costs to site 3 are reduced by $12, we should continue this shifting until all 10 remaining trucks at plant *A* are assigned to site 1.

Let us demonstrate that the delivery costs are in fact reduced by $12.

For Table 1–5, costs of delivery to site 1 are:

$$5(12) + 10(22) = \$280$$

Costs of delivery to site 3 are:

$$5(18) + 10(16) = \$250$$

Thus, total delivery costs for Table 1–5 are:

$$\$280 + \$250 = \$530$$

For Table 1–7, delivery costs are:

$$6(12) + 9(22) + 4(18) + 11(16) = \$518$$

Costs of delivery to site 2 have been ignored because they are the same for each table. This discussion is intended to demonstrate that the nature of the cost relationships will require that a continuous shift must take place until one cannot shift any more. In other words, starting with the plan proposed in matrix 2 (page 19), one would not stop with the plan suggested in the mixed matrix in Table 1–5, but would continue until matrix 1 was reached. Conversely, if the costs from plant *A* to site 1 and from plant *B* to site 1 were reversed and one started with matrix 1, one would not stop at the matrix in Table 1–5, but would continue to trade off until arriving at matrix 2.

Each of the relevant alternatives is found by first exhausting the needs at one site and then filling the remaining needs. Thus, delivery of plant *B* to site 2 yields matrix 3. Delivery of plant *A* to site 3 yields matrix 3 and matrix 4. It can be seen that once 15 trucks from plant *A* have been assigned to site 3, the remaining 15 trucks from plant *A* may be assigned to site 1 or site 2. If the remaining trucks are assigned to site 1, matrix 3 results, because this completes the needs for site 1 and all 20 trucks from plant *B* must be assigned to site 2 to fill its needs. If the remaining trucks are assigned to site 2, matrix 4 results, because five trucks from plant *B* must also be assigned to site 2 to complete its needs. This leaves 15 trucks from plant *B* which must be assigned to site 1 to complete its needs. All remaining strategies are found by a similar process. Note the duplication. These alternatives may be shown in table form (see Table 1–8).

Table 1–8

| Initial delivery | | |
From:	To:	Matrices
A	1	3, 5
A	2	1, 2
A	3	3, 4
B	1	2, 4
B	2	3
B	3	1, 5

We may now calculate the total cost for each of the five relevant alternatives, as follows:

Matrix 1. $10(12) + 20(20) + 5(22) + 15(16) = \$870$
Matrix 2. $15(22) + 20(20) + 10(18) + 5(16) = \$990$
Matrix 3. $15(12) + 20(15) + 15(18) \qquad\quad = \$750$
Matrix 4. $15(22) + 15(20) + 5(15) + 15(18) = \$975$
Matrix 5. $15(12) + 15(20) + 5(15) + 15(16) = \$795$

Hence the minimum cost occurs when trucks are assigned according to matrix 3.

Much of this chapter has been devoted to an extensive discussion of an example of managerial analysis. The findings are not startling, nor is the approach unduly difficult, even for the mathematically naïve. The methodology was built from a base which assumes very little mathematical preparation but which is enhanced by mathematical preparation. This example does act as a good reference base for the first seven chapters, which attempt to explain fully the process of managerial analysis. The process of managerial analysis is not an analytical or computational technique. It is the totality of the analysis. Thus, it is hoped that this example will act as a reference point for investigating that process.

DISCUSSION TOPICS AND PROBLEMS

1. Define managerial analysis, systems analysis, and quantitative analysis.

2. Discuss systems analysis and quantitative analysis. How do these approaches differ?

3. What is meant by the term *criterion?* What is the importance of establishing a criterion in problem solving?

4. What is the relationship between the managerial analyst and the decision maker?

5. What is meant by the scientific method? What are the characteristics of this approach?

6. Outline and summarize the steps in the process of managerial analysis.

7. Attempt to justify the inclusion of the extensive example used in this chapter.

8. What are some of the possible effects of the implementation of a model in a business setting?

9. Identify the three phases of managerial analysis and indicate the extent of managerial know-how, analytical know-how, and judgment necessary to conduct each phase.

10. The intercompany delivery service delivers packages and documents between company buildings. It has one truck and five pickup and delivery points. Packages picked up at any one point may require delivery at any other point. The diagram on page 25 pictorially presents the time it takes to move from any one point to any other point. Time is shown in minutes.

Every time the truck stops at a delivery point, there is a 10-minute allowance for pickup and sorting time. The truck contains sorting bins; the material to be delivered at any given building is simply placed in that particular bin, and at the time of delivery is removed from the bin and taken to the particular building where it goes.

The analytical staff has been asked to minimize the cost to the company attached to delivering these packages. It has further been told that delivery must be assured from any one point to any other point at least once a day. The truck is available for seven hours during any given day. The analytical staff has determined that the following delivery pattern will minimize the operation time of the truck while assuring delivery from any one point to any other point at least once a day.

DELIVERY POINTS AND TIME (IN MINUTES)
REQUIRED TO TRAVERSE THE DISTANCE
BETWEEN PICKUP POINTS

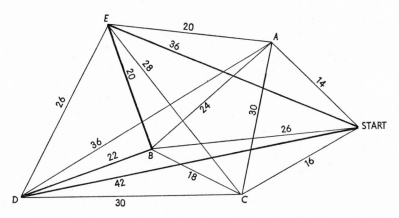

The movement pattern is:

$$S \to C \to D \to E \to A \to B \to C \to D \to E \to A \to B \to S$$

which takes 260 minutes of travel time plus 100 minutes of pickup and sorting time, thus utilizing a total of 360 of the available 420 minutes. Inasmuch as the truck is not in operation for the 60 extra minutes, there are savings resulting from the fact that the truck has not been operated, and the truck operator is of course available for other duties for those 60 minutes.

Problem:

a) Do you agree with the assumption that minimizing operation time will minimize operating costs? Explain.

b) Accept the assumption that minimizing operation time will minimize operating costs. Further, accept the fact that the delivery pattern prescribed does in fact minimize the time needed for delivery. Do you then agree that the analytical staff has properly completed its assignment? Explain.

SELECTED REFERENCES

Ackoff, Russell L., and Rivett, Patrick. *A Manager's Guide to Operations Research*. New York: John Wiley & Sons, Inc., 1963.

Churchman, C. West; Ackoff, Russell L.; and Arnoff, E. Leonard. *Introduction to Operations Research*, pp. 1–199. New York: John Wiley & Sons, Inc., 1957.

Miller, David W., and Starr, Martin K. *Executive Decisions and Operations Research*, especially pp. 1–170. Englewood Cliffs, N.J.: Prentice-Hall, Inc., 1960.

Schuchman, Abe. *Scientific Decision Making in Business*. New York: Holt, Rinehart & Winston, Inc., 1963.

2

Major analytical approaches used for managerial analysis

I. INTRODUCTION

It is highly probable that the reader has been exposed to a number of confusing references to analytical approaches. This section briefly identifies and relates approaches to managerial analysis. The general analytical *approaches* include such things as operations research, management science, statistical analysis, economic analysis, econometrics, and others that are an integral element in managerial analysis. The underlying mathematical tools used to derive solutions to the models which are developed include calculus, probability theory, and matrix algebra. Throughout this text, various models of common processes will be shown. These models have been found to recur frequently. They include inventory theory, linear programming, and queuing theory.

None of these approaches, tools, or models of common processes are necessarily managerial analysis per se. The purpose of using these approaches and tools in the conduct of managerial analysis is to assist the manager to make better decisions. For example, statistical analysis, which provides information about relationships between variables within the environment, is used to find these relationships so that the analyst may use them in order to assist the manager in making a better decision.

The scientist, however, is validly concerned with understanding the relationship between the variables in the environment as an end in itself. Consequently, statistical analysis without the end objective of assisting the manager to make decisions is not a part of managerial analysis. The same is true of many of the other analytical tools and approaches. As long as the end purpose is to assist the manager in making a decision, they are then validly tools and approaches used for managerial analysis. The following paragraphs relate some of the general analytical approaches to managerial analysis. It should be remembered that the scope of most of these analytical approaches is not uniformly agreed upon.

II. ORGANIZATION ANALYSIS

Organization analysis, as used in this text, refers to the general process of relating individuals and subunits to the organization. Organization analysis has two major uses. One is to look at the reason for the existence of the organization, i.e., to identify organizational objectives. The second deals with establishing the relationship between individuals and subunits.

One may expect to see quite a different set of objectives for the traditional manufacturing firm, with heavy emphasis upon profits, as opposed to a private research firm, whose reason for existence may be to provide the owners the opportunity to conduct their own research and only secondarily to insure adequate financial income to continue. Thus, it is first necessary to identify organizational objectives before attempting to improve organizational performance.

The process of establishing a relationship between individuals and subunits frequently progresses with the use of an organization chart and with the use of job descriptions which identify the activities, responsibilities, and scope of authority of individuals within the organization. The end purpose of understanding the relationship of individuals to one another is to identify (1) the actual decision maker, (2) what kinds of constraints he operates under, and (3) the necessary information to restrict the subsequent analysis to something over which the organization or the individual making the decision actually has control. It is of course unless to suggest that the manager undertake a program that deals with variables he cannot control.

Organization analysis can be used to assist in the implementation and control of managerial analysis by providing information about the extent to which the organization can use a recommended course of action.

III. STATISTICAL ANALYSIS

Statistical analysis is a means of developing information about the nature of relationships between variables in the environment. The analyst seeks this information so that he may construct or identify the particular values to be used in the model of the environment.

Thus, statistical analysis operates to provide input information for subsequent analysis. Statistical analysis is used in quantitative analysis and systems analysis because it provides input information for both. It may, however, be used in a different fashion in quantitative analysis than in systems analysis.

IV. ECONOMIC ANALYSIS

Economic analysis includes normative analysis and positive analysis. Positive economic analysis attempts to describe rigorously economic phenomena and their structure. Positive economics includes econometrics and mathematical economics. Normative economics is a field of economics which attempts to use the descriptions and findings of positive economics to assist the decision maker, especially governmental decision makers.

John Johnston identifies econometrics as the manipulation of statistical inference problems in the context of economic models.[1] In other words, econometrics is a means of identifying and/or explaining relationships between economic variables. Usually, the econometrician has an interest in using the statistical methodology to explain or understand economic relationships in order to improve economic forecasting. For example, to assist in the development of public policy, economists must rely upon forecasts of future conditions supplied by econometricians.

On the other hand, mathematical economics is primarily concerned with developing mathematical models to explain a theoretical economic structure or a theoretical economic model. Mathematical economics attempts rigorously to portray or represent the economic environment.

As we have seen, the econometricians primarily provide data inputs by way of their forecasts, and mathematical economists try to explain economic structure. Normative economic analysis attempts to assist the policy maker in making policy decisions by using a model to derive a solution in terms of a controllable variable.

Thus, economic analysis may be used as a partial input to quantitative analysis and is also a meaningful analytical approach for systems analysis.

V. OPERATIONS RESEARCH

Operations research is a term that is widely used and that assumes very different meanings, depending upon the user. Very clearly, the most successful operations researchers are individuals who proceed on the basis of a particular methodology to analyze or research operations. The methodology is very generally stated, and it might be considered a

---

[1] John Johnston, *Econometric Methods* (New York: McGraw-Hill Book Co., Inc., 1963).

process. The phases of operations research identified by C. West Church-man, Russell L. Ackoff, and E. Leonard Arnoff in the classical text, *Introduction to Operations Research*,[2] are:

1. Formulating the problem
2. Constructing a mathematical model to represent the system under study
3. Deriving a solution from the model
4. Testing the model and the solution derived from it
5. Establishing controls over the solution
6. Putting the solution to work (implementation)

In practice, operations research has been very successful in completing the phases identified in the above methodological framework, using well-established models of common processes such as linear programming. Thus, operations research may be considered a methodological framework or a set of successful models of common processes.

Only one of two things can be accomplished with any form of analysis. One may take the resources as given and attempt to fulfill the objectives most effectively, or one may specify a desired level of fulfillment of the objective and attempt to identify the alternative course of action that will give that desired level of fulfillment with the least cost. You cannot both maximize the objective and minimize the use of resources.

Frequently, operations research focuses upon cost minimization, thus minimizing the use of resources while taking demand (the objective) as given.

Operations research is most applicable to quantitative analysis, although some of the tools may also be applicable to systems analysis, especially when they deal with some of the game and game-theoretic approaches.

VI. MANAGEMENT SCIENCE

Management science may be equated by different individuals with different terms. Management science is frequently identified closely with operations research. On the other hand, some individuals would also relate management science to the entire process we call managerial analysis. Like operations research, management science may be identified as a process or methodology that incorporates the same steps identified in the discussion of operations research.

If management science has any distinguishable features from operations research, it is its concern with policy level decisions. Management science tends to focus more heavily than operations research on human and man-machine situations. Management science tends also to be more cogni-tive of market or demand conditions. Management science relies heavily on the same kind of analytical tools as operations research, but is also

---

[2] New York: John Wiley & Sons, Inc., 1957.

cognitive of analytical tools oriented toward psychological and economic analysis. Management science and operations research personnel, although usually conversant with the same methodological and process requirements, tend to be differently trained. The individuals in operations research are normally trained in engineering and mathematical disciplines, whereas management scientists tend to be trained in statistical and economic or other social science disciplines.

VII. COST-BENEFIT ANALYSIS

Cost-benefit analysis is, more than any of the previous analytical approaches, strictly an approach. Cost-benefit analysis is very extensive, but includes certain characteristics of an analytical tool. The approach of cost-benefit analysis, as the name might indicate, is to identify the costs of a course of action and the benefits to be derived by taking that course of action. Then the benefits are reduced by the cost to provide the net benefits. Cost-benefits analysis is mentioned here due to its recent popularity.

For example, equipment replacement analysis, which has long been recognized as part of financial management, is a classical cost-benefit analysis. Cost-benefit analysis usually recognizes the period of time over which the alternative operates and uses present-value analysis to bring the annual (or monthly) benefits and expenditures to a single period in time, thus allowing meaningful dollar comparisons between alternatives. Cost-benefit analysis further may be used to compare a series of alternatives where the costs are measured in one dimension and the benefits in another. Expenditures to increase or maintain employee morale through recreational facilities cannot be evaluated in dollar terms. However, in choosing between a company campground or gymnasium, one can find the cost per man-day of use of each alternative, thus comparing dollars of cost with man-days of use.

Since cost-benefit analysis identifies alternative courses of action, it is considered an analytical approach for systems analysis.

VIII. MATHEMATICAL TOOLS

The modeling process and the process of deriving a solution are essentially separate and distinct activities. Therefore the underlying mathematical tool that allows one to move from the model to the solution must be recognized. Most of the models of common processes are identified by their mathematical characteristics; for example, linear programming is a separate tool that uses certain mathematical bases to derive a solution. By recognizing mathematical tools and models of common processes, one clearly identifies that the way in which he structures the model has a significant impact on the solution.

In order to obtain valid conclusions, one structures the model and then attempts to find the mathematical tool that will give him the best answer to the model. It is not sound to look only at the available models of common processes and try to fit them to the existing situation.

Mathematical methods may be categorized in four major segments relevant to managerial analysis. The first would be classical methods of optimization based on the concepts of calculus. Although these are somewhat limited in their application to managerial problems, the simple optimization processes provided by them often can give considerable insight in dealing with a management model. A second area is linear and matrix algebra. Since many management problems involve large, complex sets of alternatives (e.g., the illustrative problem of Chapter 1), these methods are extremely important. As all decision problems deal with the future, a third area—probability theory—is also of great importance. Finally, recent mathematical methods for dealing with discrete phenomena (integer programming and dynamic programming) will be increasingly important as they are developed further and their relevance is demonstrated.

In summary, mathematical tools provide bases for deriving a solution to the models developed under the preceding steps.

IX. SENSITIVITY ANALYSIS

Determining and maintaining validity (phase 3 of the steps in managerial analysis) have not been well developed in the literature. There are, however, some analytical methods that assist in the determination of validity. One of these, and the only one that this text will discuss, is sensitivity analysis. Sensitivity analysis investigates the change in results if (1) the input information was in error or (2) the structure of the model was in error.

Sensitivity analysis may test the extreme values of one or more of the forecast variables or parameters and then measure the impact this would have on the decision. If the decision is sensitive to certain forecast errors, a serious question is raised about the validity of our derived solution.

Sensitivity analysis may also be used to evaluate errors in the data by looking at the extremes the data could take and the impact of those extremes on the derived solution. Also, a slightly different model might be constructed in order to compare the decision derived from the second model with that of the first.

Defined here, sensitivity analysis includes a field that is frequently referred to as reliability analysis. The area of reliability and sensitivity

Figure 2–1

<small>Diagram of the steps in managerial analysis and of the relationship
of analytical approaches to managerial analysis</small>

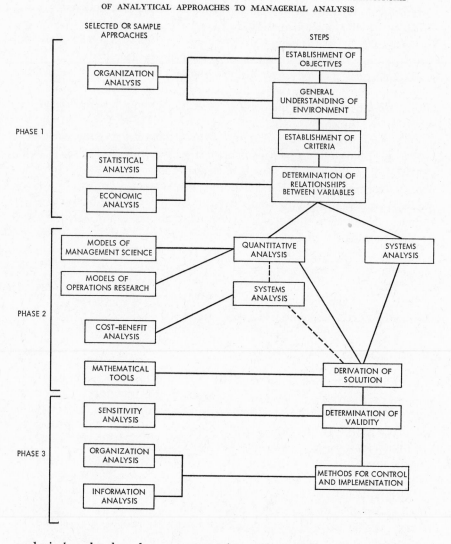

analysis has developed a very extensive and sophisticated methodology
and jargon which we shall not deal with here.

Sensitivity analysis is equally useful for quantitative analysis or systems
analysis.

X. INFORMATION ANALYSIS

Information analysis is a means of acquiring new input data so that the
model may be updated and the solution modified if necessary. This

requires an analysis of incoming information and a method of relating it to the model. Information analysis also prescribes methods for modifying the procedure.

Information analysis is equally useful in quantitative analysis and systems analysis.

XI. SUMMARY

The diagram in Figure 2–1 of the steps in managerial analysis and of the relationship of analytical approaches to managerial analysis is designed to provide a framework for integrating the material of Chapters 1 and 2 so that one can see how these different approaches and steps relate to one another.

DISCUSSION TOPICS AND PROBLEMS

1. Distinguish between approaches, tools, and models of common processes.

2. How does operations research relate to managerial analysis?

3. How do statistical analysis and economic analysis relate to managerial analysis?

4. Evaluate and explain the logic of Figure 2–1.

5. Define and explain each of the following: organization analysis, statistical analysis, economic analysis, operations research, management science, cost-benefit analysis, sensitivity analysis, and information analysis.

SELECTED REFERENCES

Ackoff, Russell L., and Rivett, Patrick. *A Manager's Guide to Operations Research.* New York: John Wiley & Sons, Inc., 1963.

Baumol, William J. *Economic Theory and Operations Analysis.* Englewood Cliffs, N.J.: Prentice-Hall, Inc., 1965.

Churchman, C. West; Ackoff, Russell L.; and Arnoff, E. Leonard. *Introduction to Operations Research.* New York: John Wiley & Sons, Inc., 1957.

Johnston, John. *Econometric Methods.* New York: McGraw-Hill Book Co., Inc., 1963.

Lindsay, Franklin A. *New Techniques for Management Decision Making.* New York: McGraw-Hill Book Co., Inc., 1958.

Miller, David W., and Starr, Martin K. *Executive Decisions and Operations Research.* Englewood Cliffs, N.J.: Prentice-Hall, Inc., 1960.

Morris, William T. *Management Science.* Englewood Cliffs, N.J.: Prentice-Hall, Inc., 1968.

3

A history of
managerial analysis

I. INTRODUCTION

The previous two chapters have demonstrated that managerial analysis is an analytical process which is dependent upon a definitive order or procedure, but which is aided by a specific analytical methodology and analytical tools. The birth of an analytical tool or a specific analytical field can frequently be dated by the point in time when the first material was published on the matter. The birth of a process or methodology, however, cannot be so clearly identified. It is a thesis of this chapter that the essential steps in the process of managerial analysis have been recognized since the turn of the century, and possibly since 1830.

II. THE YEARS 1775–1850

The works of such notable individuals as Eli Whitney and Charles Babbage demonstrate (inferentially, at least) an understanding of the process of managerial analysis. Although it becomes difficult to stereotype these well-known individuals, it is obvious that they understood scientific methodology and approach. It is also clear that to them scientific methodology and approach were not conducted in the dusty confines of a library or a laboratory. In that period of time, one could not clearly distinguish between the scientist and the practitioner. Both Babbage and Whitney directly applied their research ideas.

Eli Whitney is known to every schoolboy as the inventor of the cotton gin and to most students of business administration as an early pioneer in interchangeable manufacturing (mass production). However, the use of enlightened analysis by Whitney and his partner Phineas Miller to develop a loose model of manufacturing costs is typical of managerial analysis during that period. We shall use the following quotation from J. Mirsky and A. Nevins to indicate this depth of understanding:

Their actual calculations [for use of their gin] do not exist, but their method can be surmised. Experiments had given them the ratio of cleaned cotton to uncleaned cotton—the weight of the former was 1/3 the weight of the latter. . . . In setting up their system of charges they used 5 lbs. of uncleaned cotton as the unit which yielded one and two-thirds pounds of cleaned cotton. Of this they returned one pound to the owner and retained for themselves 2/3rds of a pound. From this gross profit, they covered their manufacturing and shipping expenses plus an annual prorating of the cost of the gin to be paid off during the term of their patent; it also included installing, operating, and maintaining their ginneries, sums expended for the purchase of water sites, and the erection of elaborate gear and buildings. To this was added their labor costs—in each ginnery allowance had to be made for feeding the white overseer, who was "to receive and deliver the cotton, repair the gins and superintend their work, paying for the labor of the negroes who are required to attend the gins and bag the cotton at the rate of two shillings per day for the men and one shilling and six-pence for the women."[1]

Even this much information does not allow us accurately to appraise their real understanding of the composition of costs, especially since this is a reconstruction by Mirsky and Nevins. However, Miller and Whitney appear to have considered all cost variables (except opportunity costs). Although their conclusions or actions may be open to question, the ability to determine and understand their manufacturing costs is not. The next two statements by Mirsky and Nevins point up more clearly Whitney and Miller's understanding of cost elements (Miller was the financier and probably the better manager of the two):

At a time [1801] when expenses were estimated on the basis of labor costs plus the costs of the raw materials—with a dollar or so added on to cover all other items—he insisted on including interest on the invested capital and insurance charges as part of the cost of a musket.[2]

In 1824 thru Whitney's influence, cost of manufacture at government armories was computed; so that the interest on the entire capital . . . insurance . . . with the addition of such further percentage for wear and decay as shall be sufficient to preserve the said capital unimpaired, shall be charged as making a part of the cost of manufacturing arms. . . .[3]

However, motion economy at the individual workplace—the area frequently, although incorrectly, identified as scientific management—is also reported by Mirsky and Nevins:

---

[1] J. Mirsky and A. Nevins, *The World of Eli Whitney* (New York: Macmillan Co., 1952), pp. 96–97.

[2] *Ibid.*, p. 324.

[3] *Ibid.*, p. 273.

The partners [Whitney and Miller] minutely considered the internal organization of their enterprise. Meticulous keeping of all kinds of records was routine;
but that they would schedule the many separate elements—the cleaning, pack-
ing, baling, shipping, every step of which was new—submit each particular
process to experiment, and standardize the preferred technique, is arrestingly
modern.[4]

Charles Babbage has received much recognition as the inventor of the
forerunner of the computer which he called a computing engine. However, his book, *The Economy of Manufacturers*,[5] is a classic on rational
management.

The idea of a choice among alternatives which coordinate the activities
of the enterprise toward a goal or goals received implied attention during
this period. In order to have a choice among alternatives, both the means
of recognizing the alternatives and the means of making the choice are
necessary. In addition, the effectiveness of the choice is dependent upon
the following factors: (1) the recognition and clear definition of the goal
or goals, (2) the availability and accuracy of information from which to
make decisions, (3) the availability of tools for processing the available
information for making the best decisions, and (4) the use that is made of
the information and tools. The idea of a choice among alternatives can be
illustrated by using a quotation from Babbage:

> In order to judge the value of such a machine [i.e., a pinmaking machine]
> compared with hand-labour, it would be necessary to ascertain: 1) the defects
> to which pins so made are liable; 2) their advantages, if any, over those so
> made in the usual way; 3) the prime cost of the machine for making them;
> 4) the expense of keeping it in repair; 5) the expense of moving the machine
> and of attending to it.[6]

This presentation by Babbage shows that management must not use rules
of thumb to make decisions but must consider the variables affecting the
system. In the above quotation, Babbage attempts to enumerate the variables to be considered in the choice between a pinmaking machine and
hand labor so that they may be accurately determined and taken into
account. Later, Babbage lists four variables to consider in making the
choice of products to market.[7]

Babbage's pin factory example represents production organization designed to take advantage of the principle of specialization.[8] If the decision

---

[4] *Ibid.*, p. 98.

[5] Charles Babbage, *The Economy of Manufacturers* (Baltimore: Charles Knight, 1832).

[6] *Ibid.*, p. 185.

[7] *Ibid.*, p. 238.

[8] *Ibid.*, p. 185.

so to organize production is based upon comparative cost analysis, Babbage's suggestion may be considered managerial analysis.

III. THE YEARS 1880–1940

F. W. Taylor and Henri Fayol more clearly recognized the principles of managerial analysis.[9] These individuals had both a scientific and an applied or operational background. All of the gentlemen discussed so far brought to the work environment a systematic methodology for analysis.

Taylor began as an engineer and completed his career as a manager. As a manager, he was concerned with systematically investigating the relationships between variables in the environment he was attempting to direct and with making decisions on the basis of that systematic investigation. Fayol was first a scientist and then a manager. He also was concerned with systematically investigating the factors which affected the operations of his organizations. The two gentlemen did tend to focus on different kinds of factors. Taylor focused on mechanical and machine kinds of factors because of his emphasis on shop management. Fayol focused more strongly on human kinds of factors because of his emphasis on top management. Taylor and Fayol operated in the period from 1890 to 1925, a period during which the complexity of operations was vastly increasing and in which the recognition of the necessity of approaching operations systematically was becoming more widespread.

Some of the work from 1915 to 1940 closely approximates some of the work that now is being done in the area of managerial analysis. Trefethen reports that during World War I, Thomas Alva Edison made studies of antisubmarine warfare for the Naval Consulting Board.[10] In Trefethen's words: "His work included the computation of statistics to be used in determining the best methods for evading and for destroying submarines, the use of a 'tactical game board' for solving problems of avoiding submarine attack, and an analysis of the value of zigzagging as a method for protecting merchant shipping." Later in this book, we shall investigate the economic order formula. This formula was published in 1926;[11] and to this day, it is one of the standard tools in the area of managerial analysis.

IV. THE YEARS 1940 TO THE PRESENT

In retrospect, it is easy to see that improvement in analysis was strongly constrained by a lack of effective techniques available to study and derive

---

[9] See F. N. Trefethen, "A History of Operations Research," in T. F. McCloskey and F. N. Trefothen (eds.), *Operations Research for Management* (Baltimore: Johns Hopkins Press, 1954), p. 10.

[10] *Ibid.*, p. 4.

[11] B. Cooper, "How to Determine Economical Manufacturing Quantities," *Industrial Management*, Vol. LXXII, No. 4 (1926), pp. 228–33.

better solutions to managerial problems. Effective analytical techniques, probably more than anything else, have been developed and vastly improved since World War II. It was also during this period that the electronic computer was used to assist in conducting systematic analyses of operations. In addition, during this period, many new analytical tools became operational.

Some of the more recent contributors in the area of managerial analysis have worked in operations research. P. M. S. Blackett of the University of Manchester was the director of a group brought together by the British government to improve military operations in 1940. Blackett and his group, known as Blackett's circus, made a substantial contribution to the war effort. This group is considered the originator of operations research.[12] Operations research owes its origin primarily to military applications.[13]

It was inevitable that the industrial community would recognize the potential of operations research. In the early 1950's, a group was formed at Case Institute of Technology to investigate and apply operations research in industry. The culmination of that effort was the first textbook in the field, entitled *Introduction to Operations Research*, written by C. West Churchman, Russell L. Ackoff, and E. Leonard Arnoff.[14] Typical applications of managerial analysis from 1945 to 1960 dealt with a fairly restricted definition of the environment.

V. CONCLUSION

The preceding discussion has focused fairly heavily on what one might term the three historical phases of managerial analysis and the contributions of certain individuals who are very prominent in the development of the particular phase. However, one thesis of this chapter is that progress to date is strongly dependent upon the availability of analytical tools and supporting information-processing tools. Managerial analysis is becoming more and more important in assisting managerial decision making, not because of the increased recognition of the process, a very significant factor in itself, but more importantly because the tools themselves have only recently been developed.

There are two very significant factors that have affected the development of the tools. One is the increasing availability, understanding, and use of the electronic computer. Initially, the electronic computer processed routine data, and it has gone through its own developmental process to the point where it can now effectively assist in the conduct of analysis.

---

[12] Trefethen, *op. cit.,* pp. 6–7.

[13] Witness the preponderance of references to military applications in Trefethen, *ibid.,* pp. 3–28.

[14] New York: John Wiley & Sons, Inc., 1957.

Simulation is a tool that we shall look at later in this text. It is a tool that has existed conceptually for a long period of time, but has become operative only because of the advent of the electronic computer. Many of the other analytical tools have been improved by its increased computational power.

The second technological breakthrough is the development of more powerful mathematical tools. The increased interest in and understanding of mathematics, leading to increased emphasis on research and development of new mathematical tools, have strongly enhanced the power of managerial analysis. In summary, the framework of managerial analysis is old, but the mathematical and computational tools necessary for its effective use have been only recently developed.

DISCUSSION TOPICS AND PROBLEMS

1. Indicate when you feel that the essential steps in the process of managerial analysis were recognized in documented form. Support your conclusion.

2. Identify the following and indicate their contribution to managerial analysis: Eli Whitney, Charles Babbage, F. W. Taylor, Henri Fayol, and P. M. S. Blackett.

3. Do you think future developments in managerial analysis will depend on an increased understanding and usage of the computer? Why?

SELECTED REFERENCES

George, Claude S., Jr. *The History of Management Thought.* Englewood Cliffs, N.J.: Prentice-Hall, Inc., 1968.

McCloskey, T. F., and Trefethen, F. N. (eds.). *Operations Research for Management.* Baltimore: Johns Hopkins Press, 1954.

SECTION TWO

The process

4

Problem
identification and
general background

I. INTRODUCTION

Obviously, the starting point for analysis begins with the identification of the problem. Because managerial problems are so pervasive and interconnected, this step is both crucial and difficult. Organizations should have a formal mechanism for identifying potential problem areas.

The investigation which precedes acceptable identification of the problem must not be shortchanged. The organization that solves the wrong problem is not very effective. It is of little benefit to control inventory costs for a product that should not be produced. Thus, one aspect of problem identification requires a thorough investigation and understanding of the interrelationship of the problem area to the organization as a whole. The department which installs an improvement which reduces its costs but causes more than offsetting increased costs in another department is not benefiting the organization.

II. THE ORGANIZATION AS A SYSTEM

The knowledge necessary to begin the analysis effectively relies upon an understanding of the organization as a system with its various subsystems. Organization analysis is the process of identifying the relevant systems and relating them to the potential problem. Finally, the understanding generated by a knowledge of the systems must be utilized to identify the problem. The remainder of this chapter is concerned with a discussion of these topics as well as a discussion of formal mechanisms for finding potential problems.

The external systems

One cannot proceed to analyze a specific probelm in a specific situation without establishing a general understanding of the relevant systems. The environment of any organization may be classified into the external systems and the internal systems. The external systems represent all of the external operating conditions which affect the organization. The private industrial firm must understand competitors' behavior, consumers' behavior, governmental considerations, suppliers' behavior, and the behavior of the general public. One of the most important considerations is to establish complete information about demand for the products or services (both existent and not yet existent) of the organization. Demand may be primary or derived.

Some business firms face a derived demand, since the primary product to which their product contributes must be demanded before theirs is also demanded. For example, construction materials are demanded because they are components of houses and other buildings. All firms with derived demand must look to the industry from which their demand is derived in order to forecast future demand. Demand and resulting sales forecasts are very important ingredients in most problems.

The internal systems

A knowledge of the internal systems requires an understanding of the physical, human, and financial makeup of the firm. Internal systems are at least partially under the control of the manager. The external systems cannot be controlled, but can merely be accounted for. All organizations operate with certain resources available from the general supply of those resources. Consequently, it is well to recognize that we must have some understanding of the limitations of the resources.

A knowledge of the external systems allows the firm to account for rather than control customer behavior. The firm cannot require a customer to purchase its goods, but it can price the goods attractively enough so that the customer will purchase them. The internal systems allow the firm greater discretion. For example, the company may place its machinery in a particular fashion. However, the way the firm places its machinery is limited by the available space and capabilities of the machinery and the end purpose, etc. Thus, no behavior is entirely discretionary. Each decision further delineates the realm of future discretionary actions. For example, the company wishing to diversify has virtually unlimited control over the area into which it may diversify. The only theoretical constraint is the availability of resources to undertake any given diversification. However, any rational organization would set up a number of criteria for diversification. The criteria would reduce the freedom of the firm.

III. ORGANIZATION ANALYSIS

Organization analysis is used to obtain an understanding of the internal systems of the firm.[1] The content of and approach to organization analysis are not well defined. This is partially due to the fact that some researchers use organization analysis to understand or identify characteristics which allow comparison of different organizations. Others, the managerial analyst included, use organization analysis to understand a specific organization. Although organization analysis can be used for both purposes, obviously the elements of organization analysis discussed here are for use in managerial analysis.

When organization analysis is used for managerial analysis, it contains two primary ingredients. One element requires an analysis of the organization chart, and of the duties and responsibilities of top and middle-level managers. Since any basic management text contains a thorough discussion of the ingredients in desirable organization structure, this aspect will not be discussed further. However, a thorough understanding of the organization structure is essential to the second element of organization analysis.

The second element of organization analysis looks at the organization to ascertain the decision centers and means whereby information flows to and from these decision centers. This includes an identification of the actual and potential information which flows within the organization.

Looking at an organization in this particular fashion accomplishes many purposes. It pinpoints deficiencies in the way information flows as well as assuring that the organization does not have overlapping areas of responsibility. We must look at the decision centers as well as the information centers in the firm to identify the operating conditions and the constraints that will affect the organizational analysis. Thus, we are only concerned with charting the existing, not the ideal organization.

This analysis includes charting the information system, including the communications systems.[2] Knowledge about the information system is

---

[1] For a deeper investigation, reference may be made to the following: Charles P. Bonini, *Simulation of Information and Decision Systems in the Firm* (Englewood Cliffs, N.J.: Prentice-Hall, Inc., 1963); Rensis Likert, *The Human Organization* (New York: McGraw-Hill Book Co., Inc., 1967); and J. D. Thompson (ed.), *Approaches to Organizational Design* (Pittsburgh: University of Pittsburgh Press, 1966).

[2] For more detailed analysis, reference may be made to the following: C. West Churchman, Russell L. Ackoff, and E. Leonard Arnoff, *Introduction to Operations Research* (New York: John Wiley & Sons, Inc., 1957), pp. 20–56; Johnson F. Craig

used for two purposes. The analyst must know where information exists within the organization. In addition, he needs information about who makes what decisions and when. This analysis gives him a knowledge of the role of the recipient of the analysis and the impact of the analysis on the organization. The analyst must further review sources of relevant information within the firm, including information about the financial, human, and physical resources. This author has found it useful to look at the organization chart and to look at the availability of information about the following subsystems of the industrial organization producing a product.

Production

Information from the production system might include information on the raw material inventory, finished goods inventories, work-in-process inventories, and component parts inventories. Information about maintenance and characteristics of production equipment might be used for equipment replacement analysis. Further information about the composition of the work force, the availability of work force skills, turnover, vacations, and shifts might be useful. Finally, one might ascertain what cost information is available for the production environment. This cost information might be used for cost control purposes and might be quite relevant for other analytical purposes.

Marketing

Useful information on the marketing system might include historical data and demographic information about the recipient of the product and other data that might accompany sales. Further, any information about the relationship of sales to the factors affecting sales and information about the promotional policies and programs might be useful.

Finance

Information about cash needs, cash availability, funding programs, funding needs, funding availabilities, and financial performance of the organization or subunits, such as rates of return or other relevant ways of measuring the firm's performance, might be useful.

---

and G. R. Klave. "General Models of Communications Research: A Survey of the Development of a Decade," *Journal of Communication*, Vol. N (March, 1961), pp. 13–26; B. H. Westley, and M. S. Machean, "A Conceptual Model for Communications Research," *Audio-Visual Communications Review*, Vol. III (Winter, 1955), pp. 3–12.

Overall administration

Finally, any available information on the administrative system ought to be useful to the analyst, including an inventory of administrative personnel, the availability of supplies, and any other relevant information.

Interrelatedness of systems

Each of the above-described systems is itself related to other systems, thus, in a sense, forming a supersystem, because each system could be considered a component. Since this is so, it is vital to recognize interrelationships between systems.

Concluding comments

The end product of this orientation period, the process of obtaining an understanding of the environment, is a relatively meaningful understanding of the way the firm operates. Thus the analyst may proceed with this knowledge.

IV. GOALS, RESOURCES, AND OPPORTUNITIES

An understanding of the organization cannot proceed without an understanding of the organization's goals, resources, and opportunities. These factors are highly interrelated. Obviously, the resources and opportunities constitute the material leading to fulfillment of the goals. *Opportunities* simply refers to the goods and services the company *could* supply and the measure of value each contains. Measuring value is far from easy, but some recognition of value is necessary before any decision to use resources in its production can be made. Opportunities are meant to imply not only existing but not yet existing goods and services.

The goods and services a company supplies should be based upon consumer desires and the company's capabilities. The capabilities of the firm are in a sense the expression of the various combinations of products the firm could produce with the resources available to it. Although the kinds of resources severely limit the range of goods or services that can be produced with any degree of efficiency, the remaining possibilities are still virtually infinite. Further, available resources are not fixed but are dependent upon the company's ability to obtain resources. In turn, the firm's ability to obtain resources is dependent upon its existing resources and their utilization. Thus the available resources are in a constant state of flux. For the purposes of this chapter, we shall assume that a fixed level of resources exists.

If the resources are limited, it is useful to recognize the limits as constraints. In the subsequent chapters of this book, we shall deal quite extensively with quantifiable costs and measures of productive capacity which are the traditional measures of resource constraints. For example, we talk about financial resources in terms of dollars available to fund the purchase of material and equipment. Or we talk about our capacity to produce up to the limit of equipment and labor capabilities. These can be termed *operational constraints*. However, other types of subtler constraints should be recognized. We shall now discuss institutional as opposed to operational constraints. Then we shall look at constraints imposed by the interaction of resources and goods.

V. INSTITUTIONAL VERSUS OPERATIONAL CONSTRAINTS

One might recognize that objectives must be subject to institutional constraints as well as operational constraints. Institutional constraints are expressions of social values which allow the system to operate in harmony with its surroundings. Institutional constraints may be represented by certain legal constraints on activity by organizational executives. Consequently, the sale of certain drugs is prohibited by law, presumably as a reflection of society's belief that harmful products or services should be withheld from the general public. There may be other constraints that exist because of moral suasion. After World War II, automotive companies restrained from pricing to take full advantage of pent-up demand partly because they feared it would have an adverse effect on customer relations and partly because they feared government intervention.

Operational constraints are those constraints on activities which are imposed due to lack of resources or because some objectives are in conflict with other objectives of the organization. Lack of financial resources to expand into a new product line is a common manifestation of an operational constraint. Low inventory levels may be inconsistent with high sales volume. Thus, one places a constraint on the expected level of the other.

If we look at different managerial philosophies, we shall see that, to an extent, they represent different institutional constraints. Some of them indicate that although profits are the end goal of the firm, profits are available only if certain constraints are met.

Managerial philosophies

Basic objectives are essentially statements or reflections of managerial philosophy. The five most common managerial philosophies found in private business are as follows:

1. **Classical.** The classical philosophy is that the sole goal of the busi-

ness organization is to make as large a profit as possible for the owners in the long run.

2. *Humanist.* The humanist philosophy is that the sole goal of business organizations is to benefit society. Consequently, profits merely act as a constraint upon the degree of benefit which the business organization can disseminate.

3. *The combination classical/humanist.* This philosophy essentially says that some level of profits is desirable and necessary, but once it is attained, the business organization should act to benefit society.

4. *The mediator.* This philosophy is that the manager acts as the mediator between conflicting claimants. The claimants are (*a*) the employees, (*b*) the customers, (*c*) the owners, (*d*) the suppliers, and (*e*) the general public. It could be argued that these claimants are merely an explicit statement of what constitutes society and that this manager is thus a humanist.

5. *The quasi-public philosophy.* This philosophy is applicable only to very large corporations; it states that those very large corporations are quasi-public corporations which are so vital to the economic health of the nation that their primary role is survival while adequately providing for those with whom they come in contact. In other words, any change in policy must be considered from the standpoint of its effect upon the economic health of the country or any demographic or socioeconomic subgroups with which the organization has previously dealt. Obviously, this type of organization is highly institutionalized.

VI. THE INTERACTION OF RESOURCES AND GOALS

Resource availability places a limit on the attainment of goals. As an example, assume that an organization desires to pursue both a goal of market share and a goal of profitability. The market share objective is one which is pursued because it is considered a means of assuring long-run profitability. The organization avoids attaining a market share above a given level because of the possibility of antitrust action. In this instance, suppose the organization also sets minimums which must be attained. This information can be summarized in Figure 4–1. This figure recognizes only goals and institutional constraints upon goal fulfillment. Let us now add the effect of operational constraints (Figure 4–2). The area below line *AB* is attainable with resource 1. The area below line *EF* is attainable with resource 2. The reader will note that the area in the triangle *IEB* is attainable with resource 1 but unattainable with resource 2. Thus, it is unattainable to the organization. Recognizing the institutional constraints, the area of attainable goals is the rectangle *GHIJ*. This information poses a problem to the decision maker because it does not tell him what action to take within the area of attainable goals. However, it does help depict

Figure 4–1

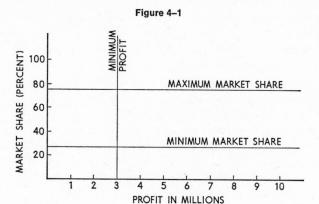

Figure 4–2

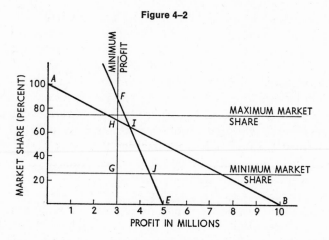

his action possibilities. Further, it demonstrates the interaction between goals and resources when both are recognized as constraints.

In the next chapter, we shall discuss the necessity of comparing and evaluating multiple objectives. Much later in the book, we shall discuss decision theory. In this discussion, we shall point out that the decision maker's objectives are the basis of a rule to identify the best course of action from among many possible courses of action. Translating to this situation, institutional and operational constraints delimit the area of possible action, but deeper analysis is necessary to identify where in the area of attainable solutions the best solution occurs.

The objective of this chapter is to develop an understanding of the organization. The concepts of this section can (at least conceptually) be used in order to develop a better fix on the objectives implied by the actions taken. For example, a firm operating at point H in Figure 4–2 seems to be maximizing market share, subject to the institutional constraints on minimum profit and maximum market share. It is entirely possible that an organization has never looked at the objectives implied by its actions. It may be quite surprised and decide that it ought to modify its behavior to reemphasize its true objectives if they are different from the implied objectives.[3]

In this text, is not possible to present a detailed methodology for understanding the general environment. The approaches and sources of information are so diverse and complex that it would be impossible to include them all in this text.

VII. IDENTIFYING THE PROBLEM

There are two stages in problem identification. The first step is a recognition that a potential problem exists. This is usually accomplished by comparing some quantitative or qualitative measure of performance with actual performance. This search for a standard is part of the subject matter of the next section. The process of identifying potential problems begins with searching for (or stumbling into) evidence of a deficiency. The deficiency may be merely an intuitive feeling that there is a problem or potential problem. Thus the company which is aware of the possibilities of applying linear programming to utilize its production facilities effectively may have no additional evidence that these facilities are not being effectively used. Identifying the problem requires some organizational mechanism for identifying the necessity of the individual conducting managerial analysis to investigate any particular area or problem. For the purposes of this discussion, we shall assume that there has arisen some particular need for problem identification (i.e., that there is, in fact, some condition in the organization which requires attention). The second stage of identifying the problem is to assure that we have identified the underlying or true problem facing the organization, so that we may conduct analysis toward the proper end.

The process of identifying the various systems discussed earlier should in itself converge on a proper identification of the problem. Thus, when management, for example, identifies a problem of an excess inventory, the managerial analyst must clearly recognize that the excess inventory investment may be simply a manifestation of a more basic underlying cause. The factors that affect that underlying cause may be many and varied.

In the following chapter, we shall discuss the measurable statement of

---

[3] See V. Buck, "A Model for Viewing an Organization as a System of Constraints," in James D. Thompson (ed.), *Approaches to Organizational Design* (Pittsburgh: University of Pittsburgh Press, 1966), pp. 103–72. In this article, Buck develops some of the concepts of this section.

the objective. If possible, the objective of the industrial organization ought to be tied to the overall objective of profit maximization or, at the very least, cost minimization. Thus, when management raises the question of excess inventories, the analyst must investigate the benefits of having inventories at various sizes so that *excess* means that the size of the inventory does not benefit the organization beyond the cost of having inventory of that size.

In conclusion, it can be seen that the process of identifying the problem is greatly simplified if one can focus on the overall objective so that one has a direct standard against which to compare the performance in a problem area.

VIII. FORMAL MECHANISMS FOR IDENTIFYING POTENTIAL PROBLEMS

The identification of a potential problem arises when someone recognizes an existent or expected deviation of conditions from a real or imaginary standard. Inventory levels are excessive only if someone objectively or subjectively identifies them as excessive. Consequently, a mechanism to identify problems for consideration by anyone responsible for managerial analysis requires (1) standards and (2) recognition and communication of those standards.

Standards are objective or identifiable criteria for acceptable levels of organizational performance. Most readers will be familiar with production or cost standards. Cost standards attempt to identify the expected cost to produce a given item. When the cost is excessive, a problem is said to exist. The occasion of excessive costs usually initiates a search for the cause so that they may be reduced to normal levels. The cost accounting system, if properly used, provides a continuous monitor on the standards it incorporates. By the same token, the organization needs standards for all managerial activities. Obviously, identification of standards for some activities is easier than for other activities. It is not the function of this text to dwell at length upon the problems of and necessity for establishment of performance standards at all levels. However, the vital importance of such standards should be recognized.

Given such standards, the organization should have a formal means for *recognizing* and *communicating* deviations from such standards. The cost control system can provide a continuous monitor which recognizes and communicates such deviations. A means should exist to uncover all potential problems via formal standards and formal means for recognizing and communicating potential problems. Further, existing standards should be constantly reevaluated.

There are essentially three elements in a formal process of identifying potential problems. One is a continuous monitor system. Many companies have a cost control system to control production costs. Although the criteria used to judge performance may differ for nonproduction segments of the firm, the concept of a control system which monitors performance for nonproduction segments of the organization is the same. Thus the organization should have a complete, continuous monitor control system.

Secondly, potential problem areas should be recognizable by the manager. Via this mechanism, the manager notifies the organizational subgroup responsible for managerial analysis of his perception of a potential problem. In this fashion the manager has direct access to analysis which the formal monitor system cannot pick up.

Thirdly, the organizational subgroup responsible for conducting managerial analysis should periodically review each functional area to evaluate both the current standards and performance in general. The evaluation of performance in general provides the analytical group the opportunity of investigating without traditional restrictions. Hence, more opportunity is provided for looking at performance and functions in the context of the organization as a whole.

DISCUSSION TOPICS AND PROBLEMS[4]

1. Prepare a schematic diagram of the systems which are of concern to the managerial analyst in a business firm. Explain your logic.

2. Prepare a schematic diagram identifying information sources, information recipients, and types of information necessary for the top-level manager in a business firm. Explain your logic.

3. Prepare a schematic diagram identifying information sources, information recipients, and types of information necessary for the manager of a functional unit for a business organization with which you are familiar.

4. How should a business organization's goals, resources, and opportunities relate to its product line?

5. How should a government's goals, resources, and opportunities relate to its product line?

6. Compare and contrast institutional versus operational constraints.

7. Assume that you are the manager of the only department store in a community of 25,000. The nearest department store is 20 miles away. Discuss the goals, resources, opportunities, institutional constraints, and operational constraints facing you. Be sure to indicate how they are interrelated. The store is wholly owned by a family whose sole interest is in the long-run profits as long as their annual return on investment does not drop below the prevailing interest rate on certificates of deposit.

---

[4] Make and state any assumptions necessary to answer these questions meaningfully.

SELECTED REFERENCES

Anthony, Robert N. *Planning and Control Systems*. Cambridge: Bureau of Business Research, School of Business, Harvard University, 1967.

Bonini, Charles P. *Simulation of Information and Decision Systems in the Firm*. Englewood Cliffs, N.J.: Prentice-Hall, Inc., 1963.

Dearden, John, and McFarlan, F. Warren. *Management Information Systems: Text and Cases*. Homewood, Ill.: Richard D. Irwin, Inc., 1966.

Donald, A. G. *Management Information and Systems*. New York: Pergamon Press, Inc., 1967.

Koontz, Harold, and O'Donnell, Cyril. *Principles of Management*. 3d ed. New York: McGraw-Hill Book Co., Inc., 1966.

Likert, Rensis. *The Human Organization*. New York: McGraw-Hill Book Co., Inc., 1967.

Schoderbek, Peter. *Management Systems*. New York: McGraw-Hill Book Co., Inc., 1967.

Thompson, J. D. (ed.). *Approaches to Organizational Design*. Pittsburgh: University of Pittsburgh Press. 1966.

5

Organizational objectives and their measurement

I. INTRODUCTION

In the last chapter, we discussed objectives and their relationship to resources and opportunities as a means of developing a general understanding of the organization. In this chapter, we are concerned with identifying objectives so that they may be used as a basis for deciding on the desirability of any course of action. This requires the translation of objectives into measurable terms so that the desirability of any course of action can be measured in terms of the extent to which it fulfills objectives.

II. THE ROLE OF OBJECTIVES

All organizations, be they profit-oriented public organizations, charitable organizations, or other kinds of organizations, exist to fulfill one or more purposes or objectives. The true value of managerial analysis hinges on the ability to identify the objectives of the organization and hence ascertain the best course of action needed to fulfill those objectives. These objectives or purposes are difficult to fulfill if the organization does not clearly state them.

Every action taken by every employee of an organization should contribute to the overall objective of that organization. Thus, all of the activities of the organization should not add up to the organizational objectives; but the organization, having established its objectives, should move on to establish the activities necessary to fulfill those objectives.

Therefore the process of establishing organizational objectives and objectives for all of the subunits of the organization provides the organization its basic direction. The establishment of the basic objectives of the organization provide a basis against which any action can be measured to ascertain whether it is contributing to fulfillment of the overall objectives of the organization. The overriding or basic objectives are always of a very general, normally nonquantifiable nature.

It is often standard practice to identify the overall objectives of a business firm as that of maximizing long-run profit. Since no means exist to assure that an organization is maximizing long-run profits, it is necessary to identify subsidiary operational objectives that will allow it to take those actions which it believes will maximize long-run profits. To assure that the activities of individuals in the organization contribute toward the overall objectives of the organization, a hierarchy of rules for the conduct of the enterprise must be developed. These rules must exist either implicitly or explicitly. The level of the rules is differentiated by referring to objectives, policies, and procedures. Each will now be described.

Objectives

Objectives may be described as hoped-for results, goals or targets. They may be further described as hoped-for states of affairs. Obviously, objectives can be quite specific or very general. A specific objective might be a 10 percent rate of return on investment, whereas a general objective might be an increase in profits. The more specific an objective, the easier it is to appraise how well it has been fulfilled.

Objectives may also be long-run or short-run. A short-run objective might be to improve the working capital position of the organization. This objective is short-run because it was probably developed due to a deficiency in the working capital position (hopefully an abnormal deficiency). A long-run objective might be to produce only a quality product. A short-run objective is generally more specific and directed toward a specific problem area.

This author advocates the division of objectives into two categories, basic and fulfilling. The only admissible basic objectives for a business organization are (1) profits (in practice, this must be stated in a more definitive manner); and/or (2) psychological rewards, over and above those derived from profits, to the owner and/or managers (in practice, this must be stated in a more specific manner). It is assumed that pursuing social goals provides a psychological reward; and in fact, this pursuit may be considered a personal goal of the owners or managers. It is to be expected that for most corporations, the sole basic objective is profits. Fulfilling objectives recognizes more specific goals which contribute to the basic objective.

Policies

Policies may be described as guides for managers in the pursuit of objectives. They may be further described as general rules for action. It is most important to recognize that they stem from fulfilling objectives. Thus, an objective of a quality product may lead to a policy of extensive inspection during and after production. Obviously, each fulfilling objective requires many policies in order to carry out that objective. Hence, another policy stemming from the objective of a quality product may be the purchase of only top-quality raw materials which are used in the production of the product.

Procedures

Procedures may be described as routine rules of action in fulfillment of a policy. They are specific actions to be taken for specific situations. They may, for example, detail the time, place, and kind of inspection to fulfill the policy of extensive inspection.

III. THE MEANS-END CHAIN

The reader is now in a position to see the hierarchy or means-end chain in establishing objectives and policies. In the above example, the production of a quality product was the fulfilling objective designed to fill the basic objective of profits. In turn, extensive inspection during and after production was a policy designed to carry out the fulfilling objective of a high-quality product. The hierarchy then looks as follows:

Profits
Quality product
Extensive inspection

The means-end chain is a reflection of the fact that every step in the hierarchy is a means to an end. For example, extensive inspection is a means to an end of a quality product, but now we start the process all over again because quality is a means to the end of profits. Thus a chain occurs because each of the objectives, policies, and procedures are linked to one another.

A further example

The means-end chain that might be identified for any arm of the government must stem from some understanding of the primary objective of government, coupled with the legislative sanction which creates or created the need for the particular agency. In general, we may recognize that governmental operations exist to maintain and enhance the welfare of the public. Welfare may be dichotomized into economic welfare and social welfare, social welfare being frequently a catchall for all noneconomic welfare. Early governmental activity existed primarily to provide for the maintenance of the physical well-being of the individual, particularly well-being from physical harm through the creation of armies and internal policing functions. Governmental activities now become more subtly concerned with something we might call psychological welfare. Agencies with this responsibility attempt to provide minority groups with equal social and economic opportunities. Even at this abstract level, we have moved from the very abstract objective of maintenance and improvement of welfare to something more specific in terms of the ways the particular agencies contribute to welfare, on the assumption that the agencies themselves, in contributing to this specific element of welfare, contribute to the overall welfare.

The order in which objectives and activities are established

Since all organizations come into being as a result of human desires to form the organization, some of the activities are already identified upon formation of the organization. Ideally, the objectives of the organization should precede the identification of any of the activities the organization would be involved in. For example, a business firm should first identify the objectives and secondly the kind of product or service that it will provide as a means of best fulfilling those objectives. It is very doubtful that any business organizations have evolved on the basis of this rationale. Almost all organizations, whether they be private enterprise or governmental organizations, begin with the identification of a product of service to be delivered, frequently with a specific identification of the product or service.

In any organization the organizational subunits derive their objectives from the overall objectives of the organization itself. Normally, one could readily identify the objectives of the subunit, since the subunit has been established to provide assistance to fulfill the major objective of the organization and that is the subunit's prime basis for existence. For example, the production planning and control department exists to assist in the planning and efficient conduct of the activity of producing the prime product.

IV. THE MOVEMENT FROM GENERAL OBJECTIVES TO MEASURABLE CRITERIA

It has often been said that profit-oriented enterprises can be managed more effectively because they have the profit objective, which is readily measured in dollars. In addition, this argument continues, the output or product of the enterprise is tangible, and its value is therefore readily identified. However, the student of business finds all is not so simple. He finds no agreement on the presence, correctness, and measurability of profit. Further, he can name numerous intangible products (or services) provided by business. The major advantage business has over not-for-profit organizations is the universality of the dollar (or appropriate currency) as the common denominator for measuring costs and value.

We have already indicated that short-run profitability is easier to measure than long-run profitability. We have also indicated that profits may not be the sole or even a partial goal. Recognizing the legitimacy of nonprofit goals, this book always assumes the sole goal is profits. Given this, the analyst will still find it difficult to measure or identify the effect of certain fulfilling objectives, policies, and procedures on overall profits.

If such measurement were possible, we would not need to concern ourselves with intermediate measures. Let us further identify what we mean by intermediate measures. An intermediate measure is simply a measure which, we believe, if maximized or minimized (subject to the appropriate constraints), will lead to improvement in the long-run or overall goal. The most frequently used intermediate measure in profit-oriented organizations is short-run profitability. Many readers will recall the elementary economic model of a firm which says to produce at the level where marginal revenue equals marginal cost ($MR = MC$). This model, in addition to the many variables which it ignores, is applicable for only one point in time, thus maximizing only short-run profit.

In the previous section, we looked at a firm that chose to produce a quality product because it believed that a quality product would, in the long run, lead to maximum profits. It is highly doubtful that any concrete evidence exists to support or reject this very major assumption. However, it is demonstrative of the kind of assumed relationship between intermediate measures and the overall goal.

Accepting the desirability of a quality product as a fulfilling goal, can we measure this goal? Since quality is intangible, it cannot be directly measured. However, quality does possess certain characteristics or attributes which might be identified and measured, either objectively or subjectively. If one can devise a scale so that these attributes can be intercompared, then we can measure quality. Given this measure, we can compare alternative ways of attaining quality. The annual cost attached to a given quality score is shown in Table 5–1. This presents a dilemma because of the difficulty of comparing quality score and cost. Accepting the quality score and annual cost as correct and meaningful, let us rank the scores and costs as shown in Table 5–2. The last column shows the additional costs of attaining the next highest level of quality. Thus, movement from a quality score of 78 to 82 costs $5,000. Suppose 3 and 4 were the only

Table 5–1

Product alternative	Quality score	Annual cost*
1........................87		$100,000
2........................93		120,000
3........................78		80,000
4........................82		85,000

* This is the annual cost at a constant level of output.

Table 5–2

Product alternative	Quality score	Annual cost*	Marginal cost†
3..................78		$ 80,000	......
4..................82		85,000	5,000
1..................87		100,000	15,000
2..................93		120,000	20,000

* This is the annual cost at a constant level of output.
† See Chapter 12 for a discussion of marginal analysis, including marginal cost.

alternatives open to the decision maker. His problem then is to decide: Are the four additional quality points worth $5,000? As an analyst, you can give him no help unless you know the impact of these four quality points on demand. This will then allow you to ascertain the effect on revenue. Since revenue minus costs equals (short-run) profits, the knowledge about the impact of these four quality points on demand would allow you to convert quality to dollars.

Three things should be illuminated by this discussion. The first is the important role of executive judgment which has limited the analysis because of the (executive's) assumption that a quality product is necessary for long-run profitability. If it were possible to identify all possible products and the impact on profits of each, then the quality objective would be unnecessary because the products could be chosen by their direct impact on profits. However, the number of products which would need analysis is infinite. Thus, some method for reducing those considered is necessary because of the prohibitive time and cost necessary to analyze them all.

The second factor which this discussion should illuminate is what happens when the quality scores (or other nondollar measure) cannot be converted to dollars (in this case via profits). Then the executive has one of two choices. He can say either: (1) Find the least-cost alternative which will give me a quality score of X, or (2) give me the highest quality for an annual cost of Y. The first calls for minimizing costs subject to X, and the second calls for maximizing quality subject to Y. One cannot both maximize quality and minimize cost.

The third factor is to recognize that whenever possible the managerial analyst converts all objectives to a dollar base so that costs may be lowered or minimized (subject to specified constraints) or profits may be increased or maximized.

We shall now go on to discuss ways of measuring objectives and converting multiple objectives to a common denominator so that alternatives can be compared among all objectives. When a decision is made without consideration of all objectives, suboptimization may occur. When optimization of a single objective means that one or more of the remaining objectives is not optimized, some way must be found to compare the objectives so that the best overall objective is fulfilled. Consideration of a single objective may mean that the overall objective is not fulfilled. These considerations should become clear in the next section.

V. MEASURABLE AND MULTIPLE CRITERIA

The purpose of this chapter is to identify the measurable form the objective will take in order to maximize, minimize, or improve the performance of the organization toward that objective. Thus, previously identified but abstract organizational objectives will be converted to some dollar base. Therefore the discussion will center upon minimization of costs, maximization of profits, improvement of profits, or lowering of costs.

It is frequently difficult to deal with service objectives in either public or private organizations. A private firm provides certain customer services in the belief that provision of these services contributes to the overall organizational objective of profitability. However, the relationship between the service and overall profitability is very difficult to identify and measure. For example, a retail store cannot accurately measure the cost of failing to have sufficient goods in inventory to meet its demand, since it may lose the customer for future sales as well as losing the present sale.

Suppose, for example, that the store mentioned above does decide that it must maintain a policy of adequate inventories as a means of servicing the customer. Somehow, this general statement must be converted to a specific statement against which we can measure the degree to which the adequate inventory policy has been fulfilled. The specific statement is referred to as the criterion. In this case the criterion might be the dollar value of the inventory relative to the dollar value of sales.

The store might set as a goal a monthly sales-to-inventory ratio of 0.5. Thus the store is saying that the monthly sales should be one half the average value of the inventory during the month or, in other words, that the average monthly value of the inventory should be twice the value of sales for the month. This ratio is fairly common among department stores. It is based on the assumption that the customer desires to choose from a variety of goods. Obviously, religious adherence to this ratio would dictate a much greater inventory during periods of high sales. If a store carries basically the same merchandise the entire year, it may expect the necessity to increase its inventory to accommodate a larger volume but not a larger variety during periods of high sales. Hence, it does not really need to increase its inventory proportionately when sales volume is above normal. On the other hand, when sales are below normal, a proportionate cut in inventory might necessitate a cut in variety, which in turn might reduce sales further. Thus, when sales are below normal, the inventory should be reduced, but not proportionately to the reduction of sales. For example, if sales are 90 percent of normal, the inventory should be more than 90 percent of normal (but less than 100 percent of normal).

A more rational goal might be to make the inventory dependent upon the level of sales, with the following quantified objective.

$$AI = NI \left(\frac{AS}{NS}\right)^{\frac{1}{2}}$$

AI = Desired inventory
AS = Actual monthly sales
NS = Normal monthly sales

Assume NS = \$1,000,000 and normal inventory (NI) is \$2,000,000.[1] If AS = \$1,100,000 then AI = (\$2,000,000)(1.1)^{1/2} = \$2,097,320. Table 5–3 shows various inventories for various levels of sales, assuming NS = \$1,000,000. Thus, it can be seen that increases in sales need not be

Table 5–3

AS	$\left(\frac{AS}{NS}\right)^{\frac{1}{2}}$	AI	Change in sales from normal	Change in inventory from normal
1.1............1.0487		2,097,320	100,000	97,320
1.0............1.0000		2,000,000	....	....
0.9............0.9487		1,897,400	100,000	102,600

---

[1] The reader will note that if $AI = NI\left(\frac{AS}{NS}\right)$, the ratio of *AS* to *AI* will always be 0.5. Thus the square root is essential to this model. If $\left(\frac{AS}{NS}\right)$ were carried to a power greater than one, the model could accommodate the goal of an inventory above a normal ratio in periods of high sales and below a normal ratio in periods of low sales.

accompanied by proportionate increases in inventory. Also, decreases in sales need not be accompanied by proportionate decreases in inventory.

It can further be seen that if actual sales are above normal, the desired ratio is greater than 0.5 and if actual sales are below normal, the desired ratio is less than 0.5.

Although this may be useful as a means of checking the adequacy of an inventory policy, it is preferable to try to relate the necessity for adequate inventory to the dollar so that the cost of obtaining this goal may be recognized. Thus, one might develop an equation to measure the cost of inadequate inventory such as:

$$C_I = \left(\frac{S}{I}\right)^3 10,000$$

C_I = Monthly cost of inadequate inventory
S = Monthly sales
I = Monthly inventory

Thus, at $\frac{S}{I} = 0.5$, $C_I = \$1,250$; but at $\frac{S}{I} = 1$, $C_I = \$10,000$. Consequently, halving the inventory makes the cost of inadequate inventory eight times as high. As more and more inventory is carried, the cost of inadequate inventory declines. However, this inventory costs money to carry. Now assume that the cost of carrying inventory is primarily the cost of capital tied up in inventory. If the cost of capital is 24 percent per year, one might express the monthly cost per dollar of inventory (letting C_E represent the monthly cost per dollar of inventory investment) as $C_E = 0.02$. Thus,

Table 5–4

Value of inventory V_I	$\frac{S}{I}$	Cost of inadequate inventory C_I	Cost of carrying inventory C_C	Total inventory costs C_T
$ 250,000............	4.0	$640,000	$ 5,000	$645,000
500,000.............	2.0	80,000	10,000	90,000
1,000,000.............	1.0	10,000	20,000	30,000
2,000,000.............	0.5	1,250	30,000	31,250

monthly carrying costs (C_C) are $C_E V_I$ where V_I is the value of the inventory for the given month. If normal sales are $1 million per month, then Table 5–4 would question the desirability of a sales-to-inventory ratio of 0.5. The lowest total cost occurs when $\frac{S}{I} = 1$.

In some instances the conversion to cost or profits is less necessary. Thus the personnel department may have a recreational budget, which presumably contributes to employee morale and which in turn contributes to productivity. One criterion might be, given the recreational budget, to maximize weighted man-hours of recreational participation.

One of the problems of using criteria other than profit is that pursuit of the major objectives may not truly fulfill the nonquantifiable objective. For example, a recreational program yielding the greatest man-hours of participation may appeal to a small proportion of the total work force who participate intensely. Hence, one may have to add a condition that at least X percent of the work force participates in the program. One may also identify two criteria. If possible, once these criteria are identified, there should be a means for reducing them to some common denominator, so that they may be intercompared and the right mix of these objectives may be identified as the means of most effectively carrying out the overall objective.

VI. REDUCING MULTIPLE OBJECTIVES TO A COMMON BASE

The Asphalt Paving Company, mentioned in Chapter 1, recognizes the fact that its objectives must be long-run profits. It further is aware that minimizing costs on any given job is only one factor which contributes to long-run profits. The company undertakes each job on the basis of a contractual agreement which specifies the job to be done and the minimal standards for the materials and for the resulting roadway. However, the company recognizes that the willingness of the contracting agency to grant future contracts depends, at least in part, upon the willingness of the company to provide materials above the minimal standards and to schedule its operations for the convenience of the contracting agency. Consequently, in this situation the company has the following two objectives: (1) to minimize current operating costs and (2) to insure future contracts.

It should be noted that the dilemma of minimizing current costs while at the same time assuring future revenues faces all business firms.

The company believes that market share is the best predictor of future contracts (market share is the ratio of present contracts in dollar value to the total contracts awarded in dollar value). Thus, if the paving company operates in a two-state area and the value of its paving contracts for the last year was $10 million and total contracts awarded are $40 million, this figure is 0.25. Further, suppose that the company must make a decision on the kind of material to be purchased for a particular contract. Suppose the expected profitability on this $1-million job is $50,000. The job calls for at least grade C material, and the company must decide whether to purchase grade A, B, or C. The relationship of the grade purchased to immediate profits is as shown in Table 5-5. The first objective of immediate profit is maximized when grade C is purchased. Assume that the company feels

Table 5–5

Course of action	Actual profit	Percent of $50,000 profit which is obtained
Purchase *A*..................	$37,500	75%
Purchase *B*..................	45,000	90
Purchase *C*..................	50,000	100

that it should have 25 percent of the market to insure future profitability. The relationship of the grade purchased to long-run revenue is as indicated in Table 5–6. Considering this objective alone, the company should purchase grade *A*. This dilemma may be resolved if a normalized weight is attached to each objective. This means that percentages should be assigned each objective so that the total percentage is 100 percent. Let us say that immediate profits are three times as important as market share. Thus the weights are 75 percent for immediate profitability and 25 percent for long-run revenues.[2] The dilemma facing this decision maker is

Table 5–6

Course of action	Actual market share	Percent of market share objective which is obtained
Purchase *A*..................	0.250	100%
Purchase *B*..................	0.225	90
Purchase *C*..................	0.200	80

that he cannot directly compare market share with immediate profitability. Consequently, he must find a method for making them directly comparable. The previously formed information can now be used to make a comparison. Let us present that data in Table 5–7. If *A* is purchased, 100 percent of the objective weighing 25 percent is fulfilled, thus contributing 0.25 = 25 percent toward the overall objective of meeting both objectives. However, only 75 percent of the objective worth 75 percent is met, thus contributing $0.75 \times 0.75 = 0.5625 = 56.25$ percent

---

[2] Normalized weights are calculated with the following formula:

$$w_i = \frac{a_i}{\sum_{i=1}^{n} a_i}$$

In this case, $a_1 = 3$ (immediate profits) and $a_2 = 1$ (market share). Since $n = 2$, $w_1 = 3/4 = 0.75$ and $w_2 = 1/4 = 0.25$.

Table 5–7

Course of action	Weight 0.75: Percent of fulfillment of objective 1	Weight 0.25: Percent of fulfillment of objective 2
Purchase *A*................0.75		1.00
Purchase *B*................0.90		0.90
Purchase *C*................1.00		0.80

toward the overall objective, or a total of $0.25 + 0.5625 = 0.8125 = 81.25$ percent of the overall objective is met. Likewise, the contribution of the purchase of *B* and *C* is:

$$B = 0.90(0.75) + 0.90(0.25) = 0.90 = 90\%$$
$$C = 1.00(0.75) = 0.80(0.25) = 0.95 = 95\%$$

In view of this, the company concludes that it should purchase *C* because a more expensive grade does not contribute enough to future revenues to warrant that purchase.

This exercise demonstrates a universal method for converting dissimilar objectives to a common base.[3] This procedure is, however, based upon a series of conversions of data that may be difficult to make in practice. Identification of specific levels of each of the objectives (i.e., a specific desired market share and profit) may be difficult, but identification of the extent to which those objectives are fulfilled becomes even more difficult. Fulfillment of the profit objective is relatively easy to identify in the above example, since the cost of purchasing each of the alternative grades of material is known. It would be much more difficult to estimate the market share obtained as a result of the purchase of grade *A*, *B*, or *C* materials. Further, placing the weight on each of the objectives (i.e., 75 percent to profit and 25 percent to market share) is an even more difficult task. However, this procedure does give us an operative way to decide upon the most desirable course of action to be taken in the face of multiple and noncomparable objectives. Coupling this procedure with the procedure of sensitivity analysis, which will be discussed later in Chapter 21, provides information with which to make a decision of this nature. For example, if we allow the percent of fulfillment of each of the objectives to remain the same but modify the weight, we note that the weight of objective 2 must be greater than 0.5 before the decision is changed. Consequently, the decision appears to be quite insensitive to the weighting scheme; thus, one may place a fair amount of faith in the answer in light of these limited objectives.

[3] Assuming that the utility or desirability of deviations from 100 percent fulfillment are proportionate (i.e., being 20 percent below 100 percent fulfillment is twice as undesirable as being 10 percent below 100 percent fulfillment).

A more desirable method of conversion would be to construct objective 2 in some form of dollar or profit figures, as we did for the retail store earlier. Thus, if one could convert the future profitability from the purchase of grade *A* or *B* material to dollars, a comparison of the cost of the purchase versus the contribution to future profitability could be made.

VII. A FURTHER EXAMPLE

Suppose that the organization has been going through a maturation process and has, until recently, attempted to maximize only the single objective of short-run profitability. This is a fairly common procedure. Suppose that, historically, the dollar value of the contracts let for the two-state area serviced by the Asphalt Paving Company has totaled $40 million annually and that the company, up until the last three years (when it modified its decision-making procedure to account for the second objective of long-run profits), has maintained a market share of 25 percent and an after-tax profit amounting to 5 percent of sales, or $50,000. Further, suppose that under the newly promulgated dual objective the market share has increased to 28 percent and the actual profit level is 4.5 percent of sales, as opposed to the previous profit level of 5 percent of sales.

The relationship between market share and the ratio of cost to sales can be expressed as an equation, the equation being $MS = 0.55 - 6(R)$ where R is the return per dollar of sales and MS is the market share.[4] Since return refers to return per dollar, total profit can be calculated as follows:

$$TP = MS(40,000,000)R$$

because total sales in the market are $40 million. Substituting in the equation for MS gives:

$$TP = (0.55 - 6R)40,000,000R$$
$$= 22,000,000R - 240,000,000R^2$$

Thus, at $R = 0.05$:

---

[4] This was calculated using the two-point equation for a line. This equation is discussed in Chapter 9. The points given above yield:

$$\frac{MS - 0.25}{R - 0.05} = \frac{0.25 - 0.28}{0.05 - 0.045} = \frac{-0.03}{0.005} = -6$$

and

$$MS - 0.25 = -6(R - 0.05)$$
$$MS = -6R + 0.55$$

where

$$R = \text{Return per dollar of sales}$$
$$MS = \text{Market share}$$

$$TP = 22{,}000{,}000\,(0.05) - 240{,}000{,}000\,(0.0025) = 1{,}100{,}000 - 600{,}000$$
$$= 500{,}000$$

which checks. Given this, the company may apply a particular methodology (discussed in Chapter 12) to this problem to identify the return per dollar which maximizes profit. This conclusion is subject to numerous restrictions and assumptions. One restriction is that MS and R must be greater than zero; two major assumptions are that the relationship between MS and R is linear and that the company can control R.

VIII. NONMONETARY CRITERIA

Another similar problem is illustrated by the following situation. An advertising manager for a retail store wishes to decide what kind of promotion to engage in to attract sufficient customers to insure profitability. He is concerned with providing only enough information to generate the customers. In order to accomplish this objective, the organization has provided him with a promotion budget. His problem is to allocate that budget to the proper promotion categories. Assume that his measurable criterion (i.e., that which we wish to maximize) is the number of different potential customers exposed to the advertising message. He may then look at various alternatives.

Suppose that the following media are available to disseminate information about his goods: radio, newspaper, and local television. He has no idea of the profitability of any of these alternatives. The promotion manager, however, may be able to ascertain the number of exposures that each media provides to a relevant group of potential customers. Assume that the promotion manager has $2,000 to dispense for promotion in any given month. Assume further that the relevant audience for the TV spot promotion amounts to 12,000 per spot announcement but that the new TV audience for subsequent announcements is reduced, depending upon the number of announcements. The second audience of new potential customers is one half of the previous audience of new customers. Thus, if there were two TV spot announcements, the first audience would be 12,000. Of the second audience, one half, or 6,000, would be new viewers. Therefore the total potential customers from two TV spot announcements is 18,000. Further, assume that the relevant radio audience is 3,000 per spot announcement and that it also decreases, so that each subsequent announcement reaches one half of the previous number of new members of the audience. Also, assume that the newspaper audience is 5,000 per spot announcement and that this number decreases by one half of the previous audience. Further assume that the cost of the TV spot announcement is $1,000; the radio announcement, $500; and the newspaper advertisement, $500. For the moment, we shall assume that the duplication of audiences between the three media is nil and may therefore be ignored.

On this basis, the advertising manager has nine alternatives which exactly use the $2,000 budget; and for each of these, he may identify the number of original exposures. The alternatives are shown in Table 5–8.

Table 5–8

The alternatives	Number of this alternative	Total original exposures
All TV.................................1		18,000
All radio...............................2		5,625
All newspaper..........................3		9,375
One TV, one radio, one newspaper..........4		20,000
One TV, two radio......................5		16,500
One TV, two newspaper..................6		19,500
Two radio, two newspaper................7		12,000
Three radio, one newspaper...............8		10,250
Three newspaper, one radio...............9		11,750

The advertising manager is now able to ascertain the most desirable action needed in order to obtain the maximum number of original exposures. He should then choose alternative 4 which says: Take one TV, one radio, and one newspaper ad. This procedure has allowed him to compare the nine relevant alternatives. He could go further and attempt to arrive at a scheme for weighting the desirability of different media exposures. Thus, he might say that the presence of both audio and visual stimuli on TV is worth 50 percent more than either radio or newspapers. In this case, he will only use TV. This scheme provides us with an implied weighting that equates each of the three media.

IX. SUMMARY

In this chapter, we have discussed both the problem of identifying measurable objectives and the problem of making objectives and alternatives comparable. In fact, we emphasize the latter because the former is almost an art that comes with experience. In this chapter and other chapters, we have discussed the movement from general statements of objectives to specific, measurable statements or objectives. For example, we discussed the importance of the service objective and the movement from that to the provision of adequate inventories as necessary to fulfill the service objective. Further, we could identify the extent to which the inventory objective was fulfilled by looking at the ratio of investment in inventory to sales.

As we move from the abstract to the concrete, we are making a series of assumptions that the concrete measurement is in fact that element which contributes to the abstract objective. To the extent that we are correct in this assumption, the activities in which the firm is engaged are correctly fulfilling the abstract objective. The process is one in which all organizations implicitly or explicitly must be involved. It was further pointed out that the common denominator must be found so that objectives may be readily compared with the fulfillment of the overall objective. We have focused fairly extensively on the nonmonetary objectives, but we have also pointed out that it is most desirable to convert the objective to monetary form if possible.

DISCUSSION TOPICS AND PROBLEMS

1. Indicate the difference, if any, between each term in the pair for the following pairs of terms:

> Goals and objectives
> Objectives and policies
> Policies and procedures
> Objectives and criteria

2. Explain and illustrate the means-end chain.

3. It has been said that the first and most crucial ingredient of accounting is measurement. Could the same thing be said of managerial analysis? Explain.

4. A restaurant has the following three objectives: (*a*) an average customer service time of eight minutes, (*b*) a 10 percent market share, and (*c*) a 10 percent return on investment. The restaurant also has three courses of action which it is considering. The following table shows what happens to each objective when each course of action is taken:

Course of action	Average service time	Market share	Return on investment
A	7 minutes	9%	10%
B	8 minutes	10	9
C	10 minutes	9	8

If each objective is given equal weight, which course of action should the company follow?

5. A promotion manager has $2,000 to spend on promotion. He estimates that the relevant audiences for the first TV, radio, and newspaper spot announcements are 10,000, 4,000, and 8,000 respectively. Also, in all cases the audience for the next announcement is one half the audience of new customers from the previous announcement. The price for a TV spot is $1,000; for the radio and newspaper, $500. There is no duplication of audiences. If the manager assumes the TV spot to be twice as effective as the radio and four times as effective as the newspaper, how should he allocate his $2,000?

SELECTED REFERENCES

Koontz, Harold, and O'Donnell, Cyril. *Principles of Management.* 3d ed. New York: McGraw-Hill Book Co., Inc., 1966.

Litterer, Joseph A. *Organizations: Structure and Behavior.* New York: John Wiley & Sons, Inc., 1963.

Moore, Franklin G. *Management Organization and Practice.* New York: Harper and Row, 1964.

Simon, Herbert A. *Administrative Behavior.* 2d ed. New York: Macmillan Co., 1958.

6

Data collection and measurement

I. INTRODUCTION

Managerial analysis does not become operational without meaningful data with which to specify the nature of the relationships within the environment. The usefulness of the final analysis is restricted by the meaningfulness of the data used in the analysis. However trite, the expression "Garbage in, garbage out" is apropros.

Before discussing the sources of data and their validity, we must discuss the process of determining relationships between variables in an unbiased manner. This requires the use of the scientific method.

II. DETERMINING RELATIONSHIPS

The development of a useful model requires a quantitative means of describing the relevant aspects of the environment. An element in the environment may be quantitatively described either by declaration or by collection of data which are further analyzed. In either case, it may be described as a certain or as an uncertain event. A declared value may be based upon judgment or logic. Judgment and logic in this case have different meanings. An example of logic is a conclusion that the distance between point A and C in the following diagram

is equal to

$$\sqrt{AB^2 + BC^2}$$

Judgment may be strictly intuitive or aided by general knowledge. An event that occurs with certainty is an event for which the outcome is always the same. An example of a certain event would be the hourly wage rate for an employee. An uncertain event is an event which cannot be described by the same value each time. An example of an uncertain event is the time it takes to travel the distance between points A and B. In this instance, one uses measures of central tendencies and/or measures of variation to describe the event.

Normally, this description will begin with identification of a postulated set of descriptive measures of the environment and their interrelationships. In the example in Chapter 1, it was postulated that the total costs of operating a motor vehicle were composed of three elements.[1] Analysis later demonstrated that operating costs were dependent in a specific way on the following:

1. Distance traveled (in miles)
2. Travel time (in minutes)
3. Number of vehicular stops

First, it was necessary to acquire a set of data to be used in determining the exact nature of the relationship between the three independent variables and the dependent variable (vehicle operating costs). Then, to predict the average operating cost for any trip, it was necessary to describe the trip by these same variables. Consequently, the elements in the environment need descriptive measurement, such as the average length of time required to travel a route. Also, the exact description of the relationships between variables, as in the following equation, was needed:

$$VOC = 0.05M + 0.02T + 0.0055S$$

where:

VOC = Variable operating costs
M = Distance traveled (in miles)
T = Travel time (in minutes)
S = Number of stops

It can be seen that these relationships are determined by postulating a given relationship or a given form of relationship and then confirming or denying this hypothesis. When the criteria used to confirm or deny this hypothesis are determined in advance, one is using the scientific method. Statistical analysis offers various means for confirming or denying hypothesized relationships.

It is assumed that the reader is familiar with the various measures of central tendency and variance or that he will refer to a statistics text to provide himself with this information. Both the correctness of the meas-

---

[1] See Chap. 1, p. 17.

ures and their use in a model have serious impact on the validity of an analysis. For example, a deliveryman has two alternative delivery routes which can be traversed in an average of 10 and 12 minutes, respectively; and the standard deviation is 6 and 2 minutes, respectively. It is quite possible that the variation in delivery time for alternative 1 will have an impact on operating costs.

The prime emphasis of the remainder of this chapter will be upon data collection and validity, leaving the discussion of finding relationships to later chapters. In general, the validity of the data is dependent upon the representativeness of the sample and the truth of the information.

The data collected here are used to provide maximum composite information from a limited amount of raw information. The information provided may be unacceptable, minimally acceptable, or very acceptable, depending upon the following:

1. The amount of data available
2. The validity and relevance of the available data
3. Use made of the data which were available

The amount of available data is limited by economic considerations. An analyst may compile varying amounts of data except that, at some point, additional data either become unnecessary or prohibitively costly. The rule of thumb which should be used is that the value of the ultimate analysis must more than offset the cost of conducting the analysis. One of the primary costs of conducting the analysis is the cost of acquiring data.

III. THE SCIENTIFIC METHOD IN STATISTICAL ANALYSIS

Statistical analysis should, in the purest sense, be based upon the use of the scientific method. The scientific method has two essential characteristics: The first is a systematic approach, in order to draw the ultimate and proper conclusion in confirmation or denial of a hypothesis which has been made. Such a hypothesis represents an initial feeling by the researcher about the relationship which exists between the variables with which he is concerned. The second essential characteristic of the scientific method is that it is an approach which is intended to reduce the possibility of contaminating the inputs so that the conclusions will not be biased.

The scientific method allows the scientist some means of ascertaining whether his general observations about nature are true or not true. Obviously, this means that the scientist must begin by making some general observations about nature. In this process, he must take his general observations about nature and structure those observations in a specific manner so that a hypothesis may be made. The next step after making the hypothesis is to set up the procedure that will be used to test the hypothesis objectively. Then, and only then, are the data gathered. Once the observations have been made, the next step is to go ahead and apply the procedure previously decided upon to test the hypothesis. Finally, on the basis of this information, the hypothesis is accepted or denied.

Since the scientist knows how the data will be used to confirm or deny his hypothesis, it is possible for him to record the observations to favor the outcome he has previously hypothesized. Of course, he must not attempt to influence the outcome of his hypothesis. With a good scientist, who strives to remain objective, this would not be a problem. But it is difficult to devise an alternative to avoid the possibility of such influences; one could first gather the information and then set up some procedure by which he would attempt to confirm or deny his hypothesis. Then we are faced with the possibility that the procedure to confirm or deny the hypothesis will be influenced by the nature of the information that has been gathered. More importantly, the analyst may merely manipulate the data until he finds a relationship. This ever-present possibility means that the scientist must always strive to be nonbiased and objective.

Let us now review the steps of the scientific method. The first step is general observation of the phenomena. The second step is to make some hypothesis about these phenomena. The third step is to develop a means of testing that hypothesis. The fourth step is to gather data in order to conduct the test prescribed in the previous step. The fifth step is to test the hypothesis by the procedures described, using the data that have been gathered. The sixth step is to confirm or deny the hypothesis.

This discussion of the scientific method has been presented to emphasize that, in conducting statistical analysis, the researcher must adhere to the two prime tenets of the scientific method: (1) the tenet of objectivity and (2) the tenet of systematically approaching the analysis. The discussion also emphasizes that to evaluate the work of someone else, the analyst must view it in terms of the elements discussed.

IV. DATA SOURCES

There are two common ways to obtain data. One is to create it by experimentation or measurement of some kind; the second is to use existing data. The managerial analyst will frequently use existing data drawn from two primary sources, i.e., sources within the organization and sources external to the organization. Frequently, data that deal with the external environment, such as data about demand for the product or services of the industry, will be found outside the organization in various public sources too numerous to list here.

The proper source of data depends entirely upon the type of research being conducted. Many disciplines will have published material which is familiar to knowledgeable researchers. On the other hand, many of the data used for managerial analysis are found within the organization, and it is the role of the researcher to locate the source of those data. Organizations maintain a host of existing records on operations of the organization. The researcher intending to use internal data must ask a series of questions about their validity. He must know exactly how the data are gathered and the ability of the individual or the instrument to measure the exact value of the object being measured.

Many measurement pitfalls exist. These pitfalls will be specifically discussed under the heading "Data Validity" in the section immediately following.

Given a knowledge of exactly how the data have been gathered and thereby a feeling for its validity, the researcher must then know how to process the data properly. This knowledge is necessary to insure that the researcher (1) is aware of the possibility of errors in the transcription of the data and (2) is completely conscious of the elements that make up the information he has received. For example, in standard inventory control analysis the researcher will frequently be provided with a figure which represents the cost of carrying a dollar's worth of inventory. Certainly the process of calculating this particular figure has an abundant amount of history behind it. That figure may play a substantial role in the decision that is ultimately made regarding the size of the inventory needed by the firm. Consequently, the researcher needs to know how the figure was derived in order to assess its validity and thus the validity of the recommended decision.

V. DATA VALIDITY

Data validity is verified by looking at (1) accuracy, (2) impartiality, and (3) representativeness. If these three characteristics are present, it may be assumed that the data are valid.

Accuracy

The criterion of accuracy deals with the ability correctly to measure and identify what is being gathered. When data are collected, they are assembled by some predesigned method, which in turn means that some way must be decided upon to measure the relevant variables. Thus the first element in gathering accurate data is to identify clearly and distinctly exactly what it is that is wanted. This, of course, can take place only if we have properly identified the organizational objectives, the problem, and the general characteristics of the environment.

The second element in accuracy is the ability to communicate unambiguously what is being measured. This communication problem is partially dependent upon the kind of data being gathered. If one is attempting to collect information about demand for items held in inventory in order to derive an effective inventory control model, one must be able to specify unambiguously the exact nature of demand. For example, in a retail store, does a sale take place and is the inventory reduced when the customer orders the item, when the item is delivered, or when the bill is paid?

Another element of accuracy deals with the question of whether the individual or instrument responsible for recording the item being measured can in fact properly record that item. For example, one of the valid ingredients in an inventory control model for a retail store deals with the amount of demand which exists for items which are out of stock at the time customers wish to purchase them. In fact, some retail stores have out-of-stock forms on which the clerks are asked to record requests for items which are out of stock. The ability of a clerk to record specific out-of-stock items is dependent upon his ability to obtain such information from the customer.

It is of course entirely possible that the customer does not know exactly what item he wants until he sees it. Consequently, the clerk is unable to record unavailable information. He cannot measure the item because he cannot extract a description of it from the customer. Even a machine is, of course, subject to questions of its ability to record.

Another element of accuracy deals with interest. When data are recorded by humans, accuracy is also influenced by the interest of the recorder. In the out-of-stock example the proper recording of requests for items is obviously strongly influenced by the interest of the clerk in supplying this kind of information. If the clerk is not interested, some of the information will go unrecorded and will not be a part of the data.

Data used in managerial analysis are sometimes gathered by observation. In that case the factors which block valid or correct data may be attributable either to the individual being observed (if an individual is being observed) or to the individual doing the observing.

One of the factors which may block recording of the data may be that the individual being observed does not wish to be observed. Another factor may be that the individual being observed wishes a different thing to be observed than that which is actually taking place. For example, it is an acceptable tenet of gathering information about income and assets of individuals that these figures will normally be understated by a significant percentage.[2]

Part of the problem of accuracy stems from the sources of the data. For example, data on unemployment are drawn or may be drawn in a number of different ways. Some of the data on unemployment exist

---

[2] See Robert Ferber, *The Reliability of Consumer Reports of Financial Assets and Debts* (Urbana: Bureau of Business and Economic Research, University of Illinois, 1966).

because some employers are required by law to submit reports. Data published by the government are of differential accuracy, depending primarily upon the ability or inclination of the receiving agency to check or verify the information contained within the report.

Obviously, the government cannot police the accuracy of that information, and therefore the reporter's attitude toward that information will have a significant impact on its validity. A particularly good reference that criticizes some of the public sources with respect to accuracy of information was published in *Fortune* magazine by Oskar Morgenstern, entitled "Qui Numerare Incipit Errare Incipit" ("He Who Begins to Count Begins to Err").[3]

Impartiality

Next, the researcher is faced with the characteristic of impartiality. For instance, the clerk preparing out-of-stock forms may overstate demand to make his potential sales look higher, thus blaming a lackluster performance on out-of-stock goods. The overstatement of demand may be deliberate or unconscious. The requirement for impartiality is applicable only to data which are gathered by individuals rather than data gathered by mechanical means.

Representativeness

The representativeness of the sample is dependent upon (1) the size of the sample and (2) whether the sample in fact represents the universe. The universe refers to the entire group of individuals or things about which one is concerned. If we are dealing with the entire universe, representativeness is not relevant. Usually, it is impractical or impossible to obtain anything more than sample information.

To illustrate the importance of the representativeness of the sample, one need merely to look at the opinion poll prediction made by the *Literary Digest* about the outcome of the 1936 Presidential election. When a random sample was drawn from the telephone directory in order to make that prediction a very high prediction, error occurred because the telephone directory did not contain a representative sample of the universe of voters. Even today, nonownership and unlisted phones create a significant problem in phone studies.

In the example in Chapter 1, the average length of time required to traverse a particular route is X number of minutes, and that conclusion has to be drawn by a sampling process. The question of whether the sample is representative strongly affects the validity of our answer with

---

[3] *Fortune*, October, 1963, pp. 142–44, 173–80

respect to the best alternative route. Since the paving operation cannot take place at night, night travel is not part of the universe of relevant travel time. Also, since it is highly unlikely that the work crew would be traveling during nonworking hours, those hours should also be eliminated as relevant times for travel. If the work crew takes a lunch break from 12 A.M. to 1 P.M. and cannot receive the pavement truck, that period of time should not be included in our sample time.

The term *universe* is much easier to conceptualize in the case of individuals or things. Therefore, in the sample of voters for the survey discussed above, the universe is defined as all potential voters (everyone who is over 21, except in those states where the legal voting age is 18).

Although the sample size does not directly affect the representativeness of a sample, it does affect our ability to extend the specific findings of the sample in order to make conclusions about the universe. Certainly the Bureau of the Census would not proceed with a sample of 100 individuals of voting age in order to draw its conclusions. On the other hand, the Bureau of the Census has used samples which were considerably less than 1 percent of the universe. Why is this so? This stems from the law of large numbers, which, when concerned with the arithmetic means, states: "The sample mean tends to be closer and closer to the population mean as the sample size increases." One way of illustrating this phenomenon is to look at some of the work in extrasensory perception, where an ability to predict the upside of a randomly flipped coin may be claimed. Using a common criterion of accepting a false hypothesis 2.5 percent of the time, let us hypothesize that a person has extrasensory perception. That is to say, he has some ability to predict the outcome of a randomly tossed coin, regardless of the magnitude of that ability. If we take a sample of 16 flips of the coin and the individual is correct 12 or more times, we accept the conclusion that he has extrasensory perception. With a sample of 64, if he is right 40 times, we accept the conclusion that he has extrasensory perception. With a sample of 256, if he is right 144 times, we accept the conclusion that he has extrasensory perception. Thus, as the sample size changes, the percentage of correct answers necessary to accept the conclusion changes from 75 percent to 62.5 percent to 56.25 percent.[4]

The direct question of representativeness has two elements. One is the problem of whether the sample is drawn from the actual universe. This problem involves a recognition of the true universe and a means of assuring that the sample is drawn from that universe. Hence, it is incorrect to take a sample of political attitudes from a group of University of Maryland students and conclude that they are representative of all college

---

[4] In terms of formal statistics, we reject the hypothesis of no extrasensory perception.

students. The true universe is University of Maryland students. The second ingredient of representativeness requires that the individuals or elements in the sample have been randomly selected. In order to have a random selection, each member or element within the universe must have an equal chance of being chosen.

In dealing with the question of representativeness, particularly the question of sample size and randomness, one does well to consult a statistician. One method of reviewing the representativeness of the data is to make a comparison between certain characteristics of the universe and the sample. For example, in dealing with economic and demographic information, a comparison can frequently be made between certain economic and demographic characteristics of the sample which has been drawn and the information provided by the Bureau of the Census for these particular variables.

VI. DATA COMPARABILITY

One of the prime factors which will influence many of the types of analysis is the fact that the analysis uses data that have been gathered over an extensive period of time. In statistical analysis, there is a whole area devoted to *time series analysis*. Time series analysis refers to data that vary over time, frequently exhibiting growth or decline. Population statistics, production statistics, income statistics, and a whole host of economic statistics are presented on the basis of time. These statistics have meaning only insofar as the variables which effect a change in these statistics operate in an unchanged system. For instance, economists frequently view the increase in gross national product over time. If this is presented in graphic form, GNP is inevitably shown on the vertical axis and time on the horizontal axis. In terms of mathematical convention, this implies that GNP is a function of time. However, viewing GNP as a function of time will have meaning only if we have a stable economic system or if the GNP data have been made meaningfully comparable.

Gross national product is informally described as the value of expenditures on goods and services and the new investment necessary to provide those goods and services. Since GNP deals with expenditures and expenditures occur at a given point in time, how does one compare the expenditures of any given year with those of any other year? Is the comparison valid? This is the crux of most of the problems attached to using data that have been gathered over a period of time.

If we wish to measure the societal value of GNP relative to any given point in time, we must look at the cost attached to purchasing a given bundle of goods and use this as a basis for making GNP at any point in time comparable to GNP at any other point in time. We shall then establish a GNP figure that we shall call *real* GNP. This is shown in Table 6–1.

Table 6–1

Year	Gross national product	Cost of base bundle	Excess of GNP over base bundle	Real value of excess	Real GNP
1......	$100 billion	$100 billion	$ 0 billion	$ 0 billion	$100 billion
2......	150 billion	120 billion	30 billion	25 billion	125 billion

This shows that it took $1.20 in year 2 to purchase a dollar's worth of year 1 goods. Thus the $30-billion increase can only purchase $\dfrac{\$30 \text{ billion}}{\$1.2} = \$25$ billion of year 1 goods. However, we still do not have any information on the causes of a given level of GNP. If we look at historical records of GNP, we see quite a different pattern when we move from periods of depression to periods of boom or to periods of war or to other major factors that affect our economic system.

As another illustration, let us look at data on the consumption of silk in the United States. It is very important to ascertain why you are looking at particular data in order to know whether it is valid to compare those data. Normally, we look at data of this nature to predict what will happen in the future and assume that the best indicator of what will happen in the future is what happened in the past. However, if conditions change, we know that the prediction was not valid. If we look at the consumption of silk for a period of years prior to the introduction of nylon, our projections would be quite in error because the event "introduction of nylon" had a very significant impact on the use of silk. Therefore, from a predictive standpoint, we have at least three series of production records on silk: (1) the series prior to the introduction of nylon, (2) the series during the introduction of nylon, and (3) the series after the introduction of nylon. In most situations, or under most circumstances, it would be invalid to compare one with the other.

In dealing with information which is essentially attitudinal, one finds that it becomes very difficult to make comparisons. How do you compare the extent to which one individual likes a political candidate with how much another individual likes a political candidate? Another problem in comparability is that data may be of varying accuracy. For example, data which must be reported to the government by private sources may be accurate from one source and inaccurate from another source.

VII. EXTRAPOLATION TO UNWARRANTED CONCLUSIONS

When the statistician or analyst reports on the analysis, there is a great temptation to extrapolate from the well-defined universe from which the data were drawn to a larger universe. Psychologists have long received a great deal of ribbing about the use of white rats and college students as their experimental subjects. Some critics question whether the conclusions from such experiments can be extrapolated to a larger universe than white rats and college students.

DISCUSSION TOPICS AND PROBLEMS

1. It has been said that statistics is a boon to the liar. Is this so? Why?

2. Does the scientific method insure impartiality? Why?

3. Indicate where invalid data may have been present in a statistical finding you are familiar with.

4. Define and explain accuracy, impartiality, and representativeness of data.

5. A company informs you (a prospective investor) that in the last five years its sales increased from $500,000 to $600,000. Upon further inquiry, you are told that prices of the company's products follow the general trend of price changes. You know that the consumer price index has increased from 1.2 to 1.4. Has there been any real increases in sales over this period of time?

6. Which of the three characteristics (accuracy, impartiality, and representativeness) do you think is most important in determining data validity, or are they equally important? For example, would slightly inaccurate but representative data be preferable to data which are accurate but do not truly represent the universe?

SELECTED REFERENCES

Croxton, F. E.; Cowdon, Dudley J.; and Klein, Sidney. *Applied General Statistics.* 3d ed. Englewood Cliffs, N.J.: Prentice-Hall, Inc., 1967.

Nemmers, Erwin E., and Myers, John H. *Business Research.* New York: McGraw-Hill Book Co., Inc., 1966.

Sanders, Virginia L. *Measurement and Statistics.* New York: Oxford University Press, 1958.

Spurr, William A., and Bonini, Charles P. *Statistical Analysis for Business Decisions.* Homewood, Ill.: Richard D. Irwin, Inc., 1967.

7

Models and systems

I. THE CHARACTERISTICS OF A MODEL

In Chapter 1, we defined a model as a physical or symbolic representation of the relevant aspects of the reality with which we are concerned. Consequently, it can be seen that the model is nothing more than a way of depicting, representing, or somehow showing the reality or system with which one is attempting to deal. Man by his very nature is a reasoning animal. He uses some process to depict or represent the environment he is dealing with so that he can make choices. Thus the movement from the reader's present method of representing his environment to developing a physical or symbolic representation of the reality or system that the individual is concerned with may be merely a matter of formalizing what previously was ill formulated. Anytime man is faced with a choice or decision situation, he must somehow structure the information so as to make that choice or decision. Hence the usefulness of the model concept is very pervasive in man's operating environment. Most individuals will have been groping in the direction of modeling the environment, and the process now being discussed is but a natural extension of something that is almost inherent in a reasoning animal. Let us look at the characteristics explicitly discussed or represented in the definition of a model.

The most important characteristic of a model is the ingredient of representation. All of the other characteristics are basically further restrictions on what is a valid or useful representation.

The second characteristic of a model deals with the physical or symbolic method of representing the environment. For managerial analysis, the only method of representing the environment is symbolic and normally mathematical.

A third characteristic of a model is that it deals with a reality or system. It may be merely a postulated reality. Of course, a model for managerial analysis must deal with a reality that could possibly exist and most frequently does exist in the world in which one operates.

Finally, we have said that the model must deal with the relevant aspects of the reality with which we are concerned. This, of course, gives the individual who is constructing the model a wide choice in identifying what is and what is not relevant. Relevance has two characteristics. There may be variables which affect the environment but whose impact is negligible, and consequently they are not considered relevant. There are some variables which do not affect the environment and thus need not be even considered tentatively as a part of the model. It is obvious that this condition of relevancy depends very heavily upon the purpose or end use to be made of the model. Relevancy is something that can only be measured in terms of the user.

II. THE CONTINUUM FROM REALITY TO ABSTRACTION

Models are of necessity abstractions of something more complex. There is essentially a continuum of the degree of abstractness of the model. If we may use the term *the real world* to represent what actually exists, we may say that the most concrete representation is what actually exists. However, our inability to see everything that exists acts as a screen so that we can never model the real world. Thus the most we could possibly model would be what we perceive. However, we have certain restrictions on our ability to model. Therefore, at most, we can model what we perceive and are capable of modeling. Further, as we have indicated in the definition, there are some aspects of the real world which are not necessary because they will play no role in the ultimate decision. Consequently, we may identify a fourth level of abstraction, that which we actually model. Finally, we may identify the minimum which could be modeled and still be considered a meaningful model. The continuum could be depicted as follows:

	The real world	Our perceptions of the real world	Our ability to model	That which is relevant and modeled	The minimum which could be modeled	
Most concrete						Least concrete

From a practical standpoint, the analyst is only concerned with how close the actual model should be to his ability to model (i.e., between the center of the continuum and the right end).

III. ELEMENTS OF MODELS

In the process of building models, one uses certain terminology such as *constants, variables, parameters,* and other universal terms. We must also look at the degree of specificity the model contains, i.e., abstract forms, concrete forms, or account forms. Further, in order to understand the elements that contribute to a desirable model, we must deal with some conceptual framework to understand a model. We shall utilize the framework recognized by G. H. Orcutt, which includes three elements: *components*, *variables*, and *relations*.[1] This section will deal with all three of the above elements in model construction.

Constants and variables

Most readers will have some intuitive feeling for the difference between a constant and a variable. Let us use as an example an equation for units produced, which is:

$$P = 4t - 2$$

where:

P = Units produced
t = Amount of time spent on production

This equation implies that the units produced (P) are dependent upon the hours worked (t). Thus, P is the dependent variable, and t is the independent variable. In this context, P and t are variables, and the 4 and the 2 are constants. Variables are items with associated values that vary during the course of the argument. Constants are values that remain the same during the course of the argument. The restriction "during the course of the argument" implies that at some time the constant may itself be changed to a variable. If, in this production environment, we have two machines instead of one, we shall have the equation:

$$P_i = a_i t_i - b_i$$

where:

P_i = Production on the ith machine
a_i and b_i = Constants for the ith machine
t_i = Time on the ith machine

In this case, production is not only dependent upon the amount of time but also upon the particular machine that is used. The value of the items which are constant when they refer to a specific machine is dependent upon the machine being used. Thus, we might have a second equation which would read

$$P = 3t - 2$$

---

[1] G. H. Orcutt, "Simulation of Economic Systems," *American Economic Review*, Vol. L, No. 5 (December, 1960), pp. 893–908.

In this argument, not only the time may vary, but also the machine may vary, and then these constants (a_i and b_i) are not in fact constants. Consequently, it can be seen that the identification of something as a constant depends upon the context in which you are discussing the material.

Functional, operational, and accounting models

The extent to which the model we develop represents reality is dependent upon the extent to which the model has identified all values associated with some measurable quantity in the real world. Each identified value is called a parameter. A functional model is a model without values specified for the constants; hence the variables can only be identified in abstract mathematical notation. When all of the values which must be associated with some measurable quantity in the environment being represented have been identified, we have an operating model. A functional model specifies the form of the relationship, but not the exact value of that relationship. In the model we discussed earlier with respect to two machines, we said that $P_i = a_i t_i - b_i$ is a functional model. When we say that $a_1 = 4, b_1 = 2$ and $a_2 = 3, b_2 = 2$, the identification of a_1 and b_1, a_2 and b_2, has transformed the functional model to an operating model.

Certain equations are essentially tautologies because they merely represent addition of values to give a total value. They are in a sense accounts. In the above example, if we are given P_1 and P_2, the total production, P, is equal to $P_1 + P_2$. This is a tautological or accounting statement. Does it then constitute a model? For our purposes, we shall assume so, since it does appear to represent symbolically relevant aspects of the reality with which we are concerned. However, it is an accounting model.

Essential elements: Components, variables, and relations

Let us now look at the essential elements of models. Earlier, it was indicated that Orcutt's classification of components, variables, and relations would be used.[2] This classification is particularly useful for large models that can be represented only by an equation system. An equation system includes either a series of equations, all dealing with the same essential forms of relationship, or basic subsystems, which combine to represent the total environment. For example, in an economic model, one might find a subsystem or component that deals with consumer behavior. One might also find a subsystem or component that deals with the behavior of the manufacturer or producer, one which deals with the behavior of the worker, and one which deals with the behavior of

---

[2] *Ibid.,* p. 898.

the supplier. Orcutt defines relationships as a means of specifying how the values of different variables in the model are related to each other or how they are otherwise generated. Orcutt also goes on to identify categories of variables. He identifies output variables, status variables, and input variables. He says these may be discussed relative to components. Consequently, an output variable is an output of a component which is anything issuing from or generated by that component. Status variables are variables which describe the state of the component. Input variables arise outside the component and must be fed into the component. In other terminology, they are also known as exogenous variables. In the production example we have been discussing, when $P_i = a_i t_i + b_i$, all a_i and b_i are status variables because they describe productivity, all t_i are input variables (at least to this component), and all P_i are output variables (at least from this component). Note that this equation system may be only one component of a larger system or model. Also, one component's input variable may be another's output, and vice versa.

IV. FURTHER CHARACTERISTICS OF MODELS

Many different schemes for classifying models have been developed. The purpose of looking at schemes of classifying models is a means of focusing upon essential characteristics. However, the essential characteristics of models may depend upon the end purpose. Let us draw an analogy between the different types of automobiles and the different types of models. We can classify automobiles in several ways. For instance, we can consider a car's origin and differentiate between foreign and domestic cars; or we can classify automobiles by age, cost, or manufacturer. We can classify a car by the type and size of its engine; or by transmission, body style, or color; or by some combination of these. The point is that all of these factors are valid in a particular situation. If someone were conducting a study of the effects of the weather on automobilies, the paint color would be very useful in this kind of study. However, if he were concerned with automobile accidents, this particular classification would be useless, and engine type and size would be much more valuable. Model classifications are useful as a means of looking at certain characteristics the model might possess.

Iconic, analog, and symbolic models

C. West Churchman, Russell L. Ackoff, and E. Leonard Arnoff, in their classic operations research text, discuss the following types of models: iconic, analog, and symbolic.[3] An iconic model pictorially or visually

---

[3] C. West Churchman, Russell L. Ackoff, and E. Leonard Arnoff, *Introduction to Operations Research* (New York: John Wiley & Sons, Inc., 1957), pp. 158–62.

represents certain aspects of a system. An analog model employs one set of properties to represent some other set of properties which the system being studied possesses. The symbolic model employs symbols to designate properties of the system being studied. These three types of models are identified because they represent a progression in several respects. The iconic is usually the simplest to conceive, and the most specific and concrete. Its function is generally descriptive rather than explanatory; i.e., it seldom reveals causal relationships. Accordingly, it can sometimes be used to determine or predict what effects many important changes have on the actual system. The symbolic model is usually the most difficult to conceive, and the most general and abstract. Its functioning is more often explanatory than descriptive. Accordingly, it is ordinarily well suited to the prediction or determination of the effects of changes in the actual system. Analog models fall between iconic and symbolic models in both respects. In summary, then, this classification scheme represents movement from the concrete to the abstract and from description to explanation.

Many authors have attempted to deal with alternative means of classifying models. For example, (1) Claude McMillan and Richard F. Gonzalez, in their book entitled *Systems Analysis*, deal with methods of defining and describing systems and models;[4] (2) David W. Miller and Martin K. Starr, in *Executive Decisions and Operations Research*, deal with categorization of models;[5] (3) Paul A. Samuelson, in *Foundations of Economic Analysis*, deals with a system for classification of models;[6] and (4) Joseph Wright Forrester, in *Industrial Dynamics*, deals with a different scheme of classifying models.[7]

Prediction, improvement, and optimization models

This author advocates recognition of models for managerial analysis as either prediction, improvement, or optimization models. Optimization models are the result of quantitative analysis and allow the measurable criterion to assume the highest or lowest possible value, given the model structure and constraints. Improvement models are the result of systems analysis; consequently, the highest value of the criterion is chosen from among the alternatives investigated. Either of these models depends upon

---

[4] Claude McMillan and Richard F. Gonzalez, *Systems Analysis: A Computer Approach to Decision Models* (rev. ed.; Homewood, Ill.: Richard D. Irwin, Inc., 1968), pp. 1–12.

[5] David W. Miller and Martin K. Starr, *Executive Decisions and Operations Research* (Englewood Cliffs, N.J.: Prentice-Hall, Inc., 1960), pp. 113–40.

[6] Paul A. Samuelson, *Foundations of Economic Analysis* (Cambridge: Harvard University Press, 1967).

[7] Joseph Wright Forrester, *Industrial Dynamics* (Cambridge: Massachusetts Institute of Technology Press, 1961), pp. 50–52.

inputs which predict outcomes or relationships; thus, they depend upon a prediction model.

Staticness, linearity, stability, and openness

All models possess differing degrees of the following characteristics: (1) staticness, (2) linearity, (3) stability, and (4) openness.[8] A static model is one in which time plays no role; i.e., the relationships do not vary with time. A dynamic model contains time-varying interactions. A model either is or is not a static model. However, dynamic models exist on a continuum, depending upon the extent of time-varying interactions.

A linear model is one in which all of the equations or inequalities are linear. When the linear relationships are constrained, the model is still linear.[9] A model which contains one or more nonlinear equations is a nonlinear model, although the degree of nonlinearity may vary greatly from model to model.

A further basis of classification of models deals with stable and unstable models. In the words of Forrester: "A stable system is one that tends to return to its initial condition after being disturbed. It may overshoot and oscillate like a single pendulum that is set in motion, but the disturbances decline and die out. In an unstable system that starts at rest an initial disturbance is amplified, leading to growth or oscillations whose amplitude increases."[10] Forrester further goes on to say that some systems will contain restraints that will restrict the degree to which an unstable system may amplify and become explosive. Thus a further condition of stability deals with the presence or absence of constraints that cause the system to assume limited values. Another subelement of stability deals with the presence of steady-state or transient models. In the words of Forrester again: "A steady state pattern is one that is repetitive with time in which the behavior in one period is of the same nature as any other period (for some purposes, a model of a nongrowing national economy that shows business cycle patterns could be considered a steady state fluctuation even though never repeating identically any particular sequence of events)."[11] Forrester continues, describing transient behavior as those changes where the character of the system changes with time. A system that exhibits growth would show transient behavior. Transient responses are one-time phenomena that cannot repeat.

Finally, the last item deals with whether the model is open or closed; again, in the words of Forrester, "the closed dynamic model is one that

---

[8] These characteristics form the basis for Forrester's classification of models in his book (*ibid.*).

[9] This condition is contrary to Forrester's definitions.

[10] *Ibid.*, p. 51.

[11] *Ibid.*

functions without connection to externally supplied exogenous variables that are generated outside the model. A closed model is one that internally generates the values of variables through time by the interaction of variables one on another."[12] Conversely, of course, the open model is one in which some variables are supplied from the external environment.

V. SYSTEMS

The reader will recall from Chapter 1 that a system is a physical entity. A model is a way (usually symbolic) of representing the system.

The term *system* is so extensive in usage and broad in meaning that it can be confusing. A system is defined as a complex of interrelated components (or objects). The components or objects may be physical, such as machines, raw materials, clerks, or machine operators. Abstract components or objects may also be part of a system. Profit goals, sales quotas, production standards, or morale are examples.

Attributes are properties of objects or components, and an object is described by listing its attributes. Relationships which exist between and among objects and their attributes tie the system together. The attributes of a system are continually varying, either because of the operations of the system itself or because of something external to the system. Relevant components and attributes must be identified and depend upon the purpose of identifying the system.

One may see references to the "systems concept," which is a way of looking at the environment one must deal with in conducting managerial analysis.[13] This is in part referring to the fact that the managerial analyst should think of reality as a system. More importantly, it requires the analyst to recognize the total system by recognizing the interrelatedness of the components.

One will also find references to computer systems, which are normally information-processing entities built around a computer. The managerial analyst will not be modeling this system but may play a role in its design. Thus a computer system is a reality constructed by man for a specific purpose.

DISCUSSION TOPICS AND PROBLEMS

1. What are the characteristics of models used for managerial analysis?

2. Listed below are examples and illustrations used thus far in the text. For each, indicate (*a*) whether they are actual models; (*b*) if they are models,

---

[12] *Ibid.*

[13] See for example, Russell L. Ackoff and Patrick Rivett, *A Manager's Guide to Operations Research* (New York: John Wiley & Sons, Inc., 1963), p. 7.

whether they are functional, operational, or accounting models; (*c*) if they are models, whether they are prediction, improvement, or optimization models; and (*d*) if they are models, the degree of staticness, linearity, stability, and openness each possesses:

a) The example which is represented by Figure 4–2 (page 50)
b) The example found on page 62
c) The example found on page 63
d) The example found on page 67–68

3. In the example found on page 62, identify the constants and variables.

4. Attempt to justify the inclusion of the word *systems* in the title of this chapter when only 1/10 of the space is devoted to this topic.

5. In the example found in Chapter 1, identify its components, variables, and relations.

SELECTED REFERENCES

Ackoff, Russell L., and Rivett, Patrick. *A Manager's Guide to Operations Research.* New York: John Wiley & Sons, Inc., 1963.

Churchman, C. West; Ackoff, Russell L.; and Arnoff, E. Leonard. *Introduction to Operations Research.* New York: John Wiley & Sons, Inc., 1957.

Forrester, Joseph Wright. *Industrial Dynamics.* Cambridge: Massachusetts Institute of Technology Press, 1961.

McMillan, Claude, and Gonzalez, Richard F. *Systems Analysis.* Rev. ed. Homewood, Ill.: Richard D. Irwin, Inc., 1968.

Miller, David W., and Starr, Martin K. *Executive Decisions and Operations Research.* Englewood Cliffs, N.J.: Prentice-Hall, Inc., 1960.

Orcutt, G. H.; Greenberger, Martin; Korbel, John; and Rivlin, Alice M. *Microanalysis of Socioeconomic Systems.* New York: Harper & Bros., 1961.

Samuelson, Paul A. *Foundations of Economic Analysis.* Cambridge: Harvard University Press, 1947.

Schoderbek, Peter. *Management Systems.* New York: McGraw-Hill Book Co., Inc., 1967.

SECTION THREE

Analytical tools: mathematics and statistics

8

The logic of
statistical analysis

I. INTRODUCTION

Events which are related to one another occur in an orderly fashion. Events which are not related to one another occur in a random or chance fashion. Statistical inference is a technique for investigating or inferring order. The following discussion attempts to show the underlying logic which allows one to make an inference of order. This discussion is built around establishing the mere existence or presence of a relationship rather than establishing any information on the size or magnitude of the relationship between variables. The latter will be discussed in Chapter 9.

II. ESTABLISHING THE EXISTENCE OR PRESENCE OF RELATIONSHIPS

Establishing the existence of relationships between things requires an understanding of the concept of dependence and independence between variables or things. The advertising manager will tell you that, other things being equal, the more the advertising expenditure, the higher the sales. The expert is saying that sales is the dependent variable, and advertising expenditures is the independent variable. Here, the expert intends that dependence and independence be synonymous with cause and effect. However, such is not necessarily the case. In this instance, advertising expenditures are said to cause sales, advertising expenditures being the cause which affects sales.

You will note that the advertising expert cautiously preceded his statement by the words "other things being equal." The condition "other things being equal" is almost a utopian one. What is meant is that all other things one thinks might affect this condition are equal or nonoperative.

Obviously, the price will also affect the sales. If the price is the same for all time periods, it can reasonably be assumed that price will not obscure the relationship because it is not operating to the benefit of any one time period. If a difference in price does occur, this difference may be either ignored or removed. In any case the statement "other things being equal" is essential to a conclusion, and its implications should be clearly recognized.

Table 8–1

Period of time	Advertising expenditures (in hundreds of dollars)	Sales (in hundreds of dollars)
1	24.90	450
2	24.00	499
3	28.00	600
4	25.10	501
5	27.00	650
6	26.00	550
7	22.00	400
8	23.00	350

Let us look at a set of information to illustrate how the existence of a relationship is established. Table 8–1 presents the promotion expenditure and the sales (in hundreds of dollars) for eight different but equally long periods of time.

A typical way of deriving more meaning from the information is to plot the two variables on a scatter diagram. It is conventional to plot the variable one believes to be the dependent variable on the vertical axis and to plot the variable one believes to be the independent variable on the horizontal axis. A glance at the pattern of points shown in Figure 8–1

Figure 8–1

ADVERTISING EXPENDITURE

ADVERTISING EXPENDITURES

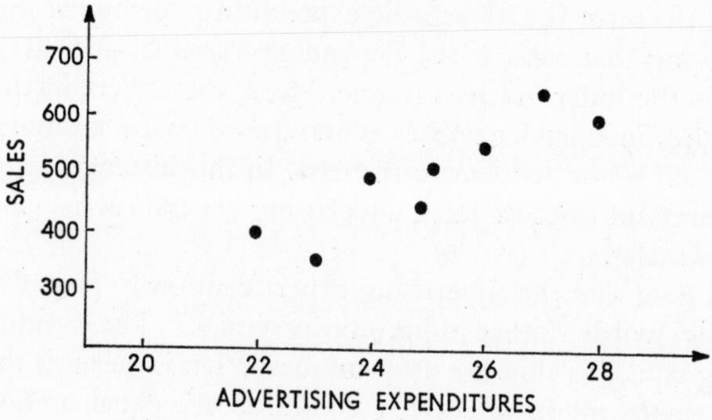

indicates that these points are not distributed in a random fashion on the scatter diagram. If they were distributed randomly, each of the eight points would be as likely to fall at any one place as at any other place; i.e., the points would show no pattern. Figure 8–1 is the scatter diagram of the data found in Table 8–1.

The point closest to the horizontal axis is the point where advertising is 23 and sales are 350. The point closest to the vertical axis is the point where advertising is 22 and sales are 400. If these points were randomly distributed, it would be equally likely to find advertising expenditures of 22 and sales of 650 as it would be to find advertising expenditures of 22 and sales of 400. A casual glance at the data tells an observer that the data are not randomly distributed. The essence of statistical analysis is to find and explain nonrandom situations; consequently, statistical analysis continuously seeks to identify the nonrandom condition.[1]

Table 8–2

ADVERTISING EXPENDITURES	SALES	
	Above median of 500	Below median of 500
Above median of 25	4	0
Below median of 25	0	4

The analyst may use a number of tools designed to test whether or not the points are randomly distributed. Table 8–2 shows one way of depicting this information. This table begins with the question: How many of the time periods with sales above the median also have advertising above the median?[2]

It can be seen that all of the periods with advertising above the median also have sales above the median, and vice versa. A condition such as this will occur only once in 70 times by chance. If one concluded on the basis of this information that there was in fact a (positive) relationship between the advertising expenditure and the sales, he would appear to be on very strong ground.[3] But just how strong is that ground?

---

[1] This search progresses by postulating that no relationship exists between the variables, i.e., that the points are random. This is called the null hypothesis. If this hypothesis is rejected, we conclude that a relationship exists.

[2] The median is a value so chosen that 50 percent of the values fall on either side.

[3] Statistically, he would reject the null hypothesis and thus accept the presence of a relationship.

It should be obvious from this discussion that whatever conclusion is drawn, it may be correct in either of two ways:

1. We may accept a relationship when it in fact exists.[4]
2. We may reject a relationship when it in fact does not exist.

The conclusion may also be in error in either of two ways:

1. We may reject a relationship when it in fact exists.
2. We may accept a relationship when it in fact does not exist.

In this instance the primary concern is whether a false relationship has been accepted. What if we are willing to be wrong 10 percent of the time? Since this relationship occurs only once in 70 times by chance, our chance of making an error by concluding that a relationship exists is 1/70, which is less than 1/10.

It should now be obvious that the statistician does not establish the existence of a relationship, but rather the *probability* of the existence of a relationship. The probability of this condition occurring once in 70 times by chance does not say anything about dependence or independence. Statistically, it makes equal sense to say that sales are dependent upon advertising expenditures or to say that advertising expenditures are dependent upon sales. The identification of the dependent and independent variable must come from judgment.

III. THE PROBABILISTIC BASIS OF STATISTICAL ANALYSIS

When a statistician makes a prediction, it is in full knowledge that the prediction may be wrong. The previous section discussed the two kinds of errors which may be made in statistical analysis:

1. We may reject the existence of a relationship when it in fact exists, or
2. We may accept the existence of a relationship when it in fact does not exist.

In statistical analysis, we normally begin to establish the existence of a relationship by stating the proportion of the time we are willing to accept the existence of a relationship when it does not exist. This is then compared to the ratio of the frequency of the relationship which actually exists to the frequency of the relationships which could exist. For instance, in our example, it was concluded that the actual relationship could exist only once and the possible relationships totaled 70. Thus, the computed probability (1/70) must be less than the proportion of time we are willing to accept the existence of a relationship when it does not exist.

As an example of one of the simple techniques used to find the existence of a relationship, let us discuss a special form of statistical analysis called

---

[4] As previously noted, we accept the conclusion that a relationship exists when we reject the so-called "null hypothesis."

[5] This section assumes an elementary knowledge of probability theory, such as that presented in Chapter 11.

the sign test. This technique is being shown to demonstrate the logic which uses the probability of occurrence of events as a means of establishing the existence (or nonexistence) of a relationship. The technique is appropriate when the independent variable is calibrated in equal segments. For example, in the hypothetical table relating sales and time (Table 8–3) the independent variable, time, occurs in equal segments.

Table 8–3

Time	Sales	Change in sales from previous years
Year 1	490	. . . .
2	500	Increase
3	498	Decrease
4	504	Increase
5	507	Increase
6	510	Increase
7	512	Increase
8	515	Increase

Since sales in the last year exceed sales in the first year, we might hypothesize that sales were increasing with time. The characteristic of interest is simply whether sales increased, and not how much. For purposes of this analysis, a 1-unit change in sales is viewed as the same as a 100-unit change in sales. Thus, we observe that between years 1 and 2, sales increased; but between years 2 and 3, they decreased.

Table 8–4

Case	Event 1: Change from year 1 to year 2	Event 2: Change from year 2 to year 3	Probability
1	Increase	Increase	0.25
2	Decrease	Increase	0.25
3	Increase	Decrease	0.25
4	Decrease	Decrease	0.25

For the moment, let us investigate only the first three years. At that time, we had an increase from year 1 to year 2 and a decrease from year 2 to year 3. Let us investigate all of the conditions which could have taken place during that time.[6] These events are shown in Table 8–4. If we had only three years of data and wished to ascertain whether the series demonstrated an increase in the level of sales, we could say that the probability of an increase and then a decrease was 0.25. Unless we specify that the proportion of time we are willing to accept the existence of a relation-

---

[6] Assuming that these events take place randomly.

ship when it does not exist is 0.25 or more, we cannot prove or disprove our hypothesis because the sample is too small. Our concern is with the probability of one or more increases out of a sample of two. This occurs in cases 1, 2, and 3. We may show this more effectively using a table showing the distribution of increases (*I*) and decreases (*D*), their frequency, and the cumulative probabilities of these events, as shown in Table 8–5 for the case just discussed. Thus the probability of one or more in-

Table 8–5

SAMPLE OF TWO

Number of increases (I) and decreases (D)	Frequency	Cumulative probability
2I............................1		0.25
1I + 1D...................2		0.75
2D.......................1		1.00
Total................4		

creases is 0.75. Clearly, we cannot, on the basis of this information, draw a conclusion that the first three years of this sequence demonstrate any pattern of increase. Ignoring order or sequencing, Tables 8–6 to 8–10 show

Table 8–6

SAMPLE OF THREE

Number of increases (I) and decreases (D)	Frequency	Cumulative probability
3I...........................1		0.125
2I + 1D...................3		0.500
1D + 2D...................3		0.875
3D.......................1		1.000
Total................8		

Table 8–7

SAMPLE OF FOUR

Number of increases (I) and decreases (D)	Frequency	Cumulative probability
4I........................ 1		0.0625
3I + 1D................. 4		0.3125
2I + 2D................. 6		0.6875
1I + 3D................. 4		0.9375
4D...................... 1		1.0000
Total................16		

Table 8–8

SAMPLE OF FIVE

Number of increases (I) and decreases (D)	Frequency	Cumulative probability
5I..........................	1	0.03125
4I + 1D..................	5	0.18800
3I + 2D..................	10	0.50000
2I + 3D..................	10	0.81250
1I + 4D..................	5	0.96875
5D..........................	1	1.00000
Total................	32	

Table 8–9

SAMPLE OF SIX

Number of increases (I) and decreases (D)	Frequency	Cumulative probability
6I..........................	1	0.015625
5I + 1D..................	6	0.109375
4I + 2D..................	15	0.343750
3I + 3D..................	20	0.656250
2I + 4D..................	15	0.890625
1I + 5D..................	6	0.984375
6D..........................	1	1.000000
Total................	64	

Table 8–10

SAMPLE OF SEVEN

Number of increases (I) and decreases (D)	Frequency	Cumulative probability
7I..........................	1	0.0078125
6I + 1D...............	7	0.0625000
5I + 2D...............	21	0.2265625
4I + 3D...............	35	0.5000000
3I + 4D...............	35	0.7734375
2I + 5D...............	21	0.9375000
1I + 6D...............	7	0.9921875
7D....................	1	1.0000000
Total..............	128	

the frequency of each combination of increases and decreases. In Table 8–10, we have six increases and one decrease. The probability of this condition (or a stronger condition) is 0.0625. If we are willing to accept a false hypothesis 10 percent of the time, we conclude that sales are increasing. This is true because the probability of six increases and one decrease, or seven increases occurring by chance, is 0.0625, which is less than 0.1.

This material has been presented to give the reader some insight into the process used to establish the existence of a relationship. A statistician would have concluded that the relationship was significant at the 0.10 level.

What is the level of significance? It is merely another way of describing the chance we are willing to take of accepting a false hypothesis. Thus, when we said that we had a 0.10 level of significance, we were saying that the chance of making an error (in drawing a conclusion that there was an increase in the level of sales) was 10 percent or less.

Let us clearly recognize that the hypothesis we were testing here was that an increase occurred. We could have tested an alternative hypothesis that a decrease occurred. What is the difference between the test for an increase rather than a decrease? Simply switch the D and I in the tables. Thus, if the order of the years were reversed, we would have six decreases and one increase. Then we would conclude that sales were decreasing (assuming that we were willing to be wrong 10 percent of the time).

DISCUSSION TOPICS AND PROBLEMS

1. A statistician has found a relationship between IQ and years of school completed. He will not say what the dependent variable is and what the independent variable is. Is he correct not to answer the question of dependence and independence? Which variable do you believe is the independent variable? Why?

2. A noted economist has found a statistically significant relationship between business activity and the extent of turbulence on the surface of the sun. He thus concludes that the two are related. Is he technically wrong to draw such a conclusion? Why? Do you agree with such a conclusion? Why?

3. What is meant by the following terms: statistical analysis and level of significance?

4. The typical statistics text identifies the following errors: type 1 error, rejecting a true (null) hypothesis; and type 2 error, accepting a false (null) hypothesis.

Explain the null hypothesis. If you have had a basic statistics course, explain the similarity and difference between the kinds of errors discussed on page 98 and the errors mentioned above.

5. A class of students have been asked to evaluate the effectiveness of a reducing diet. The instructor requires a 0.1 level of significance before accepting the presence of a relationship.

a) One student studied a sample of three people on the diet. All lost weight. The student concluded that the diet would cause a loss of weight. Do you agree? Why?

b) Another student took a sample of four. Three lost weight and one gained. He concluded that no relationship exists. Do you agree? Why?

c) Another student took a sample of five. Four lost weight and one gained. He concluded that a relationship exists. Do you agree? Why?

d) Another student took a sample of seven. Six lost weight and one gained. He concluded that a relationship exists. Do you agree? Why?

SELECTED REFERENCES

Dixon, Wilfred J., and Massey, Frank J. Jr. *Introduction to Statistical Analysis.* New York: McGraw-Hill Book Co., Inc., 1957.

Freund, John E. *Modern Elementary Statistics.* 3d ed. Englewood Cliffs, N.J.: Prentice-Hall, Inc., 1967.

Nemmers, Erwin E., and Myers, John H. *Business Research.* New York: McGraw-Hill Book Co., Inc., 1966.

Siegel, S. *Nonparametric Statistics for the Behavioral Sciences.* New York: McGraw-Hill Book Co., Inc., 1956.

Spurr, William A., and Bonini, Charles P. *Statistical Analysis for Business Decisions.* Homewood, Ill.: Richard D. Irwin, Inc., 1967.

9

Forecasting

I. INTRODUCTION

Forecasting is of importance to the managerial analyst because it provides him with structured information to use in his analysis. In Chapter 1, we discussed an equation for vehicle operating costs. The process of developing this equation is forecasting. Statistics provide techniques for processing raw information. However, the analyst exercises judgment in order to make a prediction. In other words, the activity of processing data is not identical to forecasting.

A forecast is a prediction of future events. Most techniques for processing data use historical information and make some allowance for expected differences between present conditions and future conditions. Thus the sales manager who uses gross national product (GNP) as a part of the information to decide upon a marketing strategy may find that a reasonable method of forecasting GNP is to forecast next years's GNP as 103 percent of this year's GNP. Methods of processing data for forecasting vary from extremely simple to extremely complex.

The decision maker must have a valid forecast. But identifying what constitutes a valid forecast is very difficult. Milton Friedman would say that validity is synonymous with a forecast's ability to predict.[1]

As an operational matter, we must reverse this and say that invalidity must be based upon inability to predict. This leads to a comparison of errors. But how do 10 errors of 5 percent compare to one error of 50 percent? The validity of one forecast verses another is difficult to assess. In Chapter 21, we shall discuss sensitivity analysis, which sometimes is useful in assessing different forecasts. The remainder of this chapter deals with

---

[1] See Milton Friedman (ed.), *Essays in Positive Economics* (Chicago: University of Chicago Press, 1953), pp. 1–37.

one technique for processing data to make a forecast. This technique is linear regression analysis (for one independent variable), which results in an equation which describes the relationship between two variables. Before discussing the technique, we must digress to discuss linear mathematical functions, because this form of regression analysis produces a linear mathematical function. Following this discussion, we talk about possible criteria to be used to judge the validity of a linear projection. Finally, we present the technique.

II. LINEAR MATHEMATICAL FUNCTIONS

Mathematical functions are ways of describing for further investigation the relationship between variables. These functions have many forms and characteristics. The most common form is the linear function. In Figure 9–1, we find two linear functions.

Figure 9–1

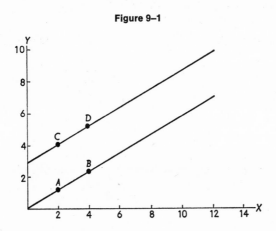

The first point (identified by A) is $X = 2, Y = 1$. By mathematical convention, this is recorded as point $(2, 1)$. Another point on the graph (identified by B) is $X = 4, Y = 2$. We call that point $(4, 2)$. If we draw a line between points A and B and extend that line upward infinitely and downward infinitely, it represents a relationship between the dependent variable Y and the independent variable X. That is to say, when the X value moves from 2 to 4, the Y value moves from 1 to 2. If this relationship continues along this line, a move in X from 4 to 6 will be accompanied by a movement in Y from 2 to 3. What we have said is that a two-unit move in X causes a one-unit move in Y. This means that the value of Y is always one half the value of X. This may be expressed in equation form as $Y = 1/2X$. If the line passes through the origin $(0, 0)$, we can always find the equation by taking the change in Y divided by the change in X. The equation is then:

$$Y = \frac{\text{Change in } Y}{\text{Change in } X} X$$

The change in Y divided by the change in X is called the slope. Thus, given any equation for the linear function, the slope is the coefficient of (i.e., the value which precedes) the X variable. If we denote point A as (X_2, Y_2) and point B as (X_1, Y_1), the slope may be expressed:

$$\frac{Y_2 - Y_1}{X_2 - X_1} = \frac{1 - 2}{2 - 4} = \frac{1}{2}$$

The order of the points does not affect the slope. Thus:

$$\frac{Y_1 - Y_2}{X_1 - X_2} = \frac{2 - 1}{4 - 2} = \frac{1}{2}$$

Since a linear equation rarely passes through the origin, we shall now show a procedure to derive the equation for a line when two points are known. The worked-out example which follows uses points C and D from Figure 9–1. C is point $(2, 4)$. D is point $(4, 5)$. The two-point formula is:

$$\frac{Y - Y_1}{X - X_1} = \frac{Y_2 - Y_1}{X_2 - X_1}$$

where:

$Y_1 = $ Value of Y for the first point, or 4
$Y_2 = $ Value of Y for the second point, or 5
$X_1 = $ Value of X for the first point, or 2
$X_2 = $ Value of X for the second point, or 4

$$\frac{Y - 4}{X - 2} = \frac{5 - 4}{4 - 2} = \frac{1}{2}$$

Multiply through by $X - 2$:

$$Y - 4 = \frac{1}{2}(X - 2)$$

$$= \frac{1}{2}X - 1$$

Add 4 to both sides:

$$Y = \frac{1}{2}X + 3$$

This derived equation has the general form:

$$Y = ax + b$$

where:

$a = $ Slope of the line
$b = $ Point at which the line intersects the Y-axis

Thus the equation derived above has a slope (a) equal to 1/2 and a Y-intercept (b) at $Y = 3$.

III. STATISTICALLY ESTABLISHING THE MAGNITUDE OF RELATIONSHIPS

Let us recall the information presented earlier in Table 8–1 (page 96) on the relationship between advertising expenditures and sales.

Figure 9–2 depicts a line relating advertising expenditures and sales.

Figure 9–2

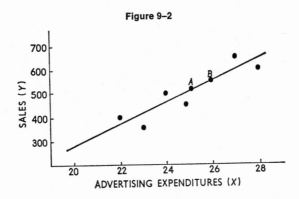

The line shown in Figure 9–2 is by observation a reasonable approximation of the relationship between the dependent variable (sales) and the independent variable (advertising expenditures). Points A and B are the only points falling exactly on the line. It remains now to demonstrate or determine the exact nature of that relationship.

Let us simply assume that the line we have shown, which passes through two specific points, is a reasonable way of showing this relationship, despite the fact that six of the eight points are not found directly on that line. Let us for the moment somewhat change the data which were presented in Table 8–1 to those found in Table 9–1.

Table 9–1

Time period	Advertising expenditure (in hundreds of dollars)	Sales (in hundreds of dollars)
1	25	450
2	24	500
3	28	600
4	25	500
5	27	650
6	26	550
7	22	400
8	23	350

The first point on the line (A) then will assume the values 25 for X and 500 for Y. The second (B) will then assume the values 26 for X and 550 for Y. Thus, using the two-point equation for a line, we find that $Y = 50X - 750$.

The ultimate objective of these calculations is to predict the sales as a result of advertising expenditures. That is to say, given the advertising expenditure, we shall be attempting to predict sales. If we look at Table 9–2, we shall see that six of the points will not be correctly predicted when we specify the advertising expenditure using the above predicting equation.

Table 9–2

Time period	Advertising expenditure (in hundreds of dollars)	Predicted sales (in hundreds of dollars)	Actual sales (in hundreds of dollars)
1	25	500	450
2	24	450	500
3	28	650	600
4	25	500	500
5	27	600	650
6	26	550	550
7	22	350	400
8	23	400	350

For example, if advertising expenditures are 27, our prediction of sales is 600. However, when advertising was 27, sales actually were 650. The difference between the predicted 600 and the actual 650 is 50. If we extend a line downward on Figure 9–2 from the point of the actual sales to our estimate, we see that the length of that line on the vertical axis is 50. Further, if we look at all six of the points that are not on the line and extend the line from the points to the prediction line, we shall see that they all have a magnitude of 50, on the vertical axis, half of them a positive and half of them a negative value. These are what we call error terms. Obviously, the farther these points fall from the line, the greater the error, and the lower our ability to predict.

In Figure 9–3, you will find an alternative line drawn through these eight points which falls on three of the eight points.

How do we decide which line is a better way of estimating the actual sales? We find that, with the exception of two points, the point where advertising is 23 and sales are 350 and the point where advertising is 27 and sales are 650, the ability to predict the remaining points appears to be better than with the other equation or line.

The statistician may use different criteria upon which to judge the desirability of any predicting equation. One criterion might be that the error sum be zero. In this case, we would choose the first predicting equation over the second predicting equation. Another criterion might be the maximum number of points which are exactly predicted. In this case, we would choose the second predicting equation over the first. Since this criterion ignores errors, it does not seem appropriate.

Another alternative would be to find that predicting equation which minimizes the absolute value of the sum of the error terms. In this instance

Figure 9–3

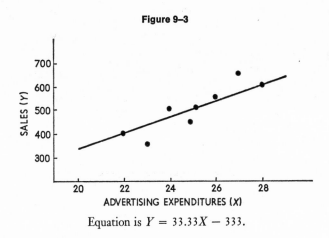

Equation is $Y = 33.33X - 333$.

the second equation gives a lower absolute value of the sum of the error terms. "Minimizing the absolute value of the sum of the error terms" says that the sum total of our predicting errors, ignoring signs, should be minimized.

The normal criterion used by the statistician is to minimize the *squared* error. "Minimizing the squared error" says essentially that we are more willing to accept a large number of small errors than a small number of large errors. Tables 9–3 and 9–4 demonstrate that although the sum of absolute error terms for the second predicting equation is lower than for the first predicting equation, the sum of the squared error terms for the second predicting equation is higher than the sum of the error terms for the first predicting equation.

Therefore, by this fourth criterion of minimizing the sum of the squared errors, we would accept the first predicting equation as better than the second predicting equation. The procedure used to calculate the squared error is the subject of the next section.

Table 9–3

FIRST PREDICTING EQUATION

$$(Y = 50X - 750)$$

Time period	Actual sales (in hundreds of dollars)	Predicted sales (in hundreds of dollars)	(X) Advertising expenditures (in hundreds of dollars)	Error (actual minus predicted)	Squared error
1................450	500	25	−50	2,500
2................500	450	24	50	2,500
3................600	650	28	−50	2,500
4................500	500	25		
5................650	600	27	50	2,500
6................550	550	26		
7................400	350	22	50	2,500
8................350	400	23	−50	2,500
		Sum...	0	15,000

Sum ignoring signs (absolute error)... 300

Table 9–4

SECOND PREDICTING EQUATION

$$(Y = 33.33X - 333)$$

Time period	Actual sales (in hundreds of dollars)	Predicted sales (in hundreds of dollars)	(X) Advertising expenditures (in hundreds of dollars)	Error (actual minus predicted)	Squared error
1................450	500.0	25	−50.0	2,500.0
2................500	466.7	24	33.3	1,108.9
3................600	600.0	28		
4................500	500.0	25		
5................650	566.7	27	83.3	6,938.9
6................550	533.3	26	−33.3	1,108.9
7................400	400.0	22		
8................350	433.3	23	−83.3	6,938.9
		Sum...	−50	18,595.6

Sum ignoring signs... 283.3

LINEAR

IV. FORECASTING: ILLUSTRATED BY REGRESSION ANALYSIS

One of the most commonly used tools of the statistician is the tool of regression analysis. We have just discussed the least squares method of finding an estimating equation. We did not explain how that method operates and how we made those calculations. Let us now show how we find the predicting equation in the regression approach for the data from Table 9–5, which relates test scores to success scores. Without explaining how we have mathematically arrived at this information, let us merely state that

Table 9–5

Individual	Test score	Success score
A.............112		82
B.............126		90
C............. 88		44
D............. 96		70

minimizing the sum of the squared deviations results in two equations. We shall call them normal equation 1 and normal equation 2.

$$\text{Normal equation 1:} \quad na + b\Sigma X = \Sigma Y$$
$$\text{Normal equation 2:} \quad a\Sigma X + b\Sigma X^2 = \Sigma(XY)$$

We now have two simultaneous equations and two unknowns. The numerical values of ΣX, ΣY, ΣXY, and ΣX^2 which are needed for these equations are computed in Table 9–6. The first three columns of Table 9–6 show the success and test score data given in Table 9–5. Using the results from columns 2–5, we may substitute the values of ΣX, ΣY, ΣX^2, and ΣXY in the normal equations and solve for a and b. When we have found a and b, the estimating equation is then $Y = a + bX$, and we can make a prediction for the value of Y, given X, for each of the observations. Table 9–6 also shows the predicted value for Y (column 6), the error between

Table 9–6

Individual	Test score X	Success score Y	X^2	YX	Predicted success $\hat{Y}$	Error $Y - \hat{Y}$	Squared error $(Y - \hat{Y})^2$
A........112	82	12,544	9,184	78.6	3.4	11.6
B........126	90	15,876	11,340	94.0	−4.0	16.0
C......... 88	44	7,744	8,872	52.3	−8.3	68.9
D........ 96	70	9,216	6,720	61.1	8.9	79.2
Total 422	286	45,380	31,116	286.0	zero	175.7

the predicted and actual (column 7), and the squared error (column 8). Finding the predicting equation:

(1) $$4a + 422b = 286$$
(2) $$422a + 45,380b = 31,116$$

Multiply formula 1 by 105.5, giving $422a + 44521b = 30173$.
Subtracting formula 1 from formula 2 gives:

(2) $422a + 45,380b = 31,116$
(1) $422a + 44,521b = 30,173$

$$859b = 943$$
$$b = \frac{943}{859} = 1.097788$$

Substituting in formula (1):

$$4a + 422(1.097788) = 286$$
$$4a + 463.27 = 286$$
$$4a = 286 - 463.27$$
$$4a = -177.27$$
$$a = \frac{-177.27}{4} = -44.3175$$

Checking in formula (2):

$$422(-44.3175) + 45,380(1.097788) = 31,116$$
$$-18,701.985 + 49,817.20 = 31,116$$
$$31,115.22 \cong 31,116$$

which checks except for rounding error.

You will note in Table 9–6 that the sum of the errors total zero. This is of course, to be expected because the least squares criterion not only minimizes the squared error but also assures that the sum of the errors is zero (except for rounding errors). This latter condition provides us with a basis for appraising our ability to predict. This will be accomplished by looking at our ability to explain the deviations from the mean of 71.5. In order to do so, we shall need to understand (1) total deviations, (2) explained deviations, and (3) unexplained deviations.

The term *total deviations* refers to the deviation of each observation from the mean of all observations. If we let $\bar{Y}$ represent the mean success

Table 9–7

TOTAL DEVIATIONS

Individual	Test score X	Success score Y	Mean success score $\bar{Y}$	Total deviations $(Y - \bar{Y})$ y
A............	112	82	71.5	10.5
B............	126	90	71.5	18.5
C............	88	44	71.5	−27.5
D............	96	70	71.5	−1.5

level and Y represent the actual success level, $y = Y - \bar{Y}$ is the total deviation and is computed in Table 9–7 and illustrated in Figure 9–4.

Figure 9–4

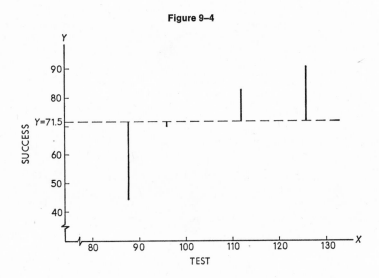

Explained deviations represent the explanation of the deviations from the mean. The regression equation provides an explanation of the deviations by suggesting that the value of Y is dependent upon the test score. If we let $\hat{Y}$ represent the estimated value of Y, then $\hat{y} = \hat{Y} - \bar{Y}$, which

Table 9–8

EXPLAINED DEVIATIONS

Individual	Test score X	Predicted success score $\hat{Y}$	Mean success score $\bar{Y}$	Explained deviations $(\hat{Y} - \bar{Y})$ $\hat{y}$
A............112		78.6	71.5	7.1
B............126		94.0	71.5	22.5
C............ 88		52.3	71.5	−19.2
D............ 96		61.1	71.5	−10.4

represents explained deviations. This is computed in Table 9–8 and illustrated in Figure 9–5.

The term *unexplained deviations* refers to the error between actual and predicted. This represents that variation which the regression equation could not account for (i.e., the last column of Table 9–9) and is

Figure 9–5

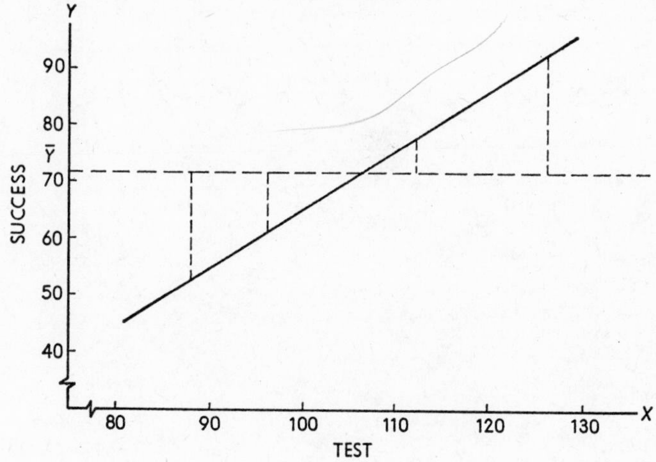

Table 9–9

UNEXPLAINED DEVIATIONS

Individual	Test score X	Success score Y	Predicted success score Ŷ	Unexplained deviations (Y − Ŷ) ỹ
A............112	82	78.6	+3.4
B............126	90	94.0	−4.0
C............ 88	44	52.3	−8.3
D............ 96	70	61.1	+8.9

$\tilde{y} = Y - \hat{Y}$. See Table 9–9 for the computations and Figure 9–6 for an illustration of the unexplained deviations. It can readily be seen that the total deviation is the sum of the explained and unexplained; i.e., $(Y - \hat{Y}) + (\hat{Y} - \bar{Y}) = (Y - \bar{Y})$, or $\tilde{y} + \hat{y} = y$. See Table 9–10 for the

Table 9–10

Individual	Test score X	Success score Y	Mean success score Ȳ	Predicted success score Ŷ	Unexplained deviation ỹ	+	Explained deviation ŷ	=	Total deviation y
A.......112	82	71.5	78.6	3.4	+	7.1	=	10.5
B.......126	90	71.5	94.0	−4.0	+	22.5	=	18.5
C....... 88	44	71.5	52.3	−8.3	+	−19.2	=	−27.5
D....... 96	70	71.5	61.1	8.9	+	−10.4	=	−1.5

Figure 9–6

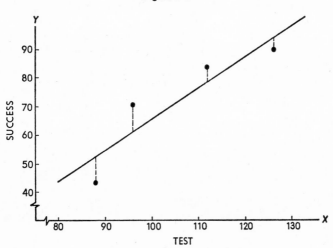

computations and Figure 9–7 for an illustration. If we take the ratio of the sum of the squared explained deviations to the sum of the squared total deviations, we have an index of the variation explained by the regression equation:

$$r^2 = \frac{1,033.46}{1,211.00} = 0.85334$$

This index is known as the coefficient of determination, indicated by the symbol r^2. In the words of F. E. Croxton and Dudley J. Cowden, "r^2 is

Figure 9–7

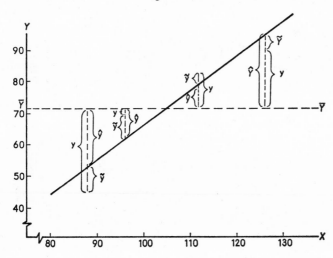

$$\frac{\Sigma\,(exp.div)^2}{\Sigma\,(TOTAL\,Div)^2} = r^2$$

the ratio of the explained variation to the total variation, and therefore, the proportion of the total variation that has been explained."[2] The square root of the coefficient of determination is known as the coefficient of correlation. As with all items drawn from a sample, the probability of obtaining a correlation coefficient this high by chance is dependent upon the sample size. Note that the coefficient of determination provides some information on the amount of variance explained by our regression equation, but further analysis must be conducted to find whether it is statistically significant. Such analysis is beyond the scope of this book.

Although it is not obvious, it follows from the method of least squares, by which the estimating equation was obtained, that the sum of squares of the three types of deviations is also additive. Symbolically:

$$\Sigma\bar{y}^2 + \Sigma\hat{y}^2 = \Sigma y^2$$

This will not be proved except by inference from Table 9–11.

Table 9–11

Given:			Then:		
$\bar{y}$	$\hat{y}$	y	$(\bar{y})^2$	$(\hat{y})^2$	$(y)^2$
3.4	7.1	10.5	11.56	50.41	110.25
−4.0	22.5	18.5	16.00	506.25	342.25
−8.3	−19.2	−27.5	68.89	368.64	756.25
8.9	−10.4	−1.5	79.21	108.16	2.25
Total.........................175.66				1,033.46	1,211.00

$$1,033.46 + 175.66 \cong 1,211.00$$

Because of rounding in columns 1, 2, and 3, there is an error of 1.88.

DISCUSSION TOPICS AND PROBLEMS

1. Distinguish between forecasting and data processing or data manipulation. In light of this discussion, attempt to justify the title of this chapter.

2. Discuss the difference between establishing the existence of a relationship and the magnitude of a relationship.

3. Discuss four different criteria upon which to judge the desirability of any predicting equation. Which is the most commonly used? Why?

4. Assume that the relationship of the number of telephones in service and population has historically varied as follows:

---

[2] F. E. Croxton and Dudley J. Cowden, *Practical Business Statistics* (3d ed.; Englewood Cliffs, N.J.: Prentice-Hall, Inc., 1966), p. 389.

Year	X Population (millions)	Y Number of phones (millions)
1	130	50
2	140	55
3	150	60
4	160	70
5	170	75
6	180	85
7	190	90
8	200	100

If the population is expected to be 250 million by year 13, forecast the number of phones that will be needed in five years:

a) By using the least squares method.
b) By using only the data from years 2 and 7.
c) Comment on your findings.

5. Find the coefficient of correlation for the regression equation in Problem 4 above by using the total, explained, and unexplained deviations.

SELECTED REFERENCES

Croxton, F. E.; Cowden, Dudley J.; and Klein, Sidney. *Applied General Statistics.* 3d ed. Englewood Cliffs, N.J.: Prentice-Hall, Inc., 1967.

Dixon, Wilfred J., and Massey, Frank J., Jr. *Introduction to Statistical Analysis.* New York: McGraw-Hill Book Co., Inc., 1957.

Freund, John E. *Modern Elementary Statistics.* 3d ed. Englewood Cliffs, N.J.: Prentice-Hall, Inc., 1967.

Nemmers, Erwin E., and Myers, John H. *Business Research.* New York: McGraw-Hill Book Co., Inc., 1966.

Spencer, Milton H., and Siegleman, Louis. *Managerial Economics.* Homewood, Ill.: Richard D. Irwin, Inc., 1964.

Spurr, William A., and Bonini, Charles P. *Statistical Analysis for Business Decisions.* Homewood, Ill.: Richard D. Irwin, Inc., 1967.

Williams, E. J. *Regression Analysis.* New York: John Wiley & Sons, Inc., 1959.

10

Mathematics for optimization*

I. INTRODUCTION

Optimization methods stem from the use of calculus. The most elementary branch of calculus is the calculus which will form the basis for the following discussion. To the mathematically naïve, calculus means an oppressive mix of mystery and awe, whose meaning and use will remain forever in the domain of the mathematician. Such should not be the case. Calculus (differential calculus) proceeds by looking at rates of change in mathematical expressions as a means of identifying points where those changes are somehow significant. It is the intent of this chapter to explain what calculus can do and how it accomplishes this.

II. MATHEMATICAL FUNCTIONS

Mathematical functions are ways of describing for further investigation the relationship between variables. These functions have many forms and characteristics. In Chapter 9, we discussed the relationship between advertising expenditures and sales, which can be expressed: $S = f(A)$. This is read: Sales are a function of advertising expenditures. A *function* expresses a relationship between two or more variables. This relationship is expressed in a general way without specifying the exact relationship. Similarly, we might express the fact that direct production costs depend on labor costs per hour, hours of labor, raw material costs per unit, and number of units produced by:

---

* Much of the material of this chapter is adopted by permission of the senior author from R. C. Meier and S. H. Archer, *An Introduction to Mathematics for Business Analysis* (New York: McGraw-Hill Book Co., Inc. 1960).

$$C = f(L_c, L_h, M_c, P)$$

where:

C = Direct production costs
L_c = Labor costs per hour
L_h = Hours of labor used
M_c = Raw material costs per unit
P = Units produced

Again, note that this is read by substituting the words *function of* for f, thus saying that direct production costs are a function of labor costs per hour, hours of labor, raw material costs per unit, and units produced. It is common practice to use abstract notations, such as:

$$Y = f(X_1, X_2, X_3, X_4)$$

and let:

Y = Direct production costs
X_1 = Labor costs per hour
X_2 = Hours of labor used
X_3 = Raw material costs per hour
X_4 = Units produced

When there are so many variables involved that it is inconvenient to count them and list them completely, the following notation is often used:

$$Y = f(X_1, X_2, \ldots, X_n)$$

This is interpreted to mean that Y is a function of n variables.

Sometimes, there are several different functions of n variables, in which case the different functions may be indicated by another set of subscripts:

$$Y_1 = f_1(X_1, X_2, \ldots, X_n)$$
$$Y_2 = f_2(X_1, X_2, \ldots, X_n)$$
$$\ldots\ldots\ldots\ldots\ldots\ldots\ldots$$
$$Y_m = f_m(X_1, X_2, \ldots, X_n)$$

Thus, there are m different functions, each of them involving n variables. This type of notation might be utilized in expressing the relationship between production costs and such variables as labor, raw material, and allocated overhead. If these three variables were the only determinants of production costs, we would have the expression for any product:

$$y = f(X_1, X_2, X_3)$$

where:

y = Production costs
X_i = Variables affecting production costs

If three products are produced, a different functional relationship would exist between the three variables and the production cost for each product. The relationships for the three products could be expressed by:

$$y_1 = f_1(X_1, X_2, X_3)$$
$$y_2 = f_2(X_1, X_2, X_3)$$
$$y_3 = f_3(X_1, X_2, X_3)$$

In the function $S = f(A)$ (where S is sales and A is advertising), we indicated that since the value of S is dependent upon A, S is the dependent variable. In the function $C = f(L_c, L_h, M_c, P)$, we would usually speak of C as being the dependent variable and L_c, L_h, M_c, and P as the independent variables. In managerial analysis, not all values of the variables are meaningful. Negative values of A in the function $S = f(A)$ would be interpreted as negative advertising, a concept which would have little practical usefulness. Likewise, advertising cannot exceed the value of the company's assets, and it would be incorrect to say that the functional relationship is true for values in excess of assets.

In mathematical terms the values the independent variable or variables may assume are called the *domain* of the function, and the corresponding values of the dependent variable are called the *range* of the function. Sometimes the domain and the range of a function are specified, but more frequently they are not, and the reader is left to his own good judgment to determine what values are eligible for use in any specific function. In some business situations, it is easy to determine at least approximately the values for which the function is valid; in other situations the proper domain and range of a function may not be so apparent.

III. EQUATIONS[1]

A specific way of expressing the relationship between two or more variables is to use an equation which indicates the specific relationship between the variables. The most common form is the linear function. In Figure 10–1, we find two linear functions.

The first point (identified by A) is $X = 2$, $Y = 1$. By mathematical convention, this is recorded as point $(2, 1)$. Another point on the graph (identified by B) is $X = 4$, $Y = 2$. We call that point $(4, 2)$. If we draw a line between points A and B and extend that line upward infinitely and downward infinitely, it represents a relationship between the dependent variable Y and the independent variable X. That is to say, when the X value moves from 2 to 4, the Y value moves from 1 to 2. If the relationship continues along this line, a move in X from 4 to 6 will be accompanied

---

[1] This section is the same as pages 105–7 of Chapter 9. It is repeated here in case Chapter 9 was not covered.

Figure 10–1

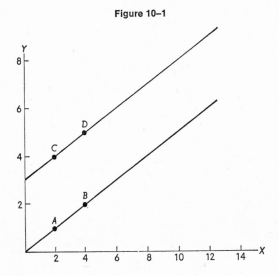

by a move in Y from 2 to 3. What we have said is that a two-unit move in X causes a one-unit move in Y. This means that the value of Y is always one half the value of X. This may be expressed in equation form: $Y = \frac{1}{2} X$. If the line passes through the origin $(0, 0)$, we can always find the equation by taking the change in Y divided by the change in X. The equation is then:

$$Y = \frac{\text{Change in } Y}{\text{Change in } X} X$$

The change in Y divided by the change in X is called the slope. Hence, given any equation for the linear function, the slope is the coefficient of (i.e., the value which precedes) the X variable. If we denote point A as (X_2, Y_2) and point B as (X_1, Y_1), the slope may be expressed:

$$\frac{Y_2 - Y_1}{X_2 - X_1} = \frac{1 - 2}{2 - 4} = \frac{1}{2}$$

The order of the points does not affect the slope. Thus:

$$\frac{Y_1 - Y_2}{X_1 - X_2} = \frac{2 - 1}{4 - 2} = \frac{1}{2}$$

Since a linear equation rarely passes through the origin, we shall now show a procedure to derive the equation for a line when two points are known. The worked-out example which follows uses points C and D from Figure 10–1. C is the point $(2, 4)$. D is the point $(4, 5)$. The formula is:

$$\frac{Y - Y_1}{X - X_1} = \frac{Y_2 - Y_1}{X_2 - X_1}$$

where:

$$Y_1 = \text{Value of } Y \text{ for the first point, or } 4$$
$$Y_2 = \text{Value of } Y \text{ for the second point, or } 5$$
$$X_1 = \text{Value of } X \text{ for the first point, or } 2$$
$$X_2 = \text{Value of } X \text{ for the second point, or } 4$$

$$\frac{Y-4}{X-2} = \frac{5-4}{4-2}$$

Multiply through by $X - 2$:

$$Y - 4 = \frac{1}{2}(X - 2) = \frac{1}{2}X - 1$$

Add 4 to both sides:

$$Y = \frac{1}{2}X + 3$$

The equation derived above has the general form:

$$Y = ax + b$$

where:

$$a = \text{Slope of the line}$$
$$b = \text{Point at which the line intersects the } Y\text{-axis.}$$

Thus, in the above equation the slope (a) equals $1/2$, and the Y-intercept equals 3.

A manufacturing department with one machine might express the relationship between the length of time it works and the number of items it produces by the function:

$$p = f(t)$$

where:

$$p = \text{Production (in units)}$$
$$t = \text{Working hours}$$

Suppose we know that it takes one-half hour to set up and clean the machine, and that four units are produced per hour of productive labor time. Accordingly, one point is $\left(\frac{1}{2}, 0\right)$. Further, we know that in an eight-hour day 30 units are produced on the machine. Thus, another point is $(8, 30)$ and using the two-point equation for a line:

$$\frac{p - 0}{t - \frac{1}{2}} = \frac{30 - 0}{8 - \frac{1}{2}}$$

and

$$p = 4t - 2$$

or (using the point-slope equation for a line):

$$\frac{Y - Y_1}{X - X_1} = m \ (m = \text{slope})$$

$$\frac{p - 30}{t - 8} = 4$$

and

$$p = 4t - 2$$

This equation is one of the most elementary types that would be found in business problems in that it now contains only one independent and one dependent variable, and the relationship between them is extremely simple. Equations in general may contain any number of variables, and the relationships between the variables may be much more complicated.

IV. MATHEMATICAL NOTATION

One of the problems frequently faced in writing equations relating to business situations is that of dealing conveniently with the large number of similar terms in an equation.

Suppose that we want to write an equation for the total overhead expense of a company for some time period. If there were six different costs involved, we could write the equation:

$$TC = x_1 + x_2 + x_3 + x_4 + x_5 + x_6$$

where TC is the total overhead expense for the period.

The costs x_1, x_2, x_3, x_4, x_5, and x_6 are different elements in overhead. The equation could be abbreviated by using a series of dots to indicate that some terms have been omitted:

$$TC = x_1 + x_2 + \ldots + x_6$$

This implies that not all x_i between x_2 and x_6 have been shown. Another abbreviation which could be used in the large sigma $\sum\limits_{i=1}^{n}$ to indicate a summation of a number of similar terms. In this notation the equation would become:

$$TC = \sum_{i=1}^{6} x_i$$

The symbol $\sum\limits_{i=1}$ means that all of the x_i from x_1 to x_6 are to be added together. The $i = 1$ below the $\sum$ means that we should start with x_1. The 6 above the $\sum$ means that we should continue and add all x_i to $i = 6$. Sometimes the notation above is abbreviated even further to:

$$TC = \sum_i x_i$$

When this notation is used, it is taken for granted that the reader can easily determine the ending x_i, which for this example is 6. The general notation is $\sum_{i=1}^{u}$, where n represents the highest numbered subscript.

More complicated summations can be abbreviated as sums of sums. Suppose that an equation must be written for total costs of components for a certain number of units of each of three products when each product contains three similar kinds of components. If we let x_i represent the number of units of the ith product and c_{ij} represent the cost of the jth component in the ith product, the equation for component costs may be expressed by:

$$\begin{aligned} \text{Component costs} = {} & x_1 c_{11} + x_1 c_{12} + x_1 c_{13} \\ & + x_2 c_{21} + x_2 c_{22} + x_2 c_{23} \\ & + x_3 c_{31} + x_3 c_{32} + x_3 c_{33} \end{aligned}$$

If a much larger number of products and components were involved, the equation would be quite long if written out term by term. Fortunately, it is not necessary to do so. The notation introduced in the previous illustration can be used to write the equation in a form which can be used to handle quickly any number of products and machines. We can successively abbreviate the equation above in the following manner:

$$\text{Component costs} = \sum_{i=1}^{3} x_i c_{i1} + \sum_{i=1}^{3} x_i c_{i2} + \sum_{i=1}^{3} x_i c_{i3}$$

$$= \sum_{i=1}^{3} \sum_{j=1}^{3} x_i c_{ij}$$

If the number of i's and j's were understood, this could be shortened still further to:

$$\text{Component costs} = \sum_{ij} x_i c_{ij}$$

The reader will note that lower case letters and capital letters are used interchangeably. Thus the general form of a linear equation may be expressed $Y = AX + B$ or $y = ax + b$. Generally the letter form is consistent throughout the discussion.

V. INEQUALITIES

The equal sign in an equation indicates an equality between the right- and left-hand members of an equation. This is a convenient way of expressing a large number of the relationships found in business, but it does not cover all of the relationships which must be expressed. It is frequently the case that we would like to indicate that something is not only equal to something else, but may also be greater than or less than something else. The following symbols are used to express these types of relationships and are called inequalities. The first two are called strict inequalities.

$<$ Less than
$>$ Greater than
$\leq$ Equal to or less than
$\geq$ Equal to or greater than

In each case the open end of the symbol points toward the larger quantity, and the closed end toward the smaller quantity.

The rules of algebra which apply to inequalities are:

1. Equal amounts may be added to both sides of the inequality without changing the inequality.
2. Equal amounts may be subtracted from both sides of the inequality without changing the inequality.
3. Both sides may be multiplied by the same positive quantity without changing the inequality.
4. Both sides may be multiplied by the same negative quantity, in which case the inequality is reversed.
5. Both sides may be divided by the same positive quantity without changing the inequality.
6. Both sides may be divided by the same negative quantity, in which case the inequality is reversed.

Rules 4 and 6 are the most important because they reverse the inequality. They may be simply illustrated by the following example. It is obviously true that $12 > 6$. If both sides of this inequality were multiplied by -1 and the inequality were not changed, we would have $-12 > -6$. This is incorrect, since -12 is less than -6. Accordingly, when both sides of an inequality are multiplied or divided by a negative number, it is necessary to reverse the inequality. In the preceding example the correct result would be $-12 < -6$.

VI. LINEAR RELATIONSHIPS AND RATES OF CHANGE

The relationship between production and time, discussed earlier, is called a linear equation and has the general form:

$$Y = ax + b$$

where:

a = Any constant except zero
b = Any constant

Table 10–1

(Arbitrarily chosen values of independent variable t)	$f(t)$ (Calculated values of dependent variable $p = 4t - 2 = f(t)$)
1	2
2	6
3	10
4	14
5	18

and the specific form $p = 4t - 2$, domain and range $\geqq 0$. We may tabulate the values of the dependent variable p by showing their values at different values of t (see Table 10–1). We may show this graphically (see Figure 10–2). In this equation, it can be seen that the slope (4) represents the change in p with a one-unit change in t. Let us now adopt the notation Δ to mean "change in." Any change in t, whether it be large or small, may then be denoted by Δt. By the same token, any change in t (Δt) must be accompanied by a change in p (Δp). In a linear function the slope represents the ratio of $\dfrac{\Delta p}{\Delta t}$, which in this case is 4.

If we wish to indicate that the value of the function $f(t)$ is to be found for some specific value of t, we may do so by inserting the value of t in the functional notation. For instance, if we wish to find the value of our function when t is 2, this may be indicated by $f(2) = 4(2) - 2 = 6$. It is not necessary that a specific number be substituted for t to use the

Figure 10–2

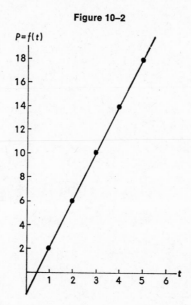

Figure 10–3

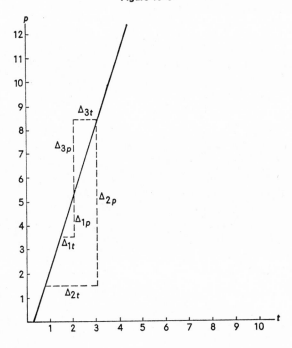

notation just described. An unspecified number, often a, may also be used. For our function

$$f(a) = 4(a) - 2$$

Figure 10–3 will show several pairs of Δp and Δt. We know that $p = f(t) = 4t - 2$ and $\dfrac{\Delta p}{\Delta t} = 4$. Looking at the graph, we see that any Δp corresponding to a certain Δt may be found by subtracting the value of the function $f(t)$ at the initial value of t from the value of the function at the changed value of t, that is, at $t + \Delta t$. In this notation, then, Δp is equal to $f(t + \Delta t) - f(t)$; and it follows that since $\dfrac{\Delta p}{\Delta t} = 4$, then

$$\frac{f(t + \Delta t) - f(t)}{\Delta t} = 4.$$

VII. LIMITS AND THE DERIVATIVE

The change in p, regardless of the size of the change in t, is always 4. If we make Δt microscopically small, so small as to be a means of representing a point not an interval, the ratio $\dfrac{\Delta p}{\Delta t}$ is still 4. Therefore, we may say that the limit of $\dfrac{\Delta p}{\Delta t}$ as Δt approaches zero is 4. This is a means of expressing the rate at which p changes when the change in t is microscopically small. It may be expressed in the following notation:

$$\lim_{\Delta t \to 0} \frac{\Delta p}{\Delta t} = 4$$

which is read: The limit of Δp divided by Δt as Δt approaches zero is 4. Note that the arrow ($\to$) is read as "approaches." Since we said earlier that Δp can be measured by $f(t + \Delta t) - f(t)$, then:

$$\lim_{\Delta t \to 0} \frac{f(t + \Delta t) - f(t)}{\Delta t} = 4$$

The limit of this ratio is known as the derivative of the function $f(t)$ with respect to t. This derivative represents the rate of change of p (the dependable variable) with respect to t (the independent variable). In this case the derivative is the same regardless of the initial value of t. A linear function such as this one is the only function where this is true; in fact, a linear function may be defined as any function with a constant derivative. The symbol for the derivative is $\dfrac{dy}{dx}$ or y' or $f'(x)$.

VIII. RATES OF CHANGE FOR NONLINEAR FUNCTIONS

The slope of a line may have a positive or negative value. The slope of a straight line remains constant through its entire length. This concept cannot be extended directly to a curve, since the slope of a curve changes

Figure 10–4

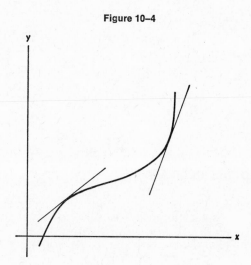

from point to point along the curve. However, the slope of a curve may be defined at any particular point as the slope of a line tangent to the curve at that point. This definition is illustrated in Figure 10–4, in which lines tangent to the curve have been drawn at two points on the curve. At any one of these points on the curve, the slope of the curve is equal to the slope of the line drawn tangent to the curve at that point. If constructing a tangent line were the only method of finding the slope of a curve at some point, it would be quite difficult to measure the slope accurately. However, the concept of a derivative can be used to measure rates of change in a nonlinear function.

IX. THE DERIVATIVE OF A NONLINEAR FUNCTION

Since the slope of a curve is constantly changing, measuring the change in the value of a nonlinear function corresponding to a certain change

Figure 10–5

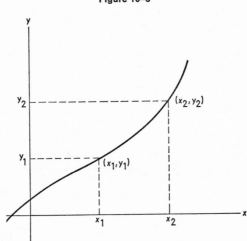

in the independent variable will not give the slope of the curve at a point, but will yield only some sort of average slope over an interval of the function. This is illustrated in the graph (Figure 10–5) of an unspecified nonlinear function $y = f(x)$. We recall that the change in y may be denoted by Δy and is equal to $y_2 - y_1$ when the change in x, Δx, is equal to $x_2 - x_1$. The slope of the line between (x_1, y_1) and (x_2, y_2) is equal to $\frac{\Delta y}{\Delta x}$ but this tells us nothing about the slope of the curve itself at any particular point. However, if the point (x_2, y_2) is moved closer to (x_1, y_1), it is apparent that the slope of the line between the two points becomes a better approximation to the slope of the curve at the point (x_1, y_1). If the point (x_2, y_2) is moved as close as possible to (x_1, y_1), the slope of the curve at the point (x_1, y_1) will have been found. Another way of saying this is to find $\lim_{\Delta x \to 0} \dfrac{\Delta y}{\Delta x}$. Since $\Delta y = f(x + \Delta x) - f(x)$, we have:

$$\lim_{\Delta x \to 0} \frac{\Delta y}{\Delta x} = \lim_{\Delta x \to 0} \frac{f(x + \Delta x) - f(x)}{\Delta x} = \text{Slope of curve at point } (x_1, y_1)$$

The derivative of a nonlinear function at some point is the slope of the curve at that point; or in other words, the derivative indicates the rate of change of the value of the function with respect to the independent variable. Since the rate of change on a curve varies continually, the derivative will be continually changing, and its value will depend on the point on the curve being considered. As a result, the expression for the derivative of a curve will not be a constant, as was the case with linear functions, but will be a function of the independent variable.

The discussion of derivatives and rates of change is also necessary to understand how one proceeds mathematically to determine the best course of action. For example, assume that a manager has been able to determine the following profit function for his operations:

$$\pi = -q^2 + 20q$$

where:

π = Daily profits

q = Units produced per day

The values of this function can be found in Table 10–2 and graphed in Figure 10–6. It would appear that the best level of daily production is 10 units.

Table 10–2

q	$\pi = f(q)$
1	19
2	36
3	51
4	64
5	75
6	84
7	91
8	96
9	99
10	100
11	99
12	96
13	91
14	84
15	75
16	64
17	51
18	36
19	19
20	0

Figure 10–6

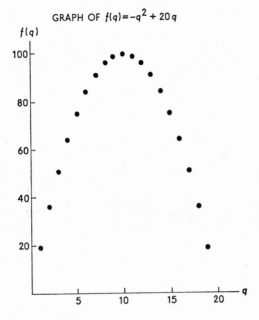

GRAPH OF $f(q) = -q^2 + 20q$

In order to use the general x and y symbols, let:

$$\pi = -q^2 + 20q$$

or:

$$y = -x^2 + 20x$$

We now proceed by finding:

$$\lim_{\Delta x \to 0} \frac{\Delta y}{\Delta x}$$

remembering that:

$$\Delta y = f(x + \Delta x) - f(x)$$

Since $f(x) = -x^2 + 20x$:

$$f(x + \Delta x) = -(x + \Delta x)^2 + 20(x + \Delta x)$$

Since $\Delta y = f(x + \Delta x) - f(x)$:

$$\Delta y = [-(x + \Delta x)^2 + 20(x + \Delta x)] - [-x^2 + 20x]$$

Then, evaluating the square:

$$\Delta y = [-x^2 - 2x\,\Delta x - \Delta x^2 + 20(x + \Delta x)] - [-x^2 + 20x]$$

Evaluating $20(x + \Delta x)$:

$$\Delta y = -x^2 - 2x\,\Delta x - \Delta x^2 + 20x + 20\,\Delta x + x^2 - 20x$$
$$= -2x\,\Delta x - \Delta x^2 + 20\,\Delta x$$

Dividing both sides by Δx to get $\dfrac{\Delta y}{\Delta x}$

$$\frac{\Delta y}{\Delta x} = -\frac{2x\Delta x}{\Delta x} - \frac{\Delta x^2}{\Delta x} + \frac{20\Delta x}{\Delta x} = -2x - \Delta x + 20$$

Therefore, as $\Delta x \to 0$, the second term becomes zero, and $\dfrac{\Delta y}{\Delta x} = 20 - 2x$.

Table 10–3

q	$f(q)$	$\Delta\pi$ over interval $q-1$ to q	Value of $\dfrac{\Delta\pi}{\Delta q} = 20 - 2q$ at given value of q (i.e., at that point)
0	0	N.A.	N.A.
1	19	19	18
2	36	17	16
3	51	15	14
4	64	13	12
5	75	11	10
6	84	9	8
7	91	7	6
8	96	5	4
9	99	3	2
10	100	1	0
11	99	− 1	− 2
12	96	− 3	− 4
13	91	− 5	− 6
14	84	− 7	− 8
15	75	− 9	−10
16	64	−11	−12
17	51	−13	−14
18	36	−15	−16
19	19	−17	−18
20	0	−19	−20

The difference between the change over an interval and the rate of change at a point will be shown in Table 10–3. In this table, we shall begin at a daily production level of zero and increase production one unit at a time to a production level of 20. Thus, at $q = 0$:

$$\pi = -(0)^2 + 20(0) = 0$$

At $q = 1$:

$$\pi = -(1)^2 + 20 = 19$$

Over the interval, profit changed from 0 to 19. The rate of change is:

$$\frac{\Delta\pi}{\Delta q} = 20 - 2q$$

Thus, at $q = 1$:

$$\frac{\Delta\pi}{\Delta q} = 20 - 2 = 18$$

This demonstrates that the rate of change at the point is lower than the rate of change over the entire interval. This is further demonstrated by Table 10–3.

You will note that the estimated rate of change of π with respect to q is always overstated by one unit when we let $\Delta q = 1$ (calculated in the third column) as opposed to letting $\Delta q \to 0$, as in the fourth column.

$\frac{\Delta\pi}{\Delta q}$ is plotted in Figure 10–7.

Figure 10–7

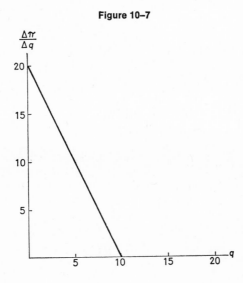

X. EXISTENCE OF DERIVATIVES

Up to this point in time, we have assumed that a derivative did in fact exist. This essentially means that the ratio $\frac{\Delta y}{\Delta x}$ has meaning. However, such may not be the case. Take as an example the total purchase cost to a company for a certain item when the company receives a discount on all units purchased after total unit purchases reach a certain level. Suppose that the price is 40 cents per unit for purchases up to 200,000 units, but that a 10 percent discount applies to all purchases if cumulative purchases are more than 200,000 units in a certain period. The total purchase cost function under these conditions is graphed in Figure 10–7.

Letting n equal the cumulative number of units purchased during a period and P equal total purchase cost, we may express the total purchase cost function, which has been graphed in Figure 10–8, by:

$$P = 0.40n \qquad 0 < n \leq 200{,}000$$
$$P = 0.36n \qquad 200{,}000 < n$$

Figure 10–8

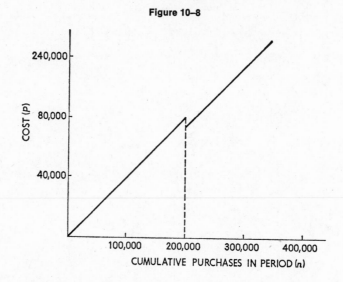

CUMULATIVE PURCHASES IN PERIOD (n)

Finding the derivative, we have:

$$\frac{dP}{dn} = 0.40 \qquad 0 < n \leq 200{,}000$$

$$\frac{dP}{dn} = 0.36 \qquad 200{,}000 < n$$

The derivative of the total purchase cost function with respect to the cumulative number of units purchased is 0.40 for n equal to or less than 200,000 and is 0.36 for n greater than 200,000 units. In going from 200,000 to 200,001 units, however, neither of these derivatives describes the rate of change of the total purchase cost function, since the function is discontinuous at 200,000 units because of the application of the discount on cumulative purchases over 200,000. Mathematically, we say that the derivative fails to exist at this point because of the discontinuity.

We may perhaps better understand the difficulty caused by this discontinuity by noting that at every other point on the graph of the total purchase cost function the derivative of the function tells what increase takes place in total cost for a unit increase in the number of units purchased. Below 200,000 units, an increase of one in the number of units purchased will result in a 40-cent increase in total cost. In each case the derivative of the proper function is the marginal cost. However, between 200,000 and 200,001 units, neither derivative gives any information about the marginal cost, which is really equal to −$7,999.64. In this particular purchase cost function, it is apparent that such a discontinuity will exist,

Figure 10–9

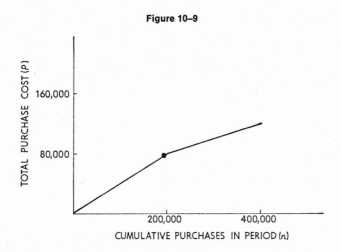

and it is not likely to cause any difficulty in interpretation. In other problems, however, the existence of discontinuities may not be so apparent, and care should be taken to investigate a function for discontinuities before the derivative is used. As was seen in the example above, the derivative cannot be used to indicate anything about the behavior of the function at the point of the discontinuity.

Another situation in which the derivative fails to exist is when the function being examined is not a smooth function but has kinks in it. At the point where a kink occurs, the derivative fails to exist.

As an example of a kinked function, consider the purchase discount example above where the 36-cent price applies only to those items purchased after the first 200,000 in a given time period. Thus a kink (but not a break) occurs in the total purchase cost function at 200,000, as shown in Figure 10–9. At the kink the derivative fails to exist in a strict mathematical sense. It should be noted, however, that there is no great difficulty in working with this function in practical problems, in spite of the kink. As with the previous example, it is necessary, of course, to be aware of any points at which the derivative will fail to exist.

In a more formal way, we say that a function $f(x)$ is continuous at the point $x = a$ if $f(a)$ is defined at this point and if:

$$\lim_{x \to a} f(x) = f(a)$$

That is, the function $f(x)$ is continuous at the point where x is equal to a if the following conditions are met:

1. Substituting a for x in the function $f(x)$ must yield a limiting value, not an undefined quantity such as zero divided by zero or a constant divided by zero.
2. The function $f(x)$ must have a limiting value of $f(a)$ as x approaches a from either direction.

XI. HIGHER ORDER DERIVATIVES

You will recall that the derivative (denote this y') of:

$$\pi = 20q - q^2$$

or:

$$y = 20x - x^2$$

was:

$$y' = 20 - 2q$$

or:

$$y' = 20 - 2x$$

However, this is also a mathematical function (which was plotted on Figure 10–5), and we can find its derivative. This subsequent derivative is called the second derivative (denoted y''). In order to avoid confusion, we shall consider the first derivative a different function, $g(x)$. Let:

$$y' = g(x) = 20 - 2x$$

Then:

$$g(x + \Delta x) = 20 - 2(x + \Delta x)$$
$$\Delta y = [20 - 2(x + \Delta x)] - [20 - 2x]$$

Evaluating $2(x + \Delta x)$:

$$\Delta y = [20 - 2x - 2\Delta x] - [20 - 2x]$$

Reducing this:

$$\Delta y = 20 - 2x - 2\Delta x - 20 + 2x$$
$$\Delta y = -2\Delta x$$

Dividing by Δx to get $\dfrac{\Delta y}{\Delta x}$ gives:

$$\frac{\Delta y}{\Delta x} = \frac{-2\Delta x}{\Delta x} = -2$$

and

$$y'' = -2$$

Also, the derivative of the derivative may be found ad infinitum until no further derivatives exist. It can be shown that further derivatives are zero for our profit function. Again, in order to avoid confusion, consider the second derivative a different function, $h(x)$. Thus:

$$y'' = h(x) = -2$$
$$h(x + \Delta x) = -2$$

and

$$\Delta y'' = [-2] - [-2]$$

which reduces to zero; and all subsequent derivatives will be zero.

XII. MAXIMA AND MINIMA

The first derivative indicates the rate at which the value of the function is changing relative to the independent variable at a given point. A positive first derivative indicates that the value of the function is increasing for increasing values of the independent variable such as the profit function

$$y = 20x - x^2$$

from $x = 0$ to 10 (but not including 10). A negative first derivative indicates a decreasing value of the function for increasing values of the independent variable such as the profit function above $x = 10$. A zero first derivative indicates that the value of the function is constant at that value of the independent variable such as the profit function at $x = 10$. We could have drawn the same conclusions if we had drawn a series of tangents in the neighborhood of $x = 10$ and noted that up to 10 they had a positive slope, and above 10 they had a negative slope, and at 10 there was no slope.

You will recall from Figure 10–6 that in the interval from $x = 0$ to $x = 20$, the highest value which the function $f(x)$ assumed was 100, and that occurred at $x = 10$. The value of the independent (x) variable where the function assumed its highest value is known as a maximum. When slightly increasing values of the independent variable cause *the first derivative* to change from positive to zero to negative, we have what is known as a maximum. When the reverse is true (i.e., slightly increasing values of the independent variable cause the first derivative to change from negative to zero to positive), we have what is known as a minimum. Note that any function may have a number of maxima and minima. The maximum which yields the highest value for the function is known as a global or absolute maximum, and the minimum which yields the lowest value for the function is known as a global or absolute minimum. All other maxima or minima are known as relative or local maxima or minima. A general term which refers to either maximum or minimum is *extremum*. Figure 10–10 will show different extrema.[2]

Figure 10–10

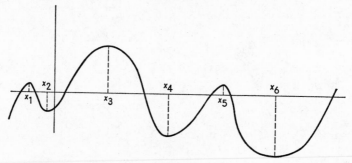

Points x_1, x_2, x_3, x_4, x_5, and x_6 are all extrema.

Points x_1, x_3, and x_5 are all maxima.

However, x_3 is clearly a global or absolute maximum, whereas x_1 and x_5 are relative or local maxima.

Points x_2, x_4, and x_6 are all minima. However, x_6 is clearly a global or absolute minimum, whereas x_2 and x_4 are relative or local minima.

The graph of the profit function $[f(x) = 20x - x^2]$ indicated a maximum at $x = 10$. We are now in a position to verify this.

We have shown that $y' = 20 - 2x$. Now we must identify all possible maxima or minima by setting $y' = 0$. Thus:

$$20 - 2x = 0$$

and

$$-2x = -20$$
$$x = 10$$

---

[2] The *um* ending in *maximum* or *minimum* or *extremum* is singular. The *a* ending is plural.

Hence, 10 is our only candidate for an extreme point. Investigating the value of y' in the neighborhood of 10, we see at $x = 9.5$ that $y' = 1$, and at $x = 10.5$ that $y' = -1$. We therefore conclude that we have met the conditions for a maximum and that $f(x)$ at $x = 10$ is a maximum because the first derivative changed from positive to zero to negative.

If we have a new function:

$$y = x^3 + 3x^2 + \frac{5}{3}x$$

and

$$y' = 3x^2 + 6x + \frac{5}{3}$$

we can find the candidates for extrema by using the quadratic equation, which is:

$$x = \frac{-b \pm \sqrt{b^2 - 4ac}}{2a}$$

for equations of the general form:[3]

$$ax^2 + bx + c = 0$$

Thus:

$$x = \frac{-6 \pm \sqrt{36 - 20}}{6} = \frac{-6 \pm 4}{6}$$

$$= \frac{-10}{6} \text{ or } \frac{-2}{6}$$

$$= -\frac{5}{3} \text{ or } -\frac{1}{3}$$

Looking at y' when x moves from $-\frac{4}{10}$ to $-\frac{1}{3}$ to $-\frac{3}{10}$, y' changes from negative to zero to positive, and $x = -\frac{1}{3}$ is therefore a minimum. Looking at y' when x moves from $-1\frac{8}{10}$ to $-1\frac{2}{3}$ to $-1\frac{6}{10}$, y' changes from positive to zero to negative, and $x = -1\frac{2}{3}$ is therefore a maximum.

In practice, it becomes tedious to check the values of y' when x is less than, equal to, and greater than the candidate for extremum. The test for maxima and minima is to insert the value of the candidate in the second derivative. If the value of the second derivative is negative, the point is a maximum. If the value of the second derivative is positive, the point is a minimum. It must be remembered that only legitimate candidates can be

---

[3] It should be remembered that the equation $y = ax^2 + bx + c = 0$ refers to the value of x when $y = 0$, i.e., the point where it crosses the x-axis. Since an equation of the above form may cross the x-axis twice, once, or no times, the quadratic equation may produce two, one, or no values of x. The equation $y = x^2 - 5x + 6$ will produce two real values of x; when the 6 becomes 6.25, it will produce one real value of x; and when the 6 becomes 7, it will produce no real value of x.

tested in this way. In the example just tested, $y'' = 6x + 6$. When $x = -\frac{5}{3}$ and $y'' = -4$, then $-\frac{5}{3}$ is a maximum, as verified earlier. When $x = -\frac{1}{3}$ and $y'' = 4$, then $-\frac{1}{3}$ is a minimum, as verified earlier.

XIII. INFLECTION POINTS

For functions of one independent variable, one other characteristic may be noted; this is the inflection point. The inflection point indicates the point where the rate of change of the function changes either from an increasing rate of change to a decreasing rate of change or from a decreasing rate of change to an increasing rate of change for successive values of x in the function. In Figure 10–11, the slope of tangents 1 and 2 as they

Figure 10–11

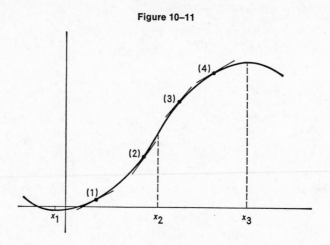

approach x_2 can be seen to be steeper and steeper; thus the rate of change is increasing. Conversely, after the point x_2, tangents 3 and 4 can be seen to be less and less steep within the interval x_2 to x_3; hence the rate of change is decreasing. The inflection point is between tangent 2 and tangent 3 in the vicinity of x_2. Mathematically, the inflection point may be found by setting $y'' = 0$. Using the function discussed, where the first derivative is identified as $g(x)$:

$$y' = g(x) = 3x^2 + 6x + \frac{5}{3}$$
$$g(x + \Delta x) = 3(x + \Delta x)^2 + 6(x + \Delta x) + \frac{5}{3}$$
$$= 3(x^2 + 2x\Delta x + \Delta x^2) + 6x + 6\Delta x + \frac{5}{3}$$
$$= 3x^2 + 6x\Delta x + 3\Delta x^2 + 6x + 6\Delta x + \frac{5}{3}$$
$$g(x + \Delta x) - g(x) = 3x^2 + 6x\Delta x + 3\Delta x^2 + 6x + 6\Delta x + \frac{5}{3} - 3x^2 - 6x - \frac{5}{3}$$
$$= 6x\Delta x + 3\Delta x^2 + 6\Delta x$$

Dividing by Δx:

$$\frac{g(x + \Delta x) - g(x)}{\Delta x} = 6x + 3\Delta x + 6$$

Since $\Delta x \to 0$, $3\Delta x \to 0$, and $y'' = 6x + 6$ when $y'' = 6x + 6 = 0$, $x = -1$, which should be the inflection point. As we approach $x = -1$ for the original function $y = x^3 + 3x^2 + 5/3x + 0$, the rate of change should change at that point. This can be partially verified by specifying values as shown in Table 10–4. Thus the rate of change from -0.9 to -1.0 was

Table 10–4

x	$f(x)$	Δy over interval
-1.2	0.592	
		0.1263
-1.1	0.4657	
		0.1324
-1.0	0.3333	
		0.1323
-0.9	0.201	
		0.1263
-0.8	0.0747	

faster than from -0.8 to -0.9, and the rate of change from -1.1 to -1.2 was slower than from -1.0 to -1.1; and we conclude that we have an inflection point at $x = -1$.

XIV. A COMPLETE EXAMPLE

As an example, we shall show how the optimum of the following function is found. It should be remembered that this requires finding the first derivative $\frac{\Delta y}{\Delta x}$ and setting it equal to zero. The value(s) of x at this point are candidates for maxima and/or minima. Then we find the second derivative. Next, we insert the candidates for maxima in the second derivative. If the value of the second derivative is positive, we have a minimum. If the value of the second derivative is negative, we have a maximum.

$$y = x^3 + 3x^2 + \tfrac{5}{3}x + 0$$
$$f(x + \Delta x) = (x + \Delta x)^3 + 3(x + \Delta x)^2 + \tfrac{5}{3}(x + \Delta x)$$
$$= (x + \Delta x)(x^2 + 2x\Delta x + \Delta x^2) + 3(x^2 + 2x\Delta x + \Delta x^2)$$
$$+ \tfrac{5}{3}x + \tfrac{5}{3}\Delta x$$
$$= (x^3 + 2x^2\Delta x + x\Delta x^2 + x^2\Delta x + 2x\Delta x^2 + \Delta x^3) + 3x^2$$
$$+ 6x\Delta x + 3\Delta x^2 + \tfrac{5}{3}x + \tfrac{5}{3}\Delta x$$

$$= +x^3 + 2x^2\Delta x + x\Delta x^2 + x^2\Delta x + 2x\Delta x^2 + \Delta x^3 + 3x^2$$
$$+ 6x\Delta x + 3\Delta x^2 + \tfrac{5}{3}x + \tfrac{5}{3}\Delta x$$

$$f(x + \Delta x) - f(x) = +x^3 + 2x^2\Delta x + x\Delta x^2 + x^2\Delta x + 2x\Delta x^2 + \Delta x^3 + 3x^2$$
$$+ 6x\Delta x + 3\Delta x^2 + \tfrac{5}{3}x + \tfrac{5}{3}\Delta x - [+x^3 + 3x^2 + \tfrac{5}{3}x]$$

$$f(x + \Delta x) - f(x) = +x^3 + 2x^2\Delta x + x\Delta x^2 + x^2\Delta x + 2x\Delta x^2 + \Delta x^3 + 3x^2$$
$$+ 6x\Delta x + 3\Delta x^2 + \tfrac{5}{3}x + \tfrac{5}{3}\Delta x - x^3 - 3x^2 - \tfrac{5}{3}x$$

$$= +3x^2\Delta x + 3x\Delta x^2 + \Delta x^3 + 6x\Delta x + 3\Delta x^2 + \tfrac{5}{3}\Delta x$$

Dividing by Δx:

$$\frac{f(x + \Delta x) - f(x)}{\Delta x} = +3x^2 + 3x\Delta x + \Delta x^2 + 6x + 3\Delta x + \tfrac{5}{3}$$

Since $\Delta x \to 0$, all terms with Δx may be eliminated:

$$y' = +3x^2 + 6x + \tfrac{5}{3}$$

The maximum and minimum are shown on page 139 and the inflection point on page 141.

XV. DIFFERENTIATION FORMULAS

It is usually possible to differentiate a function by going through the procedure outlined earlier, finding:

$$\lim_{\Delta x \to 0} \frac{f(x + \Delta x) - f(x)}{\Delta x}$$

However, this is a lengthy process to go through every time we wish to find the derivative of a function. Since certain types of functions appear quite frequently, it is much simpler to memorize the method of finding the derivative than to go through the process of finding the derivative every time as we have done. In this section, we shall develop formulas for the differentiation of some of the common functions.

No attempt will be made to prove rigorously the differentiation formulas which are given; we shall only indicate the reasonableness. In this section, we shall present some of the rules of differentiation and some examples of how they operate. The following notation will be used:

$$\frac{d}{dx}f(x) = h(x)$$

which means that the derivative of $f(x)$ with respect to x is a different function, $h(x)$.

Rule 1: Derivative of a constant

$$\frac{d}{dx}(a) = 0$$

Thus the derivative of the function $y = 4$ is zero.

Rule 2: Derivative of a variable with respect to itself

$$\frac{d}{dx}(x) = 1$$

Therefore the derivative of the function $y = x$ is one.

Rule 3: Derivative of the product of two functions

$$\frac{d}{dx}[f(x)\,g(x)] = f(x)\,\frac{d}{dx}[g(x)] + g(x)\,\frac{d}{dx}[f(x)]$$

Thus the derivative of $y = 4x$ can be found by letting $4 = f(x)$ and $x = g(x)$, and

$$\frac{d}{dx}[4x] = 4\,\frac{d}{dx}(x) + x\,\frac{d}{dx}(4)$$
$$= 4(1) + x(0) = 4$$

The case just shown is frequently referred to as a special case. Accordingly, a rule 3(a) is worthy of note.

Rule 3(a): Derivative of a constant times a function

$$\frac{d}{dx}[af(x)] = a\,\frac{d}{dx}[f(x)]$$

Thus the derivative of $y = 4x$ is:

$$4\,\frac{d}{dx}[x] = 4(1) = 4$$

Rule 4: Derivative of sum or difference of functions

$$\frac{d}{dx}[f(x) + g(x)] = \frac{d}{dx}[f(x)] + \frac{d}{dx}[g(x)]$$

Consequently, the derivative of $y = 4x + 8$ can be found by letting $f(x) = 4x$ and $g(x) = 8$, and $\frac{d}{dx}[f(x)]$ is subject to rule 3(a). Thus:

$$\frac{d}{dx}[af(x) + g(x)] = a\,\frac{d}{dx}[f(x)] + \frac{d}{dx}[g(x)]$$

and

$$\frac{d}{dx} [4x + 8] = 4$$

Rule 5:   Derivative of a power of a function

$$\frac{d}{dx} [f(x)]^n = n[f(x)]^{n-1} \frac{d}{dx} [f(x)]$$

Hence the derivative of $y = (4x + 8)^2$ is $2(4x + 8) \dfrac{d}{dx} [f(x)]$
and

$$\begin{aligned} y' &= 2(4x + 8)(4) \\ &= 32x + 64 \end{aligned}$$

It can also be seen that if $y = x^2$ and we let $f(x) = x$, we have:

$$\frac{d}{dx} [x]^2 = 2x \frac{d}{dx} [f(x)]$$
$$y' = 2x(1)$$
$$y' = 2x$$

This yields rule $5(a)$.

Rule 5(a):   Derivative of independent variable to a power

$$\frac{d}{dx} x^n = nx^{n-1}$$

Rule 6:   Derivative of the quotient of two functions

$$\frac{d}{dx} \left[\frac{f(x)}{g(x)} \right] = \frac{g(x) \dfrac{d}{dx} [f(x)] - f(x) \dfrac{d}{dx} [g(x)]}{[g(x)]^2}$$

Thus the derivative of $y = \dfrac{2}{x^2}$ is $\dfrac{x^2(0) - 2(2x)}{x^4}$:

$$y' = \frac{-4x}{x^4} = \frac{-4}{x^3}$$

Rule 6(a):   Derivative of a constant divided by the independent variable to a power

A special case of rule 6 occurs when $f(x) = \dfrac{a}{x^n}$. This function may be rewritten $f(x) = ax^{-n}$ in which case rules $3(a)$ and $5(a)$ may be applied instead of rule 6. $y = \frac{2}{x^2}$ may be expressed $y = 2x^{-2}$ and the derivative of $y = 2x^{-2}$ is $2(-2)x^{-3} = -4x^{-3}$, or $\frac{-4}{x^3}$.

XVI. EQUATION FORMS

We can tell a great deal about the shape of an equation and its characteristics from its general form. Equations of the following general form are known as polynomials:

$$y = a_1x^n + a_2x^{n-1} + \cdots + a_nx + a_{n+1}$$

It should be noted that n is an integer; consequently, all exponents of x are integers. For example, the linear equation is a polynomial of $n = 1$; thus, $y = a_1x^1 + a_2$. It is, of course, customary to omit the exponent 1 from this equation. The linear equation is known as a first-degree equation because the highest exponent is one. Since the second- and third-degree equations often occur in managerial applications, they and others frequently found will now be discussed.

Second-degree equations

The usual form of a second-degree equation is $Y = AX^2 + BX + C$. An example is $Y = 2X^2 + 3X - 4$. Computed values for the example are shown in Table 10–5. These values are plotted in Figure 10–12. At some

Table 10–5	
X	$f(X)$
3	23
2	10
1	1
0	−4
−1	−5
−2	−2
−3	5

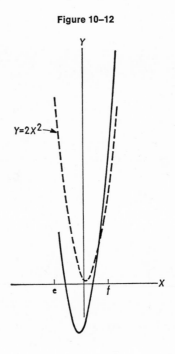

Figure 10–12

point the term with the exponent of 2 overpowers all other terms. In the above equation for all points > 3 and all points < -3 the square term controls the shape of the graph. This is further illustrated when it is noted that when B is changed from 3 to -3, the first term still overpowers all others for all points, > 3 and < -3. The sign of the first term will dictate whether the graph opens upward or downward. In this example the values of Y are positive when X^2 is large positive or negative. Thus, when the coefficient of X^2 is positive, the graph opens upward; and when the coefficient of X^2 is negative, the graph opens downward.

Further, it can be remembered that the graph of a second-degree equation can intersect the X-axis either zero, one, or two times.

If B and C were zero for the above equation, the graph would take a special form which merits separate attention. The resulting equation is shown in Figure 10–12 as $Y = 2X^2$. This equation is graphed with the above equation to show the influence of the remaining terms.

The reader can verify that the second derivative cannot be set equal to zero (since it is a constant) and only one candidate (an extremum) exists, which in general form is $\dfrac{-B}{2A}$.

Third-degree equations

The usual form of a third-degree equation is

$$Y = AX^3 + BX^2 + CX + D$$

An example is $Y = -X^3 + 2X^2 + 3X + 0$. Computed values for the example are shown in Table 10–6. These values are plotted on Figure 10–13.

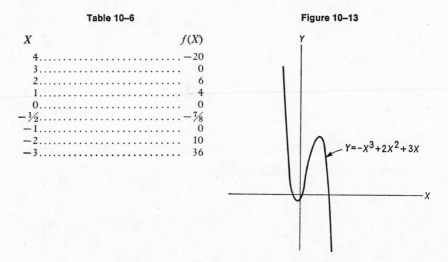

Table 10–6	
X	$f(X)$
4	-20
3	0
2	6
1	4
0	0
$-\frac{1}{2}$	$-\frac{7}{8}$
-1	0
-2	10
-3	36

Figure 10–13

$Y = -X^3 + 2X^2 + 3X$

As with the second-degree equation, at some point the first term overpowers all others. Further, it can be noted that the graph of a third-degree equation can intersect the X-axis 1, 2, or 3 times.

If the value of A is negative, the value of the first term is always positive when X is negative, and the value of the first term is always negative when X is positive. When A is positive, the opposite occurs. When A is negative, if the function has a maximum and a minimum it must have a minimum, an inflection point, and a maximum, in that order. Conversely, when A is positive, the graph must have a maximum, an inflection point, and a minimum, in that order.

It can be shown that the equation $y = x^3 - 7.5x^2 + 21x + 1$ gives $y' = 3x^2 - 15x + 21$, which has no real roots; however, it does have an inflection point at $x = 2.5$.[4]

Other common forms

We shall frequently see the equation $Y = \dfrac{\alpha}{X}$ or $Y = \dfrac{\alpha}{X^n}$. In this equation (assuming α is positive), as $X \to 0$, $Y \to \infty$; and as $X \to \infty$, $Y \to 0$. This equation can be reexpressed as $Y = aX^{-1}$ or $Y = aX^{-n}$. Sometimes, we shall see that $Y = aX^{1/2}$ or $Y = aX^{1/n}$, which is another way of expressing $Y = \alpha\sqrt{X}$ or $Y = \alpha\sqrt[n]{x}$. This equation form has economic meaning only when $X > 0$, in which case the value under the radical is always less than X except when $0 \leqq X \leqq 1$.

DISCUSSION TOPICS AND PROBLEMS

1. A company finds that crowding and other limitations cause the cost of production to increase as more units are produced.

a) Which of the following equations represent this situation?

$$PC = \alpha X^{1/2}$$

where:

PC = Production costs
X = Units produced
α = An unknown constant greater than zero

$$PC = \alpha X^2$$

---

[4] The occurrence of a negative value under the radical in $x = \dfrac{-B \pm \sqrt{B^2 - 4AC}}{2A}$ signals a nonreal number

b) If α is increased, what will happen to *PC?*

c) What is the domain and range of the PC equation?

d) Suppose management observed that the situation had changed so that:

$$PC = \alpha X^{3/2}$$

Explain the effect of such a change and probable causes.

2. *a*) Find maximum, minimum, and inflection point for the following total cost function:

$$TC = 50 - X - X^2 + X^3$$

b) Draw an approximate freehand graph of this equation.

c) Draw an approximate freehand graph of the equation if all signs in the equation are reversed (except that *TC* does not become $-TC$).

3. Find maximum, minimum, and inflection point for the following total cost function:

$$TC = 50 + \frac{5}{X} + 2X$$

4. Find the first and second derivatives of:

a) $Y = \left(2X^2 - \frac{3}{X}\right)^3$

b) $Y = \frac{3X^2 - 5}{X}$

5. Find the first and second derivatives of:

a) $Y = (3X^2 - X + 1)^3$

b) $Y = \frac{4}{X^5}$

6. Find maximum, minimum, and inflection point for the following total cost function:

$$TC = 2,000 + 5X - 10X^2 + \frac{X^3}{4}$$

7. If all signs in the equation for Problem 6 are reversed (except that *TC* does not become $-TC$), what can you say about this equation?

8. A company producing a single product finds that its fixed costs are $50 per day and that raw material costs are $2 per unit and direct labor costs are 1.40 per unit. Develop an equation to determine total production costs. Identify, if possible, the domain and range for this function.

9. Find the maximum, minimum, and inflection point, and plot the following:

a) $Y = 3X^2 - 6X + 2$
b) $Y = X^3 - 6X^2 + 3$
c) $Y = X^4 - X^2 + 1$

10. Suppose that profitability of a store is determined only by the number of clerks working in the store and the amount of inventory carried. Suppose that profitability may be described as follows:

$$P = 3,500 - (8 - X)^2 - (29 - Y)^2$$

where:

P = Net profit per quarter
X = Number of clerks working
Y = Amount of inventory carried (in thousands of dollars)

a) Without calculation, can you identify the optimum level of X and Y? Indicate why?
b) Are X and Y independent?

SELECTED REFERENCES

Bowen, Earl K. *Mathematics: With Applications in Management and Economics.* Homewood, Ill.: Richard D. Irwin, Inc., 1963.

Dean, Burton V.; Sasieni, Maurice W.; and Gupta, Shiv K. *Mathematics for Modern Management.* New York: John Wiley & Sons, Inc., 1963.

Grawoig, Dennis E. *Decision Mathematics.* New York: McGraw-Hill Book Co. Inc., 1967.

Hadley, G. *Elementary Calculus.* San Francisco: Holden-Day, Inc., 1968.

Howell, James E., and Teichroew, Daniel. *Mathematical Analysis for Business Decisions.* Homewood, Ill.: Richard D. Irwin, Inc., 1963.

Johnson, Richard E., and Kiokemeister, Fred L. *Calculus with Analytic Geometry.* Boston: Allyn and Bacon, Inc., 1957.

Klempner, Daniel, and Ramsey, Norman. *Quick Calculus.* New York: John Wiley & Sons, Inc., 1965.

Meier, Robert C., and Archer, Stephen H. *An Introduction to Mathematics for Business Analysis.* New York: McGraw-Hill Book Co., Inc., 1960.

Springer, Clifford H.; Herlihy, Robert E.; and Beggs, Robert I. *Basic Mathematics.* Homewood, Ill.: Richard D. Irwin, Inc., 1965.

Theodore, Chris A. *Applied Mathematics: An Introduction.* Homewood, Ill.: Richard D. Irwin, Inc., 1965.

Youse, Bevan K., and Stalnaker, Ashford W. *Calculus for Students of Business and Management.* Scranton: International Textbook Co., 1967.

11

Matrix algebra and
probability
concepts

I. MATRIX ALGEBRA*

A matrix is a rectangular array of numbers with m rows and n columns. Each number in the matrix is known as an element. Some examples are:

$$\begin{pmatrix} 5 & -3 \\ 4 & -2 \\ 3 & 6 \end{pmatrix} \begin{pmatrix} a_{11} & a_{12} & \dots & a_{1n} \\ a_{21} & a_{22} & \dots & a_{2n} \\ \cdot & \cdot & \dots & \\ \cdot & \cdot & \dots & \\ \cdot & \cdot & \dots & \\ a_{m1} & a_{m2} & \dots & a_{mn} \end{pmatrix}$$

The matrix on the left is a 3×2 (read 3 by 2) matrix because it contains three rows and two columns. The second is an $m \times n$ matrix, in which each element is identified by its row and column position. Hence the element a_{ij} is the element at the intersection of the ith row and the jth column. Thus, a_{21} is the element found at the intersection of the second row and first column. In the matrix on the left, the value of a_{21} is four.

A single letter (usually a capital letter) is often used to represent an entire matrix. For example:

$$A = \begin{pmatrix} 5 & -3 \\ 4 & -2 \\ 3 & 0 \end{pmatrix} B = \begin{pmatrix} 3 & 4 & 2 \\ 5 & 3 & 1 \\ 6 & 1 & -2 \end{pmatrix}$$

The B matrix shown above is a *square matrix* because it has the same number of columns as rows; i.e., $m = n$. A matrix consisting of only one col-

---

* Much of the matrix algebra material of this chapter is adopted by permission of the senior author from R. C. Meier and S. H. Archer, *An Introduction to Mathematics for Business Analysis* (New York: McGraw-Hill Book Co., Inc. 1960).

umn is known as a column vector. Since it has only one column but m rows, any matrix of dimension $m \times 1$ is a column vector. A matrix consisting of only one row is known as a row vector. Since it has one row but n columns, any matrix of dimension $1 \times n$ is a row vector.

Operations on matrices

Matrix arithmetic is basic to many of the tools of managerial analysis. Manipulations using matrices are subject to certain rules. The rules of matrix manipulations will now be discussed.

Addition and subtraction. Matrices *having the same number of rows and columns* may be added or subtracted by adding or subtracting similar elements. By way of an illustration, assume the L matrix below represents labor costs per unit, with each element representing the labor cost of the jth component of the ith product. Therefore, we have two products and three components. The M matrix below represents material costs per unit, with each element representing the material cost of the jth component of the ith product.

$$L = \begin{pmatrix} 30 & 30 & 15 \\ 18 & 0 & 10 \end{pmatrix} \quad M = \begin{pmatrix} 10 & 14 & 7 \\ 30 & 0 & 20 \end{pmatrix}$$

The total labor and material cost of each component may be found by adding L and M to give the matrix T:

$$L + M = \begin{pmatrix} 30 & 30 & 15 \\ 18 & 0 & 10 \end{pmatrix} + \begin{pmatrix} 10 & 14 & 7 \\ 30 & 0 & 20 \end{pmatrix}$$

$$= \begin{pmatrix} 30+10 & 30+14 & 15+7 \\ 18+30 & 0+0 & 10+20 \end{pmatrix}$$

$$= \begin{pmatrix} 40 & 44 & 22 \\ 48 & 0 & 30 \end{pmatrix} = T$$

If the standard direct cost of each component is given by the matrix S below, cost variances may be found by subtracting T from S, as shown. If:

$$S = \begin{pmatrix} 41 & 45 & 20 \\ 45 & 0 & 32 \end{pmatrix}$$

then:

$$S - T = \begin{pmatrix} 41 & 45 & 20 \\ 45 & 0 & 32 \end{pmatrix} - \begin{pmatrix} 40 & 44 & 22 \\ 48 & 0 & 30 \end{pmatrix}$$

$$= \begin{pmatrix} 41-40 & 45-44 & 20-22 \\ 45-48 & 0-0 & 32-30 \end{pmatrix}$$

$$= \begin{pmatrix} 1 & 1 & -2 \\ -3 & 0 \end{pmatrix}$$

Vectors with the same number of components may be added by adding similar components of the vectors. For instance, if we let each column of $S - T$ be a vector, the sum of vectors A, B, and C, which we shall call V, is found by:

$$A + B + C = \begin{pmatrix} 1 \\ -3 \end{pmatrix} + \begin{pmatrix} 1 \\ 0 \end{pmatrix} + \begin{pmatrix} -2 \\ 2 \end{pmatrix} = \begin{pmatrix} 1 + 1 - 2 \\ -3 + 0 + 2 \end{pmatrix} = \begin{pmatrix} 0 \\ -1 \end{pmatrix}$$

This matrix shows the net variance for each product. It should be noted that the matrix resulting from addition is the same regardless of which matrix is first or second. Thus:

$$A + B = B + A = C$$

Likewise:

$$C - A - B = D$$

and

$$C - B - A = D$$

The addition and subtraction of matrices results in a matrix with the same number of rows and columns.

The scalar multiple.   A matrix may be multiplied by a constant called a scalar multiple by multiplying each element in the matrix by the constant. As an example, assume we produced 12 of each product in the illustration above. Total component costs could be found by multiplying matrix T by 12, the scalar multiple.

$$12T = 12 \begin{pmatrix} 40 & 44 & 22 \\ 48 & 0 & 30 \end{pmatrix}$$

$$= \begin{pmatrix} 12 \times 40 & 12 \times 44 & 12 \times 22 \\ 12 \times 48 & 12 \times 0 & 12 \times 30 \end{pmatrix}$$

$$= \begin{pmatrix} 480 & 528 & 264 \\ 576 & 0 & 360 \end{pmatrix}$$

Again, since a vector is a special form of matrix, the same rules apply. Thus:

$$5 \begin{pmatrix} 4 \\ 2 \end{pmatrix} = \begin{pmatrix} 5 \times 4 \\ 5 \times 2 \end{pmatrix} = \begin{pmatrix} 20 \\ 10 \end{pmatrix}$$

Multiplication.   Matrix multiplication can only be carried out if the proper conditions are met. Assume that we are to multiply two matrices, A and B. We may denote the dimension of A as $m_a \times n_a$, and the dimension of B may be denoted as $m_b \times n_b$. A may be multiplied by B only if $n_a = m_b$. The reason for this will become apparent from the following example of the multiplication of one matrix by another. The dimension of the resulting matrix is $m_a \times n_b$. As an example, assume that a home builder constructs three models of houses, using four basic wood materials. The matrix showing the amount of ith wood material for the jth house follows:

$$R = \begin{pmatrix} 20 & 16 & 22 \\ 18 & 12 & 21 \\ 25 & 8 & 13 \\ 17 & 10 & 20 \end{pmatrix} \text{Wood products}$$

House style

Thus, a_{23} indicates that 21 units of the second wood product are used in the construction of the third type of house. The builder builds in two locations. The following matrix shows the number of ith homes built in the jth location:

$$C = \begin{pmatrix} 8 & 7 \\ 4 & 2 \\ 5 & 6 \end{pmatrix} \text{House style}$$

Location

Consequently, a_{32} indicates that six style 3 houses will be built at the second location.

Suppose the supply clerk wishes to know the number of each wood product to send to each location. This is found by multiplying R by C. Let us present these in abstract notation, calling the product T and remembering that the dimension of R is 4×3 and of C, 3×2. The multiplication RC is legitimate and results in a 4×2 matrix. However, the multiplication of CR is not legitimate because a 3×2 matrix cannot be multiplied by a 4×3. These matrices, in abstract notation, are:

$$\begin{pmatrix} r_{11} & r_{12} & r_{13} \\ r_{21} & r_{22} & r_{23} \\ r_{31} & r_{32} & r_{33} \\ r_{41} & r_{42} & r_{43} \end{pmatrix} \begin{pmatrix} c_{11} & c_{12} \\ c_{21} & c_{22} \\ c_{31} & c_{32} \end{pmatrix} = \begin{pmatrix} t_{11} & t_{12} \\ t_{21} & t_{22} \\ t_{31} & t_{32} \\ t_{41} & t_{42} \end{pmatrix}$$

The value of t_{ij} is found by multiplying each element in the ith row of the first matrix (R) by the corresponding element of the jth column of the second matrix (C). Thus:

$$t_{32} = r_{31}c_{12} + r_{32}c_{22} + r_{33}c_{32}$$

The third row of R is the number of the third wood product used in house styles 1, 2, and 3, respectively; and column 2 of C is the number of house styles 1, 2, and 3 built at location 2. In fact, these could be reexpressed as the following vectors:

$$V_r = (25 \quad 8 \quad 13) \quad V_c = \begin{pmatrix} 7 \\ 2 \\ 6 \end{pmatrix}$$

It can be seen that since 25 units of this product are used in the first house style and seven of that style home are being built, the builder needs 175 units of material 1 for the first-style home. In addition, he needs 8 units for each of the two second-style houses plus 13 units for each of the six third-style houses. Accordingly,

$$t_{32} = r_{31}c_{12} + c_{32}c_{22} + r_{33}c_{32} = (25)(7) + (8)(2) + (13)(6) = 175 + 16$$
$$+ 78 = 269$$

We may now compute RC:

$$\begin{pmatrix} 20 & 16 & 22 \\ 18 & 12 & 21 \\ 25 & 8 & 13 \\ 17 & 10 & 20 \end{pmatrix} \begin{pmatrix} 8 & 7 \\ 4 & 2 \\ 5 & 6 \end{pmatrix}$$

$$= \begin{pmatrix} (20)(8) + (16)(4) + (22)(5) & (20)(7) + (16)(2) + (22)(6) \\ (18)(8) + (12)(4) + (21)(5) & (18)(7) + (12)(2) + (21)(6) \\ (25)(8) + (8)(4) + (13)(5) & (25)(7) + (8)(2) + (13)(6) \\ (17)(8) + (10)(4) + (20)(5) & (17)(7) + (10)(2) + (20)(6) \end{pmatrix}$$

$$= \begin{pmatrix} 160 + 64 + 110 & 140 + 32 + 132 \\ 144 + 48 + 105 & 126 + 24 + 126 \\ 200 + 32 + 65 & 175 + 16 + 78 \\ 136 + 40 + 100 & 119 + 20 + 120 \end{pmatrix}$$

$$= \begin{pmatrix} 334 & 304 \\ 297 & 276 \\ 297 & 269 \\ 276 & 259 \end{pmatrix}$$

Matrix terminology

The *diagonal* of a square matrix is all elements, a_{ij}, where $i = j$. For example:

$$A = \begin{pmatrix} 1 & 2 & 3 \\ 2 & 1 & 2 \\ 3 & 3 & 1 \end{pmatrix}$$

The lines show the diagonal.

An *identity matrix* is a square matrix with 1's on the diagonal and 0's elsewhere. It is denoted I; thus:

$$I = \begin{pmatrix} 1 & 0 & 0 \\ 0 & 1 & 0 \\ 0 & 0 & 1 \end{pmatrix}$$

This matrix has the property that when multiplied by any other matrix, the other matrix results. Hence:

$$AI = \begin{pmatrix} 1 & 2 & 3 \\ 2 & 1 & 2 \\ 3 & 3 & 1 \end{pmatrix} \begin{pmatrix} 1 & 0 & 0 \\ 0 & 1 & 0 \\ 0 & 0 & 1 \end{pmatrix} = \begin{pmatrix} 1 & 2 & 3 \\ 2 & 1 & 2 \\ 3 & 3 & 1 \end{pmatrix}$$

It can readily be seen that this is so because any element in the resulting matrix occurs by multiplying a like element in the first matrix by 1 and all other elements by 0. For example, $a_{23} = 2 \times 0 + 1 \times 0 + 2 \times 1 = 2$. The *inverse* of a matrix is that matrix which, when multiplied by the original matrix, forms an identity matrix. The inverse of a matrix A is denoted A^{-1}. Thus, $A^{-1}A = I$. The inverse matrix also has the property that

$$AA^{-1} = A^{-1}A = I$$

Systems of linear equations

The primary use of matrix algebra is to assist in dealing with systems of linear equations. In general, a system of linear equations may be written:

$$Ax = c$$

where:

$x =$ A column vector whose m components are the m unknowns
$A =$ An $m \times n$ matrix where each component is the coefficient of the jth unknown in the ith equation
$c =$ A column vector of m constants

The fact that these symbols are really a shorthand notation for a system of m linear equations in n unknowns may be shown by carrying out the multiplication of A by x and writing out the components of c. Thus:

$$a_{11}x_1 + a_{12}x_2 + \cdots + a_{1n}x_n = c_1$$
$$a_{21}x_1 + a_{22}x_2 + \cdots + a_{2n}x_n = c_2$$
$$\vdots \qquad \vdots \qquad \cdots \qquad \vdots$$
$$a_{m1}x_1 + a_{m2}x_2 + \cdots + a_{mn}x_n = c_m$$

We shall now discuss a method for finding a solution when $m = n$, in which case A is a square matrix.

Suppose that a manufacturer makes two products, x_1 and x_2, each of which must be processed in two departments, A and B. Matrix A gives the coefficients of processing time necessary to process the jth product through the ith department. The column vector c gives the available processing time in each department. Where:

$$A = \begin{pmatrix} 3 & 5 \\ 6 & 2 \end{pmatrix}, \quad c = \begin{pmatrix} 12 \\ 10 \end{pmatrix}$$

The manufacturer wishes to utilize all available processing time. The number of units of product x_1 and product x_2 which will exactly utilize all available processing time may be found by solving the system:

$$3x_1 + 5x_2 = 12 \text{ (represents department 1)}$$
$$6x_2 + 2x_2 = 10 \text{ (represents department 2)}$$

which may be expressed:

$$Ax = c$$

Multiplying both sides by A^{-1}, we have:

$$A^{-1}Ax = A^{-1}c$$
$$IX = A^{-1}c$$
$$X = A^{-1}c$$

We would now be able to solve the system if A^{-1} were known. Let us assume we know that:

$$A^{-1} = \begin{pmatrix} -\frac{1}{12} & \frac{5}{24} \\ \frac{1}{4} & -\frac{1}{8} \end{pmatrix}$$

It may be shown that this is the inverse of A by showing that $A^{-1}A = I$. Thus:

$$\begin{pmatrix} -\frac{1}{12} & \frac{5}{24} \\ \frac{1}{4} & -\frac{1}{8} \end{pmatrix} \begin{pmatrix} 3 & 5 \\ 6 & 2 \end{pmatrix} = \begin{pmatrix} -\frac{3}{12} + \frac{30}{24} & -\frac{5}{12} + \frac{10}{24} \\ \frac{3}{4} - \frac{6}{8} & \frac{5}{4} - \frac{2}{8} \end{pmatrix}$$
$$= \begin{pmatrix} 1 & 0 \\ 0 & 1 \end{pmatrix}$$

The system may now be solved by solving $x = A^{-1}c$; hence:

$$\begin{pmatrix} x_1 \\ x_2 \end{pmatrix} = \begin{pmatrix} -\frac{1}{12} & \frac{5}{24} \\ \frac{1}{4} & -\frac{1}{8} \end{pmatrix} \begin{pmatrix} 12 \\ 10 \end{pmatrix}$$
$$= \begin{pmatrix} -\frac{12}{12} + \frac{50}{24} \\ \frac{12}{4} - \frac{10}{8} \end{pmatrix}$$
$$= \begin{pmatrix} \frac{13}{12} \\ \frac{14}{8} \end{pmatrix}$$

Thus, production of 13/12 units of x_1 and 14/8 units of x_2 will utilize all available capacity.

This may be checked by substituting these values in the original equations:

$$3(\tfrac{13}{12}) + 5(\tfrac{14}{8}) = 12$$
$$\tfrac{78}{24} + \tfrac{210}{24} = 12$$

which checks, and

$$6(1\tfrac{3}{12}) + 2(1\tfrac{4}{8}) = 10$$
$$15\tfrac{6}{24} + 8\tfrac{4}{24} = 10$$

which checks. The reader will note that he could have solved this simple system with high school mathematics. However, much larger systems must be solved with matrix methods. The reader should also note that utilizing all production capacity in no way assures maximum profits.

Finding the inverse

We shall now discuss an elementary method of finding an inverse, *if there is one*. If the system does not have a unique solution, the inverse cannot be found. This caveat should always be remembered, although this text normally proceeds under the assumption that an inverse exists.

Some of the properties of the inverse of a square matrix have now been discussed, along with the solution of a system of linear equations when the inverse of the matrix is known. However, the important step which has been left out is the method of finding the inverse, if there is one. We shall first demonstrate how the inverse of A in the production problem may be found. In the production problem, and in general for any square matrix, the inverse is defined to be a matrix such that the following is true:

$$AA^{-1} = I = A^{-1}A$$

The inverse can be found by manipulating the matrix and an identity matrix. It is worthwhile to remember: (1) Every element in a row may be divided or multiplied by any number, and (2) any row may be added to or subtracted from any other row to find a new row. Take the matrix:

$$A = \begin{pmatrix} 2 & 4 \\ 3 & 1 \end{pmatrix}$$

This method proceeds by placing an identity matrix beside the square matrix A and manipulating the system so that the first matrix is converted to an identity matrix. For example:

$$\begin{pmatrix} 2 & 4 & | & 1 & 0 \\ 3 & 1 & | & 0 & 1 \end{pmatrix}$$

Since we desire a one in the upper left corner, let us divide row 1 by 2, giving:

$$\begin{pmatrix} 1 & 2 & | & \tfrac{1}{2} & 0 \\ 3 & 1 & | & 0 & 1 \end{pmatrix}$$

We now desire a zero in the lower left-hand corner. Let us form a new row 2 by subtracting 3 times new row 1 from the old row 2:

$$\begin{pmatrix} 1 & 2 & \frac{1}{2} & 0 \\ 0 & -5 & -\frac{3}{2} & 1 \end{pmatrix}$$

$$3 - 3(1) = 0 \qquad 1 - 3(2) = -5 \qquad 0 - 3(\tfrac{1}{2}) = -\tfrac{3}{2} \qquad 1 - 3(0) = 1$$

We now wish a one in the lower element in column 2. Thus, we divide row 2 by -5:

$$\begin{pmatrix} 1 & 2 & \frac{1}{2} & 0 \\ 0 & 1 & \frac{3}{10} & -\frac{1}{5} \end{pmatrix}$$

We now desire a zero in the second element in row 1. Therefore the new row 1 is old row 1 minus two times new row 2:

$$\begin{pmatrix} 1 & 0 & -\frac{1}{10} & \frac{2}{5} \\ 0 & 1 & \frac{3}{10} & -\frac{1}{5} \end{pmatrix}$$

Consequently, the inverse is:

$$\begin{pmatrix} -\frac{1}{10} & \frac{2}{5} \\ \frac{3}{10} & -\frac{1}{5} \end{pmatrix}$$

and this may be checked by multiplying it by A to see if $AA^{-1} = I$. Thus:

$$\begin{pmatrix} 2 & 4 \\ 3 & 1 \end{pmatrix}\begin{pmatrix} -\frac{1}{10} & \frac{2}{5} \\ \frac{3}{10} & -\frac{1}{5} \end{pmatrix} = \begin{pmatrix} -\frac{2}{10} + \frac{12}{10} & \frac{4}{5} - \frac{4}{5} \\ -\frac{3}{10} + \frac{3}{10} & \frac{6}{5} - \frac{1}{5} \end{pmatrix} = \begin{pmatrix} 1 & 0 \\ 0 & 1 \end{pmatrix}$$

which demonstrates that we have found the inverse.

II. PROBABILITY THEORY

The probability concepts used throughout this book are elementary and deal with discrete rather than continuous probability. The concepts can best be introduced by using an example. Assume that you are a TV manufacturer selling both a floor model and a portable TV set which may be purchased in black and white or in color. The records of the company show that 250 of the last 1,000 sets sold were color, and 750 of the last 1,000 sets were black and white. They further show that 300 of the last 1,000 sets sold were portable sets, and 700 of the last 1,000 were floor models. The probability of the occurrence of an event is the ratio of the number of times the event occurs (or can occur) to the number of times it and all other events occur (or can occur). In this case the probability of the purchase of a color set is:

$$P(C) = \frac{C}{C + B} = 0.25$$

where C is the number of times color sets were purchased and B is the number of times black-and-white sets were purchased. It can be seen that $P(C)$ represents the relative frequency of the occurrence of C to $B + C$. How did we decide that $C + B$ were the relevant events? In this case, color is the characteristic of interest, and this characteristic can exist in only two forms (color or black and white). The case at hand seems un-ambiguous. However, such is not always the case.

The concept of sample space, sample points, and events

Relevant events can be understood by the concept of a sample space, sample points, and events. A sample space refers to the complete set of outcomes for the situation as it did or may exist. It is simplest to consider each situation an experiment. Then, in the words of Chris A. Theodore: "A *sample space* of a real or conceptual experiment is a set of elements such that every possible outcome of the experiment corresponds to one and only one element in the set. An element in a set serving as a sample space is called a *sample point*."[1] Add to this the following definition of an event: An *event* is a statement which refers to a particular subset of a sample space for an experiment. Consider the experiment of tossing first one coin and then another. Every possible outcome gives the following sample space:

$$S = [HH, HT, TH, TT]$$

Note that $S = [\quad]$ is the symbol which represents the sample space. This sample space has four outcomes or sample points: HH, HT, TH, TT. Consider a number of events which may be represented from these sample points. One event may be that both coins fall alike, which may be shown:

$$E_1 = [HH, TT; \text{alike}]$$

where the word following the semicolon indicates the characteristic of interest. If we let E_1 be the event of interest and E_2 be the subset of all remaining outcomes, then:

$$S = E_1 + E_2$$

As long as any outcome or sample point in our experiment is not af-fected by outside influences, each outcome or sample point is equally likely to occur. The assumption of each sample point being equally likely to occur is known as an *a priori assumption*. The term *a priori* refers to something which is known by reason alone. Thus, a priori probability is

---

[1] Chris A. Theodore, *Applied Mathematics: An Introduction* (Homewood, Ill.: Richard D. Irwin, Inc., 1965), p. 509.

known by reason alone. In the example being discussed, each sample point occurs with equal frequency. For example, E_1 occurs twice, E_2 occurs twice, and

$$P(E_1) = \frac{E_1}{E_1 + E_2} = \tfrac{1}{2}$$

Consider a second experiment where the events of interest are the number of heads which occur when tossing first one coin and then another. Then $E_1 = [HH; \ 2H]$; $E_2 = [HT, \ TH; \ 1H]$; $E_3 = [TT; \ 0H]$; and $S = E_1 + E_2 + E_3$. In this case, we have listed the characteristic of interest (the number of heads) by a number followed by an H for *head*. Since all sample points are listed, no subset of sample points remains, and

$$S = E_1 + E_2 + E_3$$

Since, a priori, the sample points are equally likely to occur,

$$P(E_1) = 1/4, \ P(E_2) = 1/2, \text{ and } P(E_3) \ 1/4$$

Another experiment could be that both coins fall heads. Another could be at least one falls heads. Even though this example may seem simple, the reader should now begin to appreciate the necessity of defining unambiguously the sample space, sample points, and events.

Fundamental concepts

The use of probability concepts relies on two fundamental relationships which stem from the concepts already presented. We have shown that the probability of occurrence of an event is the relative frequency of the occurrence of that event to all other relevant events. Since the number of sample points in the event is less than or equal to the number of sample points in the sample space, the probability of any event is between zero and one, inclusive. Thus:

$$P(A_1) = \frac{A_1}{\sum\limits_{i=1}^{n} A_i}$$

and

$$0 \le P(A_1) \le 1$$

where A_i is the frequency of occurrence of the ith event.

The remaining concepts can be understood with the aid of the example of the TV manufacturer, mentioned earlier. The information provided by the TV manufacturer can be summarized as shown in Table 11-1. $P(C)$ and $P(B)$ are known as marginal probabilities or uncondi-

Table 11–1

MODEL

COLOR		F	P	Total
	C	150	100	250
	B	550	200	750
		700	300	1,000

Since:

$$P(C) = \frac{250}{750 + 250} = 0.25$$

$$P(B) = \frac{750}{750 + 250} = 0.75$$

$$P(C) + P(B) = 1.00$$

Also:

$$P(F) = \frac{700}{700 + 300} = 0.7$$

$$P(P) = \frac{300}{700 + 300} = 0.3$$

$$P(F) + P(P) = 1.0$$

tional probabilities. This seems logical because these events are on the margin of the table. Marginal probabilities are mutually exclusive and collectively exhaustive events for a single basis of classification. In this example the color is one basis of classification, and the model type (i.e., floor or portable model) is another basis of classification. When the list of events includes every possible outcome, it is collectively exhaustive. Events are mutually exclusive if one and only one outcome can take place at a time. These conditions hold for the marginal probabilities shown above. The reader should note that in this context we have 1,000 sample points but only two events. Since we shall be discussing only situations where the sample points are clearly understood by the description of the events, we shall confine the remaining discussion to events and sample spaces. The material which follows will clarify the status of the events which tend to be somehow interrelated. The relationship of events is identified by statistical independence or statistical dependence, which will now be presented.

Statistically independent events

As indicated earlier, $P(A_i)$ is the probability of occurrence of the ith marginal or unconditional event. When events are statistically independent, the occurrence of one event has no effect on the probability of the occurrence of any other event. The probability of two or more independent events occurring together or in succession is the product of their marginal probabilities. Mathematically, this is defined as

$$P(AB) = P(A) \times P(B)$$

where $P(AB)$ is the probability of events A and B occurring together or in succession and $P(A)$ is the marginal probability of event A occurring and $P(B)$ the marginal probability of event B occurring. This is known as a joint probability and is a different form of probability than marginal (sometimes called unconditional) probability. Thus a single event cannot be both a joint probability and a marginal probability.

Table 11–2

MODEL

		F	P	Total
	C	175	75	250
COLOR	B	525	225	750
		700	300	1,000

In the TV manufacturer example the relative frequency of the occurrence of the event "color and portable" is:

$$P(CP) = \frac{100}{1,000} = 0.1$$

If these data exhibit statistical independence, then:

$$P(CP) = P(C)P(P)$$

Since $0.1 \neq (0.25)(0.3)$, this event is not statistically independent.

The TV manufacturer has four joint probabilities which, if statistical independence existed, would be:

$$P(PC) = (0.3)(0.25) = 0.075$$
$$P(PB) = (0.3)(0.75) = 0.225$$
$$P(FC) = (0.7)(0.25) = 0.175$$
$$P(FB) = (0.7)(0.75) = 0.525$$

Table 11–2 would have yielded such a pattern.

From the initial data, we have demonstrated that the choice of color and the choice of model are not made independently. In other words, we cannot say that regardless of whether a floor model or portable model was chosen, 25 percent would be color. Nor can we say that regardless of whether a color or black-and-white set were chosen, 30 percent would be portable models. In this context, neither can we say anything about the order in which the choice of color and model was made. However, in some situations the order of events may be important.

For example, in two tosses of a fair coin, the probability of heads on two successive tosses is the probability of heads on the first toss (shown as H_1) times the probability of heads on the second toss (shown as H_2). That is:

$$P(H_1 H_2) = P(H_1)P(H_2)$$

These events are statistically independent because the probability of any outcome is not affected by any preceding outcome. Therefore the a priori probability of heads on two successive tosses is 0.25.

Likewise the a priori probability of getting three heads on three successive tosses is:

$$P(H_1 H_2 H_3) = P(H_1)P(H_2)P(H_3) = (0.5)(0.5)(0.5) = 0.125$$

Thus far, we have considered two types of probabilities: marginal (unconditional) probability and joint probability. Symbolically, marginal probability is $P(A)$, and joint probability is $P(AB)$. There is only one other type of probability: It is known as conditional probability. Symbolically, conditional probability is written $P(A/B)$ and is read: The probability of event A, *given that event B has occurred*.

For statistically independent events the conditional probability of event A, given that event B has occurred, is simply the probability of event A. At first glance, this may seem contradictory. However, by definition, independent events are those whose probabilities are in no way affected by the occurrence of any other events. In fact, statistical independence is symbolically defined as the condition in which

$$P(A/B) = P(A).$$

For example, what is the probability that the second toss of a fair coin will result in heads, given that heads resulted on the first toss? Symbolically, this is written as $P(H_2/H_1)$. Remember that for two independent events, the results of the first toss have absolutely no effect on the results of the second toss. Since the probability of heads on the second toss is 0.5, we must say that $P(H_2/H_1) = P(H_2) = 0.5$.

Referring again to the TV manufacturer in the statistically independent case (Table 11–2), a conditional probability is $P(C/F)$. By the above rule, $P(C/F) = P(C) = 0.25$. We may check this by logic. Since we have shown that the probability of the occurrence of F has no effect on the probability of C or B, and that the occurrence of P has no effect on the probability of C or B, the ratio of color to black and white should be the

Table 11–3

Type of probability	Formula under statistical independence
Marginal (or unconditional)...............	$P(A) = P(A)$
Joint....................................	$P(AB) = P(A)P(B)$
Conditional.............................	$P(A/B) = P(A)$

same whether the purchaser is buying a floor model or a portable model; i.e., $P(C/F) = 0.25$.

For a summary of the three types of probabilities and their mathematical formulas under conditions of statistical independence, see Table 11–3.

Statistically dependent events

Statistical dependence exists when the probability of some event is dependent upon or affected by the occurrence of some other event. Just as with independent events, the types of probabilities under statistical dependence are (1) marginal, (2) conditional, and (3) joint.

The marginal probability of a statistically dependent event is exactly the same as that of a statistically independent event. This is not difficult to see if we note that a marginal probability is symbolized $P(A)$. One and only one probability is involved in the consideration.

In the TV manufacturer example of Tables 11–1 and 11–2, the marginal probabilities have identical meanings; i.e., they are mutually exclusive and collectively exhaustive for a single basis of classification.

Conditional and joint probabilities under statistical dependence are somewhat more involved than marginal probabilities. Conditional probabilities will be treated first, because the concept of joint probabilities is best illustrated by using conditional probabilities as a basis.

Assume that the TV manufacturer represents his situation by placing 1,000 slips of paper in a huge box in the distribution shown in Table 11–4. These relationships can be shown diagrammatically, as in Figure 11–1.

One question which conditional probability asks is: If a buyer purchases a portable set, what is the probability that it is colored? In order to calculate this, we must completely ignore all the information on floor

Table 11–4

Statement on paper	Number of pieces
Portable, color..................................	100
Portable, black and white........................	200
Floor model, color...............................	150
Floor model, black and white.....................	550
Total..	1,000

models. From the data in Figure 11–1, we know that of the 300 portable models purchased, 100 were color, and 200 were black and white. Our problem is now simply to find the probability of color for this restricted problem. Thus:

$$P(C_1) = \frac{(C_1)}{(C_1) + (B_1)} = \frac{100}{100 + 200} = \frac{1}{3}$$

where C_1 is the number of color TV sets sold under the restricted conditions and B_1 is the number of black-and-white sets sold under the restricted conditions.

Figure 11–1

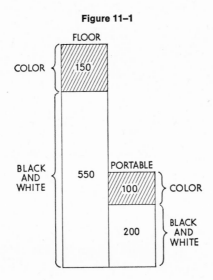

The direct formula for calculating this is:

$$P(C/P) = \frac{P(CP)}{P(P)}$$

In general symbols this is:

$$P(A/B) = \frac{P(AB)}{P(B)}$$

We have not discussed the calculation of joint probabilities for the statistically dependent case. We do know, however, the relative frequency of CP; therefore:

$$P(CP) = \frac{100}{1,000} = 0.1$$

Inserting this in the direct formula:

$$P(C/P) = \frac{0.1}{0.3} = 0.33$$

which supports the finding.

Since we have data on the joint probabilities, we may calculate all conditional probabilities:

$$P(C/P) = \frac{P(CP)}{P(P)} = \frac{0.1}{0.3} = 0.33$$

$$P(C/F) = \frac{P(CF)}{P(F)} = \frac{0.15}{0.7} = 0.2143$$

$$P(F/B) = \frac{P(FB)}{P(B)} = \frac{0.55}{0.75} = 0.733$$

$$P(F/C) = \frac{P(FC)}{P(C)} = \frac{0.15}{0.25} = 0.6$$

$$P(B/F) = \frac{P(BF)}{P(F)} = \frac{0.55}{0.7} = 0.7857$$

$$P(B/P) = \frac{P(BP)}{P(P)} = \frac{0.2}{0.3} = 0.67$$

$$P(P/C) = \frac{P(PC)}{P(C)} = \frac{0.1}{0.25} = 0.4$$

$$P(P/B) = \frac{P(PB)}{P(B)} = \frac{0.2}{0.75} = 0.267$$

We have shown that the formula for conditional probability under conditions of statistical dependence is:

$$P(A/B) = P(AB)/P(B)$$

If we solve this formula for $P(AB)$ (and this can be done simply by cross multiplication), we find that:

$$P(AB) = P(A/B) \, P(B)$$

This is the formula for joint probability under conditions of statistical dependence. It is read: The joint probability of events A and B equals the probability of event A, given that event B has occurred, times the probability of event B. Also, we can note that:

$$P(B/A) = \frac{P(AB)}{P(A)}$$

Therefore, $P(AB) = P(A)P(B/A)$.

Thus, working the data back to the joint probabilities:

$$P(CP) = P(C/P)P(P) = (\tfrac{1}{3})(0.3) \quad\; = 0.1$$
$$P(CF) = P(C/F)P(F) = (0.2143)(0.7) = 0.15$$

$$P(BF) = P(B/F)P(F) = (0.7857)(0.7) = 0.55$$
$$P(BP) = P(B/P)P(P) = (\tfrac{2}{3})(0.3) \qquad = 0.2$$

which agrees with the earlier data.

Note that the marginal probability of the event "color" can be computed by summing the probabilities of the joint events in which color is contained:

$$P(C) = P(CP) + P(CF) = 0.1 + 0.15 = 0.25$$

Similarly, the marginal probability of the event "black and white" can be computed by summing the probabilities of the joint events in which black and white are contained:

$$P(B) = P(BP) + P(BF) = 0.2 + 0.55 = 0.75$$

In like manner, the marginal probability of "portable" can be computed by summing the probabilities of the joint events in which portable is contained:

$$P(P) = P(CP) + P(BP) = 0.1 + 0.2 = 0.3$$

And finally, the marginal probability of "floor model" can be computed by summing the probabilities of the joint events in which floor model is contained:

$$P(F) = P(CF) + P(BF) = 0.15 + 0.55 = 0.7$$

These four marginal probabilities can be verified by inspection of Table 11–1 (page 161).

We have now considered the three types of probability—marginal, conditional, and joint—under conditions of statistical dependence. Table 11–5 provides a résumé.

Table 11–5

Type of probability	Formula under statistical dependence
Marginal (or unconditional).............	$P(A) = P(A)$
Joint...............................	$P(AB) = P(A/B)P(B)$
Conditional........................	$P(A/B) = \dfrac{P(AB)}{P(B)}$

Relationship between independence and dependence

Under conditions of statistical dependence, the formula for conditional probability is:

$$P(A/B) = P(AB)/P(B)$$

Under independence, the formula for joint probability is:

$$P(AB) = P(A)P(B)$$

Substituting $P(A)P(B)$ for $P(AB)$ in the formula for conditional probability, we get:

$$P(A/B) = \frac{P(A)P(B)}{P(B)}$$

Since $P(B)$ occurs in both the denominator and the numerator, we can cancel the two, as follows:

$$P(A/B) = \frac{P(A)P(B)}{P(B)} = P(A)$$

The resulting formula, $P(A/B) = P(A)$, was shown on page 163 as the formula under statistical independence. An example will show that this is true. What is the probability of heads on the second toss of a fair coin, given that tails occurred on the first toss?

Converting the formula

$$P(A/B) = \frac{P(A)P(B)}{P(B)}$$

to terms of heads and tails, we have:

$$P(H_2/T_1) = \frac{P(H_2)P(T_1)}{P(T_1)} = \frac{(0.5)\ (0.5)}{0.5} = 0.5$$

The probability of heads on the second toss is not affected by the result of the first toss. In other words:

$$P(H_2/T_1) = P(H_2)$$

Notice that this has the same form as the general formula $P(A/B) = P(A)$.

This concludes our development of probabilities under both statistical independence and statistical dependence. Table 11–6 is given as a quick reference.

Table 11–6

Type of probability	Formula under statistical independence	Formula under statistical dependence
Marginal	$P(A) = P(A)$	$P(A) = P(A)$
Joint	$P(AB) = P(A)P(B)$	$P(AB) = P(A/B)P(B)$
Conditional	$P(A/B) = P(A)$	$P(A/B) = \dfrac{P(AB)}{P(B)}$

Additivity

We have used the symbol $P(AB)$ to represent the joint probability. A joint probability is an event where both A *and* B occur. It carries the meaning "and." We may wish to refer to the probability of event A or event B occurring. In this case, either A or B, but not necessarily both, must occur. This is written symbolically: $P(A + B)$. The general formula to compute $P(A + B)$ is:

$$P(A + B) = P(A) + P(B) - P(AB)$$

Let us look at the data on the TV manufacturer. If we wish to know the probability that *either* a portable set or a color set was purchased, we may refer to Table 11–1 and find:

$$\begin{aligned} P(P + C) &= P(P) + P(C) - P(PC) \\ &= 0.3 + 0.25 - 0.1 \\ &= 0.45 \end{aligned}$$

The purpose of subtracting the joint probability is to eliminate double-counting. In the example, we can see that we have only one instance in which the set was neither portable nor color, which is the black-and-white floor model. Since $P(BF) = 0.55$, the difference between this and one is 0.45, which verifies our earlier findings. The problem may not be so simple if the number of events becomes larger.

If the events are mutually exclusive, $P(AB)$ is always zero. This can be seen by remembering that the formula for $P(AB)$ is $P(A/B)P(B)$. If the events are mutually exclusive, A cannot occur when B occurs. Thus, $P(A/B)$ is inconsistent and nonexistent.

DISCUSSION TOPICS AND PROBLEMS

1. A manufacturer sells red, white, and blue widgets to men and women. Men buy the following percentage of *all* widgets:

$$\begin{aligned} \text{Red}&\dots\dots\dots\dots\dots\dots\dots 0.1 \\ \text{White}&\dots\dots\dots\dots\dots\dots\dots 0.1 \\ \text{Blue}&\dots\dots\dots\dots\dots\dots\dots 0.2 \end{aligned}$$

Women buy widgets in the following proportions:

$$\begin{aligned} \text{Red}&\dots\dots\dots\dots\dots\dots\dots 0.2 \\ \text{White}&\dots\dots\dots\dots\dots\dots\dots 0.3 \\ \text{Blue}&\dots\dots\dots\dots\dots\dots\dots 0.5 \end{aligned}$$

a) What are the joint probabilities for each possible event?
b) What are the conditional probabilities for each possible event?
c) What are the marginal probabilities for each relevant event?
d) Are color and sex statistically independent?

2. The following information is available about a manufacturer's last 20 sales. The manufacturer sells red, white, and blue widgets for men and women.

Date		Sex	Products
August	27	M	R
	27	M	R
September	1	F	B
	3	M	R
	5	F	W
	7	F	W
	9	M	W
	11	M	B
	13	F	B
	15	F	R
	17	F	B
	19	M	R
	21	F	W
	23	F	B
	25	F	W
October	5	M	B
	7	M	B
	9	F	B
	15	M	R
	17	F	W

a) What are the joint probabilities for each possible event?
b) What are the conditional probabilities for each possible event?
c) What are the marginal probabilities for each relevant event?

3. Among a group of 100 college students, 50 had blue eyes, and 50 did not. Also, 20 had blond hair, and 80 did not. Five had blond hair and blue eyes. How many have either blond hair or blue eyes? Is hair color independent of eye color?

4. An insurance company has analyzed its policies with respect to sex. The company has only four basic policies, and the probability of the occurrence of each policy type with respect to each sex is as follows:

	Policy type			
	A	B	C	D
Men	0.2	0.2	0.2	0.4
Women	0.3	0.3	0.2	0.2

The company sells 60 percent of its policies to men.

Find all of the joint, marginal, and conditional probabilities for this situation. Are policy type and sex independent?

5. A bag contains two white and three black marbles.

a) Describe at least two sample sets.
b) Assign probabilities to these sets of outcomes. What did you assume?

c) Mr. *A* and Mr. *B* each make two draws from the bag (replacing the marble each time). They bet 25 cents each. If either draws two white marbles, he is declared the winner. In the event of no winner or two winners, they split. Describe the universe.

6. Answer the following matrix algebra questions true or false. If false, indicate why.

a) If $A + B = C$, then $B + A = C$.
b) If $AB = C$, then $BA = C$.
c) $A^{-1}A = AA^{-1}$.
d) The following conditions for the elements must exist in an identity matrix: $a_{ij} = 1$ when $i = j$, and $a_{ij} = 0$ when $i = j$.
e) A matrix of dimension $1 \times n$ is a column vector.
f) A matrix of $m_1 \times n_1$ may be multiplied by a matrix $m_2 \times n_2$ when $m_1 = n_2$.
g) Any square matrix may be multiplied by any other square matrix.
h) All matrices have an inverse.

7. We wish to evaluate the values of X_i for the following system:

$$X_1 + X_2 + X_3 = 1$$
$$-0.2X_1 + 0.1X_2 + 0.1X_3 = 0$$
$$+0.1X_1 - 0.2X_2 + 0.1X_3 = 0$$

Transcribe this system to matrix notation, and indicate in abstract notation how the X_i values are found. Now find the values for all X_i.

8. Multiply the following matrices in the order shown:

a)
$$\begin{pmatrix} 3 & 2 & 6 \\ -4 & 2 & 4 \end{pmatrix}$$
$$\begin{pmatrix} 2 & 8 \\ 5 & 3 \\ 1 & 4 \end{pmatrix}$$

b)
$$\begin{pmatrix} 5 & 7 \\ -1 & 3 \\ 2 & -5 \end{pmatrix}$$
$$\begin{pmatrix} 3 & 6 \\ -2 & 4 \\ 3 & 9 \end{pmatrix}$$

c)
$$\begin{pmatrix} 3 & 2 & 6 \\ -4 & 2 & 4 \end{pmatrix}$$
$$\begin{pmatrix} 2 & 8 \\ 5 & 3 \\ 1 & 4 \end{pmatrix}$$
$$\begin{pmatrix} 2 & 9 \\ 3 & 4 \end{pmatrix}$$

9. A company purchasing agent wishes to know how many component parts to order for the coming month's production. The company produces three

172   *Managerial analysis*

products (called products 1, 2, and 3, respectively) and uses four different component parts (called parts *A, B, C,* and *D,* respectively). Product 1 takes two units of component *A,* no units of component *B,* one unit of component *C,* and two units of component *D.* Product 2 takes three units of component *A,* one unit of component *B,* two units of component *C,* and no units of component *D.* Product 3 takes two units of component *A,* one unit of component *B,* no units of component *C,* and one unit of component *D.* The company plans to produce 100 units of product 1, 200 units of product 2, and 500 units of product 3. Use matrix methods to find the number of components *A, B, C,* and *D* the purchasing agent must order.

SELECTED REFERENCES

Bowen, Earl K. *Mathematics: With Applications in Management and Economics.* Homewood, Ill.: Richard D. Irwin, Inc., 1963.

Burford, Roger L. *Introduction to Finite Probability.* Columbus, O.: Charles E. Merrill Books, Inc., 1967.

Dean, Burton V.; Sasieni, Maurice W.; and Gupta, Shiv K. *Mathematics for Modern Management.* New York: John Wiley & Sons, Inc., 1963.

Grawoig, Dennis E. *Decision Mathematics.* New York: McGraw-Hill Book Co., Inc., 1967.

Howell, James E., and Teichroew, Daniel. *Mathematical Analysis for Business Decisions.* Homewood, Ill.: Richard D. Irwin, Inc., 1963.

King, William R. *Probability for Management Decisions.* New York: John Wiley & Sons, Inc., 1968.

Levin, Richard I., and Kirkpatrick, C. A. *Quantitative Approaches to Management.* New York: McGraw-Hill Book Co., Inc., 1965.

Meier, Robert C., and Archer, Stephen H. *An Introduction to Mathematics for Business Analysis.* New York: McGraw-Hill Book Co. Inc., 1960.

Schkade, Lawrence L. *Vectors and Matrices.* Columbus, O.: Charles E. Merrill Books, Inc., 1967.

Springer, Clifford H.; Herlihy, Robert E.; Mall, Robert T.; and Beggs, Robert I. *Probabilistic Models.* Homewood, Ill.: Richard D. Irwin, Inc., 1968.

Theodore, Chris A. *Applied Mathematics: An Introduction.* Homewood, Ill.: Richard D. Irwin, Inc., 1965.

SECTION FOUR

Models of common processes

12

Single-variable optimization: Classical economic models

I. CONDITIONS OF DATA CERTAINTY AND UNCERTAINTY

Differing degrees of knowledge exist about the relationship between actions taken by the decision maker and the outcomes that result from those actions. For example, the decision maker considering the purchase of a piece of equipment knows the price he must pay for the equipment, but he has less knowledge about the benefits of owning any particular piece of equipment. The benefits of owning any particular piece of equipment are dependent upon the use of the equipment and the length of time the equipment is used. Consequently, in order to conduct this analysis, the decision maker must project the amount of time the equipment will be used and the particular tasks the equipment will perform. When information is known with certainty, this is a condition of data certainty. A knowledge of the cost of equipment is a condition of data certainty. When the outcome is not known with certainty, this is a condition of data uncertainty. The decision maker will find that the amount of uncertainty varies widely. The demand for a stable product is known with more certainty than the demand for a completely new product.

The amount of time the equipment will be used is a condition of data uncertainty. However, the decision maker may be willing to make a point estimate and proceed on the basis of a point estimate. A point estimate is a projection of a specific value for the outcome of a given action, thus transforming a condition of data uncertainty to an apparent condition of data certainty. In other words, the decision maker may be willing to identify the most likely length of time the equipment will be used and proceed to make his decision assuming that it is a reasonable estimate. However, a more thorough and cautious decision maker may wish to obtain information on other variables that would affect the use of the equipment and predict the probability that the various conditions which affect the equipment usage will occur.

Consider the case of Ira Optimist, who has $1,000 to invest. He is concerned only with his return at the end of one year. He is considering whether to purchase blue-chip stocks, speculative stocks, or government

Table 12–1

	Economic conditions		
Action	Good conditions	Normal conditions	Bad conditions
Buy government bonds:			
Average return	0.04	0.04	0.04
Standard deviation of returns	Zero	Zero	Zero
Buy blue-chip stocks:			
Average return	0.08	0.04	Zero
Standard deviation of returns	0.01	0.01	0.01
Buy speculative stocks:			
Average return	0.15	0.05	−0.10
Standard deviation of returns	0.03	0.01	0.02
Probability of outcome	0.30	0.50	0.20

bonds. If he assumes that the return on these stocks is dependent upon general economic conditions, his action is dependent upon his willingness to make a point estimate of future economic conditions. If he believes that the future outlook is good, thus making speculative stocks attractive, his decision is to buy speculative stocks. On the other hand, he might identify the following three economic conditions as possible events: (1) good, (2) average, or (3) bad. Then, by attaching a probability of occurrence to each condition and identifying the likely return on each stock under these conditions, he can make a choice even under a condition of data uncertainty. Table 12–1 portrays his dilemma. The cells of the table show the average return per dollar and the variance. Since the average is the most likely return, the decision maker may use it as a point estimate. The most likely economic condition is normal. A point estimate applied to economic conditions would consider "normal" as the only outcome. Since deviations from normal have a marked impact, it would be foolish to consider "normal" as the only outcome (i.e., make a point estimate).

The manufacturer replacing equipment must estimate usage of the equipment on the basis of estimated demand for his product. Since demand is so complex that from all appearances it is random, a point estimate is quite reasonable. The desirability of either a point estimate or an interval estimate depends upon the application being analyzed.

If the environment can be represented by a system of equations or a single equation, we have an optimization model with deterministic inputs. It should be noted that optimization models with deterministic inputs may be solved in differing fashions.

An optimization model for which there is an analytic solution is one form of optimization model with deterministic inputs. The chapter on finding maxima, minima, and inflection points (Chapter 10) deals with classical optimization theory. Consequently, any model that can be solved with classical optimization theory fits in this first category of optimization models with deterministic inputs. The classical economic order quantity (EOQ) discussed later in Chapter 13 is an example of this type of model. It is not necessary that there be only one independent variable; there may be many independent variables, as long as they can be dealt with using classical optimization techniques.

The second category of optimization models with deterministic inputs includes models that are systems of equations for which there is an algorithm to identify the optimum solution. An algorithm is a predefined procedure for finding a solution. The linear programming algorithm discussed in Chapter 15 and 16, particularly the simplex algorithm identified in Chapter 16, is an example if the second category of optimization models with deterministic inputs. In fact, any model with deterministic inputs in which the optimum value can be identified or obtained by a preestablished search procedure other than classical optimization techniques is included with the second classification of optimization models with deterministic inputs.

Another category of optimization models deals with probabilistic inputs. One possible way of classifying models with probabilistic inputs is to look at the characteristics or nature of the probabilities that are used in the model. The probabilities may exhibit either statistical independence or statistical dependence. This distinction is partially concerned with whether the order of events has any impact on the probability of the occurrence of the next event.

II. MARGINAL ANALYSIS

Marginal analysis is a method of looking at the difference between the benefits and the costs of a course of action as one changes the course of action. It looks at the benefits minus the costs for the next incremental action. In classical economic theory the firm is faced with different revenues and costs at different levels of production. Marginal analysis

Table 12–2

Units manufactured and sold	Total costs of operations	Total revenue from sale
0	$ 25	. . . .
1	50	$ 47.50
2	75	90.00
3	100	127.50
4	125	160.00
5	150	187.50
6	175	210.00
7	200	227.50
8	225	240.00
9	250	247.50
10	275	250.00
11	300	247.50

looks at the change in profit (revenue minus cost) for each increment in the number of units produced. This is then a process of looking at rates of change, i.e., the impact of a change in production from x to $x + 1$ units.

If the reader has not completed a course in calculus or read Chapter 10, it is advised that he read pages 118–29 of that chapter. The following will assume a knowledge of that material.

Suppose that the following total cost (TC) and total revenue (TR) functions are given:

$$TC = 25 + 25q, \text{ where } q \text{ is the quantity sold}$$
$$TR = 50q - 2.5q^2$$

Table 12–2 shows TC and TR, given q. Investigating at the margin means that we decide the desirability of each level of production based upon an analysis of the effect on profits as we move from the previous level of

Table 12–3

Units	Total costs	Marginal costs	Total revenue	Marginal revenue
0	$ 25	N.A.	. . . .	N.A.
1	50	$25	$ 47.50	$47.50
2	75	25	90.00	42.50
3	100	25	127.50	37.50
4	125	25	160.00	32.50
5	150	25	187.50	27.50
6	175	25	210.00	22.50
7	200	25	227.50	17.50
8	225	25	240.00	12.50
9	250	25	247.50	7.50
10	275	25	250.00	2.50
11	300	25	247.50	−2.50

Table 12–4

Units	Total costs	Total revenue	(TR − TC) Total profits
0	$ 25	....	−$25.00
1	50	$ 47.50	−2.50
2	75	90.00	15.00
3	100	127.50	27.50
4	125	160.00	35.00
5	150	187.50	37.50
6	175	210.00	35.00
7	200	227.50	27.50
8	225	240.00	15.00
9	250	247.50	−2.50
10	275	250.00	−25.00
11	300	247.50	−52.50

production. Movement from no production to production of one unit costs $25 and contributes $47.50 to revenue. Clearly, this is desirable. Movement from one unit to two units costs $25 but adds $42.50 to profits and is thus desirable. Table 12–3 shows marginal revenues and marginal costs. We can see that the movement from the fourth to the fifth unit costs $25 and yields $27.50 in revenue. Clearly, this is desirable. However, movement from the fifth unit to the sixth unit is not desirable, since costs exceed revenues. If this conclusion is correct, profits should be maximized at production and sale of five units. This can be verified by Table 12–4. It can be seen that profits are highest when five units are produced and sold. This form of analysis requires explicit calculation of the marginal costs and revenues. Figure 12–1 depicts this situation. Thus, it can be

Figure 12–1

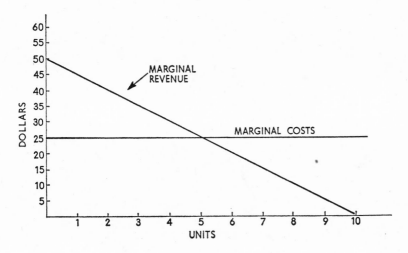

seen that at five units, marginal revenue exceeds marginal cost; but at six and subsequent units, the reverse is true.

The rule necessary to decide the desirability of a marginal course of action is $MR \geqq MC$; i.e., as long as marginal revenue exceeds or is equal to marginal costs, the action should be taken. However, one does not always deal with revenues. Revenues represent a contribution of value, and costs represent a distraction or subtraction from value. The terminology *benefit* instead of revenue is preferable. Hence the rule to decide upon the desirability of a course of action is $MB \geqq MC$, where MB is marginal benefit.

The analysis just completed has looked at the change in each function over a one-unit interval. For example, in $TR = 50q - 2.5q^2$, the change in TR for $q = 4$ to $q = 5$ is:

$$
\begin{aligned}
TR_5 - TR_4 &= 50(5) - 2.5(5)^2 - [50(4) - 2.5(4)^2] \\
&= 250 - 62.50 - (200 - 40) \\
&= 187.50 - 160 \\
&= 27.50
\end{aligned}
$$

Since this function is nonlinear, it changes throughout. Accordingly, the change from 4 to 5 is not uniform throughout, nor is it the same at 4 as at 5. In $TC = 25 + 25q$ the rate of change is a constant 25 regardless of the interval.

Direct methods[1]

Earlier, we said that a marginal course of action is desirable if $MR \geqq MC$. This rule applies only when the courses of action exist on a discrete scale. Since a firm can only produce in whole units, this appears reasonable. However, the functions referred to here are continuous functions (i.e., every value is possible).

In Chapter 10, we presented a direct method for finding the rate of change in the dependent variable. Thus, we may directly calculate the rate of change for the revenue function and the rate of change for the cost function. We may then set them equal and find the point where $MC = MR$. We may use the rule $MC = MR$ because these are continuous functions.

Using the technique shown on pages 129–33 of Chapter 10 for finding the equation expressing the rate of change for the revenue function, we see that:

$$
\begin{aligned}
f(q) &= 50q - 2.5q^2 \\
f(q + \Delta q) &= 50(q + \Delta q) - 2.5(q + \Delta q)^2
\end{aligned}
$$

---

[1] This section relies upon pages 118–33 of Chapter 10.

Since $\Delta R = f(q + \Delta q) - f(q)$:

$$\begin{aligned}
\Delta R &= [50(q + \Delta q) - 2.5(q + \Delta q)^2] - [50q - 2.5q^2] \\
&= [50q + 50\Delta q - 2.5(q^2 + 2q\Delta q + \Delta q^2)] - [50q - 2.5q^2] \\
&= 50q + 50\Delta q - 2.5q^2 - 5q\Delta q - 2.5\Delta q^2 - 50q + 2.5q^2
\end{aligned}$$

Dividing by Δq to get $\dfrac{\Delta R}{\Delta q}$:

$$\frac{\Delta R}{\Delta q} = \frac{50q}{\Delta q} + \frac{50\Delta q}{\Delta q} - \frac{2.5q^2}{\Delta q} - \frac{5q\Delta q}{\Delta q} - \frac{2.5\Delta q^2}{\Delta q} - \frac{50q}{\Delta q} + \frac{2.5q^2}{\Delta q}$$

$$= 50 - 5q - 2.5\Delta q$$

As $\Delta q \to 0$, the first term approaches zero, and

$$\frac{\Delta R}{\Delta q} = 50 - 5q$$

which is the marginal revenue function.

Since $TC = 25 + 25q$, we know that $MC = 25$.
Setting $MC = MR$, we get:

$$\begin{aligned}
25 &= 50 - 5q \\
5q &= 25 \\
q &= 5
\end{aligned}$$

which agrees with our previous findings.

Direct optimization[2]

The ultimate purpose of marginal analysis is to maximize profits (or other contributions to value). Profits may be expressed as total revenue minus total costs:

$$\begin{aligned}
P &= TR - TC \\
P &= 50q - 2.5q^2 - 25 - 25q \\
&= -2.5q^2 + 25q - 25
\end{aligned}$$

This function is graphed in Figure 12–2. As demonstrated in Chapter 10, the concepts of a limit may be used to find the rate of change of profit with respect to q. It was further demonstrated that the rate of change calculated at the point was different than that calculated over the interval. In this chapter, it is shown in Figure 12–1 that the graph of the marginal revenue function crosses the marginal cost function at the point where the profit appears to be highest.

The end purpose of marginal analysis is to maximize the dependent variable (profit) for the function combining costs and benefits. This oc-

---

[2] This section relies upon pages 118–33 of Chapter 10.

Figure 12–2

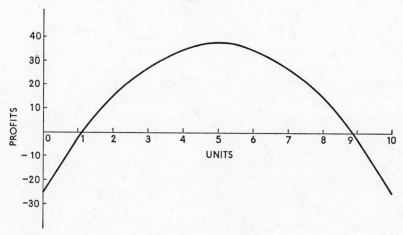

curs at the point where the rate of change of the profit function is zero. The following presentation will demonstrate that the use of marginal analysis is a means of maximizing profit (or other contributions to value).

The profit function is:

$$P = -2.5q^2 + 25q - 25$$

We may find the function identifying the rate of change of profit by finding $\frac{\Delta P}{\Delta q}$. When:

$$\Delta P = f(q + \Delta q) - f(q)$$
$$f(q) = -2.5q^2 + 25q - 25$$
$$f(q + \Delta q) = -2.5(q + \Delta q)^2 + 25(q + \Delta q) - 25$$
$$\Delta P = [-2.5(q^2 + 2q\Delta q + \Delta q^2) + 25q + 25\Delta q - 25]$$
$$- [-2.5q^2 + 25q - 25]$$
$$= -2.5q^2 - 5q\Delta q - 2.5\Delta q^2 + 25q + 25\Delta q - 25 + 2.5q^2$$
$$- 25q + 25$$
$$= -5q\Delta q - 2.5\Delta q^2 + 25\Delta q$$

Multiplying by $\frac{1}{\Delta q}$ to get $\frac{\Delta P}{\Delta q}$:

$$\frac{\Delta P}{\Delta q} = \frac{-5q\Delta q}{\Delta q} - \frac{2.5\Delta q^-}{\Delta q} + \frac{25\Delta q}{\Delta q}$$
$$= -5q - 2.5\Delta q + 25$$

As $\Delta q \to 0$, the second term cancels, leaving:

$$\frac{\Delta P}{\Delta q} = -5q + 25$$

Profit is maximized when the rate of change is zero or:

$$-5q + 25 = 0$$
$$-5q = -25$$
$$5q = 25$$
$$q = \frac{25}{5} = 5$$

which further verifies our earlier findings. However, in Table 12–3, we said that the marginal revenue was $27.50 and marginal cost was $25 at the fifth unit. This discrepancy occurred because we were looking at the change in costs from four to five units, but later we were looking at the rate of change at exactly five units. Hence, when looking at average change over the interval, we use $MR \geqq MC$; but when looking at the rate of change at a point, we use $MR = MC$.

III. CLASSICAL ECONOMIC OPTIMIZATION[3]

The classical economic model of profit maximization assumes a condition of data certainty where there are two decision variables that are functionally related. A decision variable is a variable which can be manipulated or controlled by management. In functional notation, then:

$$P = f(X_1, X_2)$$

where:

$$X_1 = f(X_2)$$

or:

$$X_2 = f(X_1)$$

The decision variables are the quantity to be produced (X_1) and the price to the charged (X_2). In the simplest example, one assumes that a firm is producing only one product. It is further assumed that since a firm knows with certainty what it can sell, it will both produce and sell that many units. Further, it is assumed that no other relevant factors influence the firm's sales except its price.[4] If the information shown in Tables 12–5 and 12–6 is given, we may develop the equation for total cost as a function of units produced, develop the equation for the quantity sold as a function of the price,[5] and optimize profits.

The equation for production costs and demand is found by mathemati-

---

[3] This section relies on pages 118–42 of Chapter 10.

[4] If the firm is a monopolist, the actions of other firms can be ignored, and this assumption becomes more plausible.

[5] Because of conditions of data certainty, it is assumed that the quantity sold is equal to the quantity demanded. Thus, this is really a demand equation.

Table 12–5

HISTORICAL PRODUCTION COSTS

Production (in units)	Total costs (in dollars)
5	50
10	75
15	100
20	125
25	150
30	175
35	200
40	225
45	250
50	275

Table 12–6

HISTORICAL SALES

Price	Units sold
9.50	5
9.00	10
8.50	15
8.00	20
7.50	25
7.00	30
6.50	35
6.00	40
5.50	45
5.00	50

cal or statistical means. A graph would show that they are linear. Also, the fact that the rate of change is constant is proof of linearity. The resulting equations are:[6]

(1)
$$TPC = 25 + 5q_p$$

where:

TPC = Total production costs
q_p = Quantity produced

(2)
$$q_d = 100 - 10p$$

where:

q_d = Quantity demanded
p = Price

Given these equations, we know that $\pi = R - C$ where π is the profit, R is the revenue, and C is total costs; further, $R = q_s p$ where q_s is the quantity sold.

In our analysis, we shall assume that maximizing the contribution to overhead and profit will lead to maximization of profit. Thus the only costs we shall recognize are TPC. The quantity available (q_a) is the sum of items in inventory at the beginning of the period and produced during the period of the analysis.

The reader will note that we have discussed (1) quantity demanded (q_d), (2) quantity produced (q_p), (3) quantity available (q_a), (4) quantity sold (q_s), and (5) quantity in inventory (q_i). However, if we have a condition of data certainty and effective decision making, the firm need not have an inventory, and $q_d = q_s = q_p = q_a$. The profit equation may be expressed:

---

[6] It would be desirable for the student to verify these equations using the two-point equation for a line.

(3) $$\pi = qp - (25 + 5q)$$

and since:

$$q = 100 - 10p$$
$$\pi = [p(100 - 10p)] - [25 + 5(100 - 10p)]$$
$$= 100p - 10p^2 - (25 + 500 - 50p)$$
$$= -10p^2 + 100p - 25 - 500 + 50p$$
(4) $$= -10p^2 + 150p - 525$$

Using one variable optimization:

$$\pi' = -20p + 150$$

Setting $\pi' = 0$ to find the candidates for an extremum:

$$20p = 150$$
$$p = 7.5$$

Finding π'' to test for a maximum or a minimum:

$$\pi'' = -20$$

The π'' is negative; therefore, 7.5 is a maximum. Let us for the moment assume that this is a global or absolute maximum. The reader may verify that $q = 25$ and $\pi = 37.5$.

IV. NECESSARY AND SUFFICIENT CONDITIONS[7]

In order that this be a true optimum, certain conditions must prevail. Figures 12–3 and 12–4, with profit (π) as the dependent variable and production (q) as the independent variable, demonstrate the pitfalls of as-

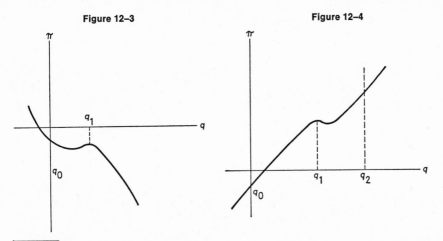

Figure 12–3   Figure 12–4

---

[7] This and subsequent sections rely upon a knowledge of differential calculus presented in Chapter 10 (pages 118–47).

suming that a maximum is the true optimum. In Figure 12–3, the derived maximum is undesirable because zero production (q_0) results in less loss than the derived maximum (q_1). In Figure 12–4 the derived maximum (q_1) is not so desirable as the maximum at the extreme of the range (q_2). In fact, extreme values of the independent variable must always be considered as possible maxima or minima.

With minor exceptions for functions of one independent variable [where $Y = f(X)$] the following conditions for locating internal extrema must occur:

1. Y' is defined and not zero.
2. Y'' is defined and not zero.
3. When $Y' = 0$, X must assume a real value, not an imaginary number.
4. The function is continuous throughout the range.
5. When the value of X at $Y' = 0$ is inserted in Y'', the result must be a positive or negative number.

V. THE EFFECTS OF A CONSTANT

The profit equation calculated on page 185
$$(\pi = -10p^2 + 150p - 525)$$
could equally well have been expressed in terms of q as:

$$\pi = -0.1q^2 + 5q - 25$$

If fixed product costs increase by \$100, this equation becomes:

$$\pi = -0.1q^2 + 5q - 125$$

Will this increase have an effect on locating the maximum? Since:

$$\frac{d\pi}{dq} = -0.2q + 5$$

setting

$$\frac{d\pi}{dq} = 0$$
$$-0.2q + 5 = 0$$
$$0.2q = 5$$
$$q = 25$$

which is the maximum q found on pages 184–85. Thus, this increase had no effect on the maximum. This is because the added \$100 merely shifts the curve down. The following values for the original equation and one with an added \$100 of fixed expenses are shown in Table 12–7 and illustrated in Figure 12–5. However, let us assume that this fixed cost occurs

Table 12–7

Original		Modified	
p	f(p)	p	f(p)
1	−385	1	−485
2	−265	2	−365
3	−165	3	−265
4	−85	4	−185
5	−25	5	−125
6	+15	6	−85
7	+35	7	−65
8	+35	8	−65
9	+15	9	−85
10	−25	10	−125

Figure 12–5

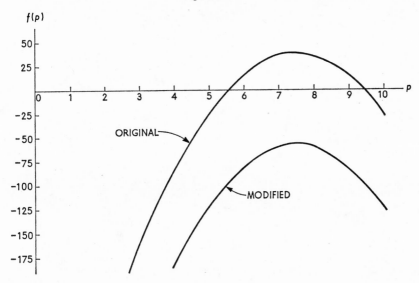

only if we actually enter production and may be more accurately identified by the following conditional equation:

$$\text{If } q = 0, \text{ then } FPC = \$25$$
$$\text{If } q > 0, \text{ then } FPC = \$125$$

where FPC is fixed production costs. In this case, we have a discontinuity at $q = 0$.

At $q = 0$, the profit equation is:

$$\pi = -0.1q^2 + 5q - 25$$

and $\pi = -25$, which is the only value π can assume, and which is the extremum at that point.

At $q > 0$, the profit equation is:

$$\pi = -0.1q^2 + 5q - 125$$
$$\frac{d\pi}{dq} = -0.2q + 5q$$

Setting $\dfrac{d\pi}{dq} = 0$:

$$q = 25$$
$$\pi'' = -0.2$$

Thus, $q = 25$ is a maximum. Substituting $q = 25$ in the profit equation gives:

$$\pi = -0.1(25)^2 + 5(25) - 125$$
$$= -0.1(625) + 125 - 125$$
$$= -62.5$$

Both equations produce a loss. However, the best policy is no production, since it produces a loss of only $25.

VI. OPTIMIZATION WHEN THE COST EQUATION IS A SECOND-DEGREE EQUATION

Let us assume that the same conditions prevail as in the preceding example except that the production cost equation is a second-degree equation. The total cost equation and demand equation are:

(6) $TC = \dfrac{1}{2}q^2 + 100$

(7) $q = 100 - 10p$

Thus:

(8) $\pi = [p(100 - 10p)] - \left[\dfrac{(100 - 10p)^2}{2} + 100 \right]$

$\quad = [(100p - 10p^2)] - \left[\dfrac{(10,000 - 2,000p + 100p^2)}{2} + 100 \right]$

$\quad = [100p - 10p^2] - [5,000 - 1,000p + 50p^2 + 100]$

$\quad = -60p^2 + 1,100p - 5,100$

$\pi' = -120p + 1,100$

Setting $\pi' = 0$:

$$p = \frac{1,100}{120} = 9.167$$

Finding π'' to check for maximum or minimum, $\pi'' = -120$, which yields a maximum. Since the function is continuous throughout the range and this is the only maximum, all conditions for finding internal extrema are met at $p = 9.167$, where $\pi = -61.34$ and $q = 8.33$. We must now check the extremes. At $+\infty$, we have a minimum because the first term will overpower the others. At $q = 0$, $\pi = -100$, which is less than -61.34. Thus, $p = 9.167$ ($q = 8.33$) is a true maximum.

VII. OPTIMIZATION FOR A MULTIPRODUCT MONOPOLIST

The same assumptions prevail as earlier, i.e., $q_d = q_s = q_a = q_p$. Fixed costs of production are assumed to exist regardless of the amount of either good produced. The following equations prevail:

$$(12) \qquad q_1 = 300 - 10p_1$$
$$(13) \qquad q_2 = 100 - 10p_2$$
$$(14) \qquad TVPC_1 = 15q_1$$
$$(15) \qquad TVPC_2 = 5q_2$$

where $TVPC_i$ is total variable production costs of the ith product.

$$(16) \qquad \pi = R_1 - TVC_1 + R_2 - TVC_2 - FC$$

where:

TVC_i = Total variable costs of the ith product
R_i = Revenue from the ith product
FC = Fixed costs = 100

Then:

$$\pi = p_1(300 - 10p_1) - 15(300 - 10p_1) + p_2(100 - 10p_2)$$
$$- 5(100 - 10p_2) - 100$$
$$= 300p_1 - 10p_1^2 - 4{,}500 + 150p_1 + 100p_2 - 10p_2^2 - 500 + 50p_2 - 100$$
$$= -10p_1^2 + 450p_1 - 10p_2^2 + 150p_2 - 5{,}100$$

One way to investigate this equation is to look at the maximum when one value of p is given. Assume that $p_2 = 7$. Then:

$$\pi = -10p_1^2 + 450p_1 - 4{,}540$$
$$\pi' = -20p_1 + 450$$

Setting $\pi' = 0$, $p_1 = 22.5$:

$$\pi'' = -20$$

Thus, 22.5 is a maximum. Note that regardless of the value of p_2, the price to charge for p_1 is still \$22.50. This process of assuming that p_2 is an unknown constant and then finding the extremes with respect to p_1 is partial differentiation. We shall now find the optimum for p_2 by letting all terms without p_2 become unknown constants. Let:

$$-10p_1^2 = C_1$$

and

$$+450p_1 = C_2$$

and

$$C_1 + C_2 - 5{,}100 = C_3$$

Then:

$$\pi = -10p_2^2 + 150p_2 + C_3$$

and

$$\frac{d\pi}{dp_2} = -20p_2 + 150$$

Setting $\pi' = 0$:

$$p_2 = 7.5$$
$$\pi'' = -20$$

Thus, 7.5 is a maximum, and the optimal prices are $p_1 = 22.5$ and $p_2 = 7.5$. The reader should note that this is a general method for optimization *only* when good 1 is strictly independent of good 2.

VIII. TWO INDEPENDENT VARIABLES

Suppose a monopolist finds that the quantity demanded is a function of two variables: price (p) and advertising expenditures (X). Given:

(12) $\qquad q = \dfrac{100}{p} + (-X^3 + 5X^2 - 3X)$

(13) $\quad TC = (25 + 5q) + X$

Then:

(14) $\qquad \pi = p\left(\dfrac{100}{p} - X^3 + 5X^2 - 3X\right) - 25$

$$- 5\left(\frac{100}{p} - X^3 + 5X^2 - 3X\right) - X$$

$$= 100 - X^3p + 5X^2p - 3Xp - 25 - \frac{500}{p} + 5X^3 - 25X^2$$

$$+ 15X - X$$

Again, we can assume that one variable is constant. Let X be constant; then:

$$\frac{d\pi}{dp} = -X^3 + 5X^2 - 3X + 500p^{-2}$$

Now, setting $\dfrac{d\pi}{dp} = 0$:

$$-500p^{-2} = -X^3 + 5X^2 - 3X$$
$$p^2(-X^3 + 5X^2 - 3X) = -500$$
$$p^2 = \frac{-500}{(-X^3 + 5X^2 - 3X)}$$
$$p = \sqrt{\frac{-500}{-X^3 + 5X^2 - 3X}}$$

This result does not provide the answer to the decision maker except by assuming a value for X or p. However, direct mathematical means do exist to solve this equation.[8] Such means are beyond this text.

IX. THE SEGMENTED OR CONDITIONAL MODEL

Suppose that a concrete company selling delivered concrete by the yard is in competition with a few other concrete companies. As a result of this competition, the demand function is discontinuous. The normal price for a yard of concrete is $5. The customer is aware of the normal price; but because of friendships, better delivery schedules, etc., he will tolerate some price differentials. The demand curve facing the company can be represented in four different sections, as follows:

(1)   If $p \geq 5.50$, $q_d = 0$.
(2)   If $5.00 \leq p < 5.50$, $q_d = 550 - 100p$.
(3)   If $4 \leq p \leq 5$, $q_d = 1,050 - 200p$.
(4)   If $p < 4.00$, $q_d = 90 - 10p$.

The cost curve is:

(5)
$$TC = \frac{q^2}{100} + 3q + 50$$

Equation (1) demonstrates that beyond a differential price of 50 cents, no customer will remain loyal. Equation (2) reveals that loyalty is a function of the price differential. Equation (3) demonstrates that the number of other customers attracted depends upon the price differential. Equation (4) shows that the competition will tolerate a price differential of only so much before reducing price.

The analytic method requires that the maximum be calculated for each profit equation, ignoring the boundaries. However, in some cases the analytic extremum is found outside the boundary. Thus the extremum is the boundary. As in the previous cases, inventory is assumed to be zero, and $q_d = q_a = q_p = q_s$; thus, we shall use the notation q. However, within each case the best possible actions and the computations with results are shown below.

---

[8] See, for example, Daniel Teichroew, *Management Science: Deterministic Models* (New York: John Wiley & Sons, Inc., 1964), pp. 243–321.

When p $\geq$ *\$5.50:*

$$q = 0 \text{ and } \pi = pq - TC$$

Thus

$$\pi = p(0) - \frac{0}{100} - 3(0) - 50 = -50$$

For 5.00 $\leq$ p < 5.50:

$$\pi = p(550 - 100p) - \frac{(550 - 100p)^2}{100} + 3(550 - 100p) + 50$$

$$= 550p - 100p^2 - \frac{302,500 - 110,000p + 10,000p^2}{100}$$

$$- 1,650 + 300p - 50$$

$$= 550p - 100p^2 - 3,025 + 1,100p - 100p^2 - 1,650 + 300p - 50$$

$$= -200p^2 + 1,950p - 4,725$$

$$\frac{d\pi}{dp} = -400p + 1950$$

At $\frac{d\pi}{dp} = 0$:

$$p = \frac{1,950}{400} = 4.875$$

which is not in the interval, thus showing that there is no maximum or minimum within the interval. We must now test the end points.

Testing end points, we find at $p = 5.00$:

$$\pi = -5,000 + 9,750 - 4,725 = 25$$

and at $p = 5.50$:

$$\pi = -6,050 + 10,725 - 4,725$$
$$= 10,725 - 10,775 = -50$$

Therefore, as $p \to 5.50$, $\pi \to -50$. This means that the optimum in this interval is $p = 5.00$, which yields a profit of \$25.

For 4.00 $\leq$ p $\leq$ 5.00:

$$\pi = p(1,050 - 200p) - \frac{(1,050 - 200p)^2}{100} - 3(1,050 - 200p) - 50$$

$$= 1,050p - 200p^2 - \frac{1,102,500 - 420,000p + 40,000p^2}{100}$$

$$- 3,150 + 600p - 50$$

$$= -600p^2 + 5,850p - 14,225$$

$$\frac{d\pi}{dp} = -1,200p + 5,850$$

Setting $\dfrac{d\pi}{dp} = 0$:

$$p = \frac{5{,}850}{1{,}200} = 4.875$$

Finding the second derivative:

$$= \pi'' - 1{,}200$$

Therefore, p is a maximum at 4.875, and $\pi = \$34$.

We must still test the end points to be sure they are not preferable. At $p = 5.00$:

$$\pi = -15{,}000 + 29{,}250 - 14{,}225 = 25$$

At **p** = *4.00:*

$$\pi = -9{,}600 + 23{,}400 - 14{,}225 = -425$$

Thus the maximum for this interval is a profit of \$34.

For **p** $<$ *4.00, we find:*

$$\pi = p(90 - 10p) - \frac{(90 - 10p)^2}{100} + 3(90 - 10p) + 50$$

$$= 90p - 10p^2 - \frac{8{,}100 - 1{,}800p + 100p^2}{100} + 270 - 30p + 50$$

$$= -11p^2 + 138p - 401$$

$$\frac{d\pi}{dp} = -22p + 138$$

Setting $\dfrac{d\pi}{dp} = 0$:

$$p = \frac{138}{22} = 6.27$$

which is outside the interval. Now, testing extremes, we find, at $p = 4.00$:

$$\pi = -176 + 552 - 401 = -25$$

Therefore, as $p \to 4.00$, $\pi \to -25$; and at $p = 0$:

$$\pi = -401$$

Thus the maximum for $p < 4.00$ occurs as $p \to 4.00$. The global or overall maximum occurs when $p = 4.875$ and profit is \$34.

In summary, the results are:

For $p > 5.50$..$\pi = -\$50$ regardless of p
For $5.00 \leq p < 5.50$, maximum occurs at $p = 5.00$............$\pi =$ 25
For $4.00 \leq p \leq 5.00$ maximum occurs at $p = 4.875$..........$\pi =$ 34
For $p < 4.00$ maximum occurs as $p \rightarrow 4.00$.................$\pi \rightarrow$ 25

It should be observed that the term $q^2/100$ in the total cost equation represents a number of real-life phenomena. For example, as the quantity produced increases, crowding and capacity limitations increase costs at an increasing rate. It is also likely that as q increases, this concrete company is selling to customers more and more distant, and thus incurring higher and higher delivery costs.

DISCUSSION TOPICS AND PROBLEMS

1. Suppose an English manufacturer of widgets can sell x number of widgets per week at a price $P = 300 - 0.02x$ cents and that the total cost to produce x number of widgets is $TPC = 100x + 30,000$ cents. What is the production level for maximizing profits?

2. Suppose that the government imposes an import tax of 10 cents for each widget sold in Problem 1, but other features remain unchanged. How much of the tax should the manufacturer absorb, and how much should he pass on to the customer to maximize his profits?

3. It costs a manufacturer c dollars to manufacture and distribute a widget. If the widgets are sold at x dollars each, it is estimated that he will sell q widgets (where $q = [t/(x - c)] + [z(50 - x)]$). The z and the t are positive constants. What selling price will bring him a maximum profit?

4. The following information has been taken from the records of a single-product monopolist:

Month	Price charged	Production (in units)	Sales costs	Sales (in units)	Ending inventory (in units)	Total variable production costs
1.........	$24.00	30	20.0	20	10	$450.00
2.........	15.00	40	35.0	50	0	800.00
3.........	21.00	40	25.0	30	10	800.00
4.........	21.00	30	25.0	30	10	450.00
5.........	22.50	20	22.5	25	5	200.00
6.........	27.00	10	15.0	10	5	50.00
7.........	24.00	15	20.0	20	0	112.00
8.........	24.00	20	20.0	20	0	200.00
9.........	22.50	35	22.5	25	10	612.50
10.........	19.50	40	27.5	35	15	800.00
11.........	15.00	40	35.0	50	5	800.00
12.........	16.50	40	32.5	45	0	800.00

Further, you are told that administrative expenses are a fixed $50 per month. Also, you have a warehousing agreement whereby the costs of warehousing your inventory are $1 per unit of ending inventory.

a) Develop the monthly total cost function for the organization.

b) Develop the total production cost function (inventory costs are assumed to be sales costs).

c) Develop the total sales cost function.

d) Assume that the company has just developed a procedure that allows it to forecast sales exactly. What is the total cost function?

e) Develop the demand function for this firm.

f) Indicate the maximum profit point under the conditions of part (*d*).

g) Attempt to maximize profit under the conditions of part (*a*).

5. The following information is given for a monopolist:

Production (in units)	Total costs
5	$ 102.50
10	150.00
15	212.50
20	300.00
25	412.50
30	550.00
35	712.50
40	900.00
45	1,152.50
50	1,350.00

Price	Number of units sold
$9.50	5
9.00	10
8.50	15
8.00	20
7.50	25
7.00	30
6.50	35
6.00	40
5.50	45
5.00	50

a) Devise the equations for total cost.

b) Devise the equation for demand.

c) Find the profit-maximizing point and indicate its economic significance.

d) Discuss the assumptions made.

6. The Red Shin Peanut company has a capacity of 200 one-pound tins of peanuts per day. Costs are of four types, and the following information is available on costs:

Type *A*. Fixed costs are $50 per day.

Type *B*. Selling costs are 10 percent of the distributor's selling price (the peanuts are sold to a distributor who will take up to 200 one-pound tins per day).

Type C. Raw material costs are shown by the equation $RMC = \dfrac{q^2}{2}$.

Type D. Labor costs are a constant 25 cents per unit produced.

The one-pound tin sells for $2 (i.e., the distributor receives $2 per tin, of which 20 cents goes to him for performing the selling function). Always assume that the quantity sold is equal to the quantity produced.

a) Determine the total cost function for this product (double-check your answer).
b) At what rate is total cost changing when $q = 100$?
c) Determine the total revenue function for this product (double-check your answer).
d) At what rate is total revenue changing when $q = 100$?
e) Determine the profit function for this product.
f) What is the maximum profit output for this firm?
g) Discuss the above findings from both their mathematical meaning and their economic meaning.
h) What is the domain and range of the equations for parts (a), (c), and (e)?

7. The XYZ Products Company produces two products, A and B. A consists of two subassemblies and other minor parts. B also consists of two subassemblies and other minor parts. Costs of subassemblies are: A1, $6; A2, $4; B1, $8; and B2, $5.

The manufacturing operation consists of an assembly department and a finishing department. All workers in the assembly and finishing departments are paid $4 per hour. Assembly time for product A is two hours; for product B four hours. Finishing time for product A is three hours; for product B, one hour. Total available time per day is 40 assembly hours and 28 finishing hours. The products are sold by a manufacturer's agent who collects a 10 percent commission on the selling price. Fixed expenses are $100 per five-day week. Other expenses are dependent upon the total number of direct labor-hours employed. Capacity may be increased by the use of overtime, which increases direct labor costs by 50 percent. The following data on production, price, sales, and other expenses is available from company records:

Week	Production A	B	Total hours	Price A	B	Sales A	B	Other expenses
1	40	10	250	$44	$62	34	6	70
2	10	30	200	49	50	14	30	50
3	20	10	150	50	60	10	10	35
4	40	20	300	40	55	50	20	95

Unless otherwise stated, assume that the XYZ Products Company is a monopolist and sales of goods A and B are independent.

a) Determine the equation for demand for good A.
b) Determine the equation for demand for good B.
c) Determine a linear approximation to the "other expenses" function (use only points found in the data provided above).

d) Ignoring capacity limitations (including limitations on product mix) and inventory-carrying costs, develop a total cost equation for good *A* (be sure to identify all elements in this equation).

e) Ignoring capacity limitations (including limitations on product mix) and inventory-carrying costs, develop a total cost equation for good *B* (be sure to identify all elements in this equation).

f) Ignoring inventory-carrying costs and capacity limitations, develop a total cost equation for both goods (be sure to identify all elements in this equation).

g) Identify the profit-maximizing point for each good.

h) In part (*c*), two different independent variables could have been used. Indicate what they are and why either is acceptable.

i) In part (*c*), you were forced to use only two points found in the table. Indicate the nature of the error induced because of this requirement.

8. The XYZ Company is the only company producing widgets and gidgets. The company is divided into six departments, as follows:

a) The sales department has a budget of 10 cents per widget and 20 cents per gidget. Since the promotional budget may be over- or underdrawn, you may assume that this is a direct and immediate expense. Salesmen are paid a commission of 25 cents and 50 cents, respectively, for widgets and gidgets.

b) The administrative department is a fixed cost of $1,000 per month (including the sales manager's salary).

c) The machining department has 450 hours of machining time available monthly. It takes this department 15 minutes to machine a widget and 30 minutes to machine a gidget. Direct expenses of machining for this department are $3 per hour of machining time, and fixed expenses are $900.

d) The assembly department has 300 hours of assembly time available. It takes this department 12 minutes to assemble a widget and 24 minutes to assemble a gidget. Direct expenses of machining are $2 per hour, and fixed expenses are $600.

e) The finishing department has 400 hours of finishing time. It takes this department 30 minutes to finish a widget and 12 minutes to finish a gidget. Direct expenses of finishing are $2 per hour, and fixed expenses are $400.

f) The production services department provides maintenance and other services. It has a fixed budget of $600 per month.

The following information is given on prices, sales, production, and inventory:

Month	Price (including sales expenses) Widget	Gidget	Sales Widget	Gidget	Production Widget	Gidget	Inventory Widget	Gidget
1.................	$6	$10	500	400	600	450	100	50
2.................	6	9	500	500	420	540	20	40
3.................	7	8	300	600	300	600	20	40
4.................	5	10	650	400	640	400	10	40
5.................	7	8	300	600	300	600	10	40
6.................	5	9	630	480	620	440	0	0

You may ignore seasonal, cyclical, and secular factors in demand. Further warehousing costs are fixed, regardless of the size of the inventory. They are included in administrative expenses. Raw material is $1 and $2, respectively, for widgets and gidgets.

a) Develop the monthly variable cost function for widgets and gidgets. Show each element separately.
b) What are the fixed costs? List and identify each separately.
c) What is the total cost function, including selling costs?
d) Develop the demand function for widgets. Assume that the demands for widgets and gidgets are independent of each other.
e) What is the profit-maximizing behavior for this firm if it produces only widgets?
f) Explain in writing how you would find the profit-maximizing behavior for this firm. Assume that the demands for widgets and gidgets are independent. Be sure to consider the feasibility of your answer.
g) How would you verify the answer to part (e)? (The fact that the second derivative is a maximum does not do this.)
h) Assume that fixed costs increase by $50 per month. What effect does this have on the profit-maximizing point?

9. A two-product monopolist gives you the following information:

Month	Price		Sales		Production		Inventory		Production costs	
	Good 1	Good 2	Good 1	Good 2	Good 1	Good 2	Good 1	Good 2	Good 1	Good 2
1....	$18	$10	120	50	150	50	30	0	$1,680	$400
2......	24	5	60	50	75	100	45	50	975	650
3......	21	12	90	0	100	50	55	100	1,200	400
4......	15	11	150	0	100	0	5	100	1,200	150

You may ignore seasonal, cyclical, and secular factors in demand. Further, you are told that administrative and selling expenses are a fixed $100 per month. You are leasing a warehouse at a cost of $100 per month. Ignore any costs except the leased warehouse when figuring inventory costs. Remember that the cost figures include allocated factory overhead.

a) Develop the monthly cost function for good 1 (ignore warehousing costs).
b) Develop the monthly cost function for good 2.
c) Develop the monthly total cost function for this firm.
d) Develop the demand function for good 1.
e) Develop the demand function for good 2.
f) What is the profit-maximizing behavior for this firm, assuming no limit on capacity?
g) Assume that the warehousing costs increase by $25 per month. What effect does this have on the profit-maximizing point?
h) Assume that the firm has a five-year lease, with three years left to run. However, the warehousing firm offers to provide a different warehouse which costs $50 per month and releases the company from the existing lease. Should the firm accept?

10. Have your answers to Questions 2, 3, and 6 of Chapter 10 satisfied the necessary and sufficient conditions discussed on pages 185–86 of this chapter? Explain.

11. Discuss the relevance of necessary and sufficient conditions applied to pages 191–94 of this chapter (the segmented or conditional model).

SELECTED REFERENCES

Baumol, William J. *Economic Theory and Operations Analysis.* Englewood Cliffs, N.J.: Prentice-Hall, Inc., 1965.

Bowen, Earl K. *Mathematics: With Applications in Management and Economics.* Homewood, Ill.: Richard D. Irwin, Inc., 1963.

Bowman, Edward H., and Fetter, Robert B. *Analysis for Production and Operations Management.* Homewood, Ill.: Richard D. Irwin, Inc., 1967.

Grawoig, Dennis E. *Decision Mathematics.* New York: McGraw-Hill Book Co., Inc., 1967.

Howell, James E., and Teichroew, Daniel. *Mathematical Analysis for Business Decisions.* Homewood, Ill.: Richard D. Irwin, Inc., 1963.

Meier, Robert C., and Archer, Stephen H. *An Introduction to Mathematics for Business Analysis.* New York: McGraw-Hill Book Co., Inc., 1960.

Theodore, Chris A. *Applied Mathematics: An Introduction.* Homewood, Ill.: Richard D. Irwin, Inc., 1965.

Youse, Bevan K., and Stalnaker, Ashford W. *Calculus for Students of Business and Management.* Scranton: International Textbook Co., 1967.

13

Inventory models

I. THE DECISION ENVIRONMENT FOR INVENTORY MODELS

This section will discuss the environment for decision making. As indicated earlier, the analyst must attempt to establish, to the best of his ability, the environmental factors which relate to the decision. We say "to the best of his ability" because we understand that particular conditions such as lack of time and lack of sufficient relevant data often prohibit the analyst from establishing all relevant factors.

The Asphalt Paving Company (hereafter referred to as APC) sells paving to road-building contractors and to homeowners for driveway paving. Asphalt pavement is made from some or all of the following ingredients: aggregate (coarse, intermediate, and fine), sand, mineral filler, and liquid asphalt. *Aggregate* refers to the stone or gravel used in the pavements. Obviously, the aggregate may refer to relatively soft stones such as sandstone or to hard stone such as granite. Let us assume that only one kind of stone is acceptable for paving by APC. Let us further assume that the company has purchased each of the three kinds of aggregate from one supplier. Further, each of the three remaining items is purchased from a different supplier. Consequently, APC has up to six major items in its raw material inventory. The company has been maintaining a one-month supply of inventory based upon the annual demand projections shown in Table 13-1. Presently, the company purchases an intermediate processed aggregate. The cost of aggregate is dependent upon the amount of processing required to provide the size breakdown found in the aggregate. One type of coarse aggregate is quick-rinsed to remove finer particles. Another type is resieved to remove larger particles. The coarse aggregate used by this company costs $4 per ton; the fine, $4.50 per ton; and the intermediate, $5 per ton.

The plant has 50-ton storage bins for all items except asphalt, which

Table 13-1

Item	Amount (in tons)	Cost per ton
Coarse aggregate................	150,000	$3–$5
Intermediate aggregate...........	150,000	$3–$5
Fine aggregate..................	150,000	$3–$5
Sand.........................	25,000	$2–$3
Asphalt.......................	24,000	$20
Mineral additives................	......	.....

is stored in a special 10-ton container. The plant's inventory and purchase policy has been to reorder 80 percent of the storage capacity when 20 percent of the capacity remains. Thus, when 10 tons of coarse aggregate are in the storage bin, 40 more tons are ordered. Capacity is defined as the lower of annual usage or actual storage capacity. Hence the capacities shown in Table 13–2 obtain.

Given this information, we wish to find the best inventory policy for this firm. Thus far, the problem and general environment have been discussed. The next step is to find criteria or measurable objectives. As indicated, these must stem from the identification of organizational objectives. Long-run profit maximization is a reasonable overall organizational goal. Therefore, for the inventory policy, long-run minimization of the costs of fulfilling the inventory function is the best measurable objective. Inventories exist to uncouple purchasing, production, and shipping. In other words, inventories allow goods in raw, finished, or partially finished state to accumulate. If APC uses a certain type of engine oil for its equipment, it purchases more than its immediate need. The company purchases large lots because it is too expensive to deliver in small lots. Hence, inventories have allowed the paving company to take advantage of large-lot savings.

Table 13-2

Location	Item	Actual capacity (in tons)	Annual demand (in tons)	Operational capacity (in tons)	Reorder point	Reorder amount
Bin 1.....	Coarse aggregate	50,000	150,000	50,000	10,000	40,000
Bin 2.....	Intermediate aggregate	50,000	150,000	50,000	10,000	40,000
Bin 3.....	Fine aggregate	50,000	150,000	50,000	10,000	40,000
Bin 4.....	Sand	50,000	25,000	25,000	5,000	20,000
Bin 5.....	Empty					
Bin 6.....	Empty					
Tank 1...	Asphalt	10,000	24,000	10,000	2,000	8,000

The next step in managerial analysis is to identify all of the factors which affect costs. This is usually expressed in functional form as follows: Inventory costs equal costs associated with ordering inventory, costs associated with carrying inventory, and costs of being out of inventory. Each of these independent variables may be expressed as a function itself. Inventory-carrying costs include:

1. Cost of the money which is tied up in inventories.
2. Cost of goods which deteriorate while in inventory.
3. Cost of providing storage space (including heat, utilities, insurance on building and inventory, rent or amortized capital investment, and other associated costs).
4. Cost of obsolescence (i.e., if the good is replaced by another good, all the goods replaced are reduced in value).

Ordering costs include all costs which are the same, regardless of order size:

1. Costs of placing an order
2. Costs of receiving and unloading an order (when they are the same, regardless of order size)
3. Costs of processing the order for payment

For a retailer, costs of inadequate inventory are dependent upon whether the sale is lost or postponed, and also upon whether future sales are lost. If the shortage does not affect future sales, it probably results in a one-time decrease in profits. If future sales are lost, this must be measured in terms of lost profits in the future. For a manufacturer, inadequate raw material inventory may result in idle equipment and ultimately in lost sales. A machine operator without materials is expensive.

Let us proceed on the assumption that the classical economic order quantity (EOQ) equation applies here.

II. THE CLASSICAL ECONOMIC ORDER FORMULA

This widely reported model assumes that order costs are fixed per order of each product. Let us assume that the cost of placing an order for liquid asphalt is $80 per order. In as much as we use 24,000 tons and order 8,000 tons each time, we place

$$\frac{24,000}{8,000} = 3 \text{ orders per year}$$

In fact, this equation always expresses the relationship between annual demand, order size, and orders per year. Let D be the annual demand; Z the order size; and C_1 the cost per order. Then:

(1) $$\text{Annual ordering costs} = \frac{D}{Z} C_1$$

Note that order costs include all fixed costs associated with *placing, receiv-ing*, and *paying* an order. Those costs, if any, which vary with the size of the order either are not relevant or are ignored in this model. If the cost of unloading an order is linearly (proportionately) related to its size, it is not relevant, because it must be incurred regardless of order size. For example, if the costs of unloading an order are:

$$UC = 10 + \frac{1}{10}(q)$$

the $10 or fixed costs are included in order costs, and the 10 cents per unit must be incurred regardless and may be added to the item's value.

Since the company contracts well in advance of delivery, let us assume that it can influence its customers to accept delivery on a schedule which uses the same amount of liquid asphalt per day. Consequently if the company works 240 days per year, it uses:

$$\frac{24,000}{240} = 100 \text{ tons of asphalt per day}$$

Since it orders three times per year and uses the asphalt at a constant rate, it has on hand an average of 4,000 gallons or one half the order size *above the 2,000 gallons always kept on hand.*

A simple example will show why the average is one half the order size. Assume that a company orders 100 components and uses 20 of them each day; at the midpoint of the first day, it has on hand 90. Table 13–3 shows

Table 13–3

Day	Number re-maining at noon
1	90
2	70
3	50
4	30
5	10
Total	250

the number in inventory at the midpoint of the day over a period of five days. Thus a total of 250 were on hand (recounting each day) over the five days, or an average of 50 per day, which is one half the order quantity. Hence, average inventory size is $\frac{Z}{2}$.

The relationship between inventory and time can be shown for liquid asphalt as in Figure 13–1. If the company did not maintain the 2,000 buffer inventory, the sawtooth graph would drop to the X-axis.

If we can identify the costs of carrying each ton of asphalt in inven-

Figure 13–1

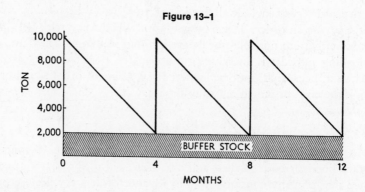

MONTHS

tory for the entire year, we can identify inventory-carrying costs. Assume that it costs 20 cents per dollar's worth of inventory to carry that inventory for one year. Also, assume that liquid asphalt costs $20 per ton. Let C_2 be the annual cost of carrying a dollar's worth of inventory and p be the price or value of the item carried in inventory. Accordingly, carrying costs are:

(2) $$\left(\frac{Z}{2}\right) C_2 p$$

and total variable costs of inventory are:

(3) $$TVC = \left(\frac{D}{Z}\right) C_1 + \left(\frac{Z}{2}\right) C_2 p$$

Graphically, this may be shown as in Figure 13–2. It so happens that this

Figure 13–2

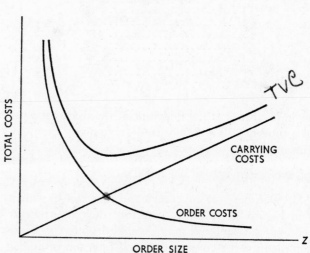

ORDER SIZE

graph has the mathematical pecularity that the minimum occurs at the point where the carrying cost and order cost curve intersect. This condition occurs for any curve of the form:

$$Y = \alpha x^{-1} + Bx$$

This means that the minimum occurs when carrying costs equal order costs. Consequently, one may locate the minimum using algebra and letting order costs equal carrying costs, or:

$$\frac{D}{Z}C_1 = \frac{Z}{2}C_2 p$$

$$2\,DC_1 = Z^2 C_2 p$$

$$Z = \sqrt{\frac{2DC_1}{C_2 p}}$$

Let $DC_1 = \alpha$ and $\dfrac{C_2 p}{2} = B$. Then:

$$\frac{\alpha}{Z} = BZ$$

Multiply both sides by Z. Then:

$$\alpha = BZ^2$$

Multiply both sides by $1/B$. Then:

$$\frac{\alpha}{B} = Z^2$$

or

$$Z^2 = \frac{\alpha}{B}$$

and

$$Z = \sqrt{\frac{\alpha}{B}}$$

Substituting for α and B:

$$Z = \sqrt{\frac{DC_1}{C_2 p/2}}$$

or

$$Z = \sqrt{\frac{2DC_1}{C_2 p}}$$

This can be verified by applying the calculus. Let $DC_1 = \alpha$ and $\dfrac{C_2 p}{2} = B$. Then:

$$TVC = \alpha Z^{-1} + BZ$$

and

$$Y' = \frac{-\alpha}{Z^2} + B$$

Setting $Y' = 0$:

$$B = \frac{\alpha}{Z^2}$$

Multiplying by Z^2:

$$Z^2 B = \alpha$$

Multiplying by $1/B$:

$$Z^2 = \frac{\alpha}{B}$$

Thus:

$$Z = \sqrt{\frac{\alpha}{B}}$$

Testing for a minimum:

$$Y'' = \frac{2\alpha}{Z^3}, \text{ at } Z = \sqrt{\frac{\alpha}{B}}$$

Y'' is positive, and therefore a minimum. Thus:

(4) $$Z = \sqrt{\frac{DC_1}{C_2 p/2}} = \sqrt{\frac{2DC_1}{C_2 p}}$$

Substituting in $D = 24{,}000$, $C_1 = \$80$, $C_2 = 0.2$, $P = 20$:

$$Z = \sqrt{\frac{2(24{,}000)80}{0.2(20)}}$$

$$= \sqrt{\frac{3{,}840{,}000}{4}}$$

$$= \sqrt{960{,}000}$$

$$\cong 980$$

Let us look closer at the carrying-cost equation, i.e., $C_c = \left(\dfrac{Z}{2}\right) C_2 p$.

The C_2 represents all of the costs associated with carrying a dollar's worth of inventory per year. Thus, C_2 is the sum of all of the elementary costs which contribute to carrying a dollar's worth of inventory. One of the primary ingredients in this cost is cost of capital (i.e., the price we must pay for funds to conduct the business). If this equation were truly representative, it might have multiple terms. Thus:

(5) $$C_c = \frac{Z}{2} C_3 p + \frac{Z}{2} C_4 p + \cdots + \frac{Z}{2} C_n p = \frac{Z}{2} p(C_3 + C_4 + \cdots + C_n)$$

When $C_2 = C_3 + C_4 + \cdots + C_n$, we have $\left(\dfrac{Z}{2}\right) C_2 p$.

Let C_3 equal the cost of capital per dollar of average annual inventory. The cost-of-capital term then assumes that each dollar released from inventory can be put to work elsewhere and generate the return indicated. For example, assume that C_3 equals 0.12. Since we use 100 tons of liquid asphalt per day, we release $100(20) = \$2,000$ per day. Thus, we are assuming that that amount can immediately be released to productive use. In most operations, it is quite true that released funds can be used to make another investment or to decrease outstanding obligations. A discussion of how the 0.12 is identified will be doubly useful here because it will show how the money might be alternatively used as well as showing how one should calculate the cost of capital.

Cost of capital may be calculated on many different bases. However, this author advocates that it be calculated on the basis of opportunity costs.[1] Opportunity costs are the return on the best alternative use of the money. Thus, if the company could use money released from a lower investment in inventory to purchase a new laborsaving device which saves 12 percent of its purchase price annually, the opportunity forgone because of the inventory investment is a 12 percent return. Therefore the cost of capital is 12 cents per dollar of average inventory.

Earlier, it was indicated that the cost-of-capital term assumes that each dollar released from inventory can be put to work elsewhere and generate the indicated return. This is quite plausible when a long-term drop in inventory investment occurs. For example, the EOQ model applied to liquid asphalt resulted in a reduction in maximum investment (excluding buffer stock) from \$160,000 (i.e., 8,000 gallons at \$20, or \$160,000) to \$19,600 (i.e., 980 gallons at \$20, or \$19,600), thus releasing

$$\$160,000 - \$19,700 = \$140,300$$

from inventory investment. However, the assumption is less plausible for each dollar released over the inventory cycle. For example, when the 980 gallons are received, the investment is \$19,600; but at the end of the cycle, it is zero dollars. Hence, over the length of the cycle, \$19,600 has been released in equal proportions. If the firm handled only one good, it would seem doubtful that each dollar could be immediately reused. However, a firm with many products in inventory may have each product at a different stage in the cycle, thus keeping its total investment relatively constant instead of continuously varying. If this is so, the problem of immediately using released dollars vanishes.

By the way of illustration, consider a firm with five items in inventory, each of which must be ordered every five days. Also, assume that each item costs \$10, and 20 of each are used per day. Further, assume that delivery takes one-half day. Consequently, no buffer stock is needed. These

---

[1] It is assumed that a company will not use capital unless it returns more than its cost. See, for example, H. Bierman and S. Smidt, *The Capital Budget Decision* (2d ed.; New York: Macmillan Co., 1966).

items are identified as items A, B, C, D, and E. On one Monday morning the firm finds that it has 20, 40, 60, 80, and 100 items A, B, C, D, and E, respectively. The investment over a five-day cycle is shown in Table 13–4. It should be noted that the above discussion focuses upon a release of funds when the EOQ model is applied. It is entirely possible that the application of the EOQ will increase inventory investment.

Another term in the carrying-cost equation deals with warehousing or

Table 13–4

Day/Item	Number in stock at noon	Investment	Number ordered
Monday:			
A........	10	$ 100	100
B........	30	300	0
C........	50	500	0
D........	70	700	0
E........	90	900	0
Total......	250	$2,500	
Tuesday:			
A........	90	$ 900	0
B........	10	100	100
C........	30	300	0
D........	50	500	0
E........	70	700	0
Total......	250	$2,500	
Wednesday:			
A........	70	$ 700	0
B........	90	900	0
C........	10	100	100
D........	30	300	0
E........	50	500	0
Total......	250	$2,500	
Thursday:			
A........	50	$ 500	0
B........	70	700	0
C........	90	900	0
D........	10	100	100
E........	30	300	0
Total......	250	$2,500	
Friday:			
A........	30	$ 300	0
B........	50	500	0
C........	70	700	0
D........	90	900	0
E........	10	100	100
Total......	250	$2,500	

storage costs. Let C_4 represent this term. Included in storage costs are costs of storage facilities, insurance on items in inventory, and any other storage costs, which vary with the size of the inventory. Accordingly, insurance costs are relevant only if they are dependent upon the size of the inventory. Let us assume that the company estimates that C_4 equals 0.035, where C_4 is the cost of storage per dollar of average inventory investment.

Another term (C_5) in the carrying-cost equation is the deterioration term. Again, only that deterioration which varies with average inventory size is relevant. Assume that the longer the asphalt is kept in storage, the less of the original is reclaimable. For example, assume that each day liquid asphalt is in storage, one 80th of 1 percent cannot be reclaimed. Thus, under present policy, average inventory is $\dfrac{4,000}{24,000}$, or one sixth of the year (60 days' worth). Therefore, for the 60 days, average inventory is 4,000 tons at $20 per ton. Deterioration is $0.0075\,(4,000)$, or 30 tons, which is $600 each 60 days, or $3,600 annually; this is $\dfrac{3,600}{20\,(4,000)}$, or 0.045 (4.5 percent of each dollar of average inventory investment). Thus, C_5 equals 0.045. In the example being discussed:

$$C_2 = C_3 + C_4 + C_5 = 0.12 + 0.035 + 0.045 = 0.20$$

Following the new policy, the costs of maintaining the 2,000 tons in the buffer inventory are the same, but the costs of providing the variable inventory are:

$$TVC = \frac{24,000}{980}\,(80) + \frac{980}{2}\,(0.2)\,(20)$$
$$= 1,959 + 1,960 = 3,919$$

Before application of the EOQ model:

$$TVC = \frac{24,000}{8,000}\,(80) + \frac{8,000}{2}\,(0.2)\,(20)$$
$$= 240 + 16,000 = 16,240$$

Thus the EOQ model produces quite a saving in this case.

III. THE ROLE OF TIME IN THE EOQ MODEL

It can be noted that the EOQ formula was developed for an annual period of time. It is reasonable to assume that demand for asphalt is partially dependent upon the season of the year. Assume that demand for the six months October, November, December, January, February, and March is 9,000 tons; and for April, May, June, July, August, and September, 15,000 tons. Can we calculate an economic order quantity relevant for each separate six-month period? The answer is yes, because the EOQ is not tied to an annual time period. The time base must be the same for all parameters. Hence, for the first six-month period:

$$D = 9,000$$
$$C_1 = \$80$$
$$C_2 = 0.10$$
$$p = \$20$$

and

$$EOQ = \sqrt{\frac{2(9,000)(80)}{0.10(20)}}$$

$$= \sqrt{\frac{1,440,000}{2}}$$

$$= \sqrt{720,000}$$
$$\cong 848$$

For the second six-month period:

$$D = 15,000$$
$$C_1 = \$80$$
$$C_2 = 0.10$$
$$p = 20$$
$$EOQ \cong 1,095$$

On the other hand, if, next year, demand increases so that expected sales for the winter months are 12,000, or one half the annual demand for this year, EOQ during the winter months would be 980 (the same as earlier calculated for the annual time period). Consequently, the formula is independent of time, but the parameter values are strongly dependent upon time.

IV. RELEVANCY OF STORAGE COSTS

Storage costs for liquid asphalt did not include any amortized cost of capital (depreciation) because it was assumed that this cost was incurred regardless of the size of inventory. Now assume that the tanks may be rented on an annual basis in multiples of 1,000 tons, according to the rental schedule shown in Table 13–5. This total container cost (TCC) can be graphed as in Figure 13–3. The dotted line shows a linear approxi-

Table 13–5

Size (in tons)	Annual rental
1,000	$ 1,000
2,000	2,000
3,000	3,000
4,000	4,000
5,000	5,000
6,000	6,000
7,000	7,000
8,000	8,000
9,000	9,000
10,000	10,000

Figure 13–3

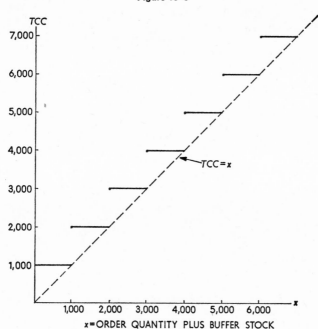

x = ORDER QUANTITY PLUS BUFFER STOCK

mation to total container costs of $1 per ton of order quantity plus buffer stock. Thus

$$C_6 X = C_6(Z + B) = TCC$$

where Z is the order quantity, B is the buffer stock and C_6 is the container cost per ton; in this example, C_6 equals one and was thus not specified in the graph in Figure 13–3. Then:

$$C_6 X = C_6 Z + C_6 B$$

and

$$TCC = C_6 Z + C_6 B$$

Where TCC equals the total container cost, B is the buffer stock, and C_6 is the total cost per ton for the container, or \$1. This equation assumes that only one container will be rented and that any size of rental container may be rented. Since buffer stock costs are fixed costs, we may ignore them here. Adding container costs to the total variable inventory costs, the cost equation is:

(6)
$$TVC = \frac{D}{Z} C_1 + \frac{Z}{2} C_2 p + Z C_6$$
$$= \frac{D}{Z} C_1 + (\frac{1}{2} C_2 p + C_6) Z$$

Since we have already shown that the minimum of the original cost curve occurs at $Z = \frac{\alpha}{B}$ when $\alpha = 1/2 C_2 p$ and $B = D C_1$, we can, for this case, let $\alpha = 1/2 C_2 p + C_6$. Then:

(7)
$$Z = \sqrt{\frac{DC_1}{\frac{1}{2} C_2 p + C_6}}$$
$$= \sqrt{\frac{24,000(80)}{\frac{1}{2}(0.2)(20) + 1}}$$
$$= \sqrt{640,000}$$
$$= 800 \text{ tons}$$

The purpose of this section is to show that the model can be modified to accommodate different inventory situations. However, this solution ignores the fact that the container cost is a step or segmented function. In fact, this approach results in the container cost being understated by zero to \$999.99. For example, at 1,001 gallons:

$$TVC = 1,918.24 + 2,002 + 2,000 = 5,920.24$$

but at 1,000 tons:

$$TVC = 1,920 + 2,000 + 1,000 = 4,920$$

The solution is to calculate the minimum in each of the ranges to identify the true minima. This approach uses the original equation plus the container costs; thus, for $0 \leq Z \leq 1,000$:

(8)
$$TVC = \frac{D}{Z} C_1 + \frac{Z}{2} C_2 p + 1,000$$

and for $1,000 < Z \leq 2,000$:

(9)
$$TVC = \frac{D}{Z} C_1 + \frac{Z}{2} C_2 p + 2,000$$

and so on. For example, when C_1 equals $150 and the remaining parameters stay the same, EOQ (ignoring container costs) is approximately 1,342. Accordingly, TVC under equation 9 above is approximately $7,364. However, if we let Z equal 1,000, TVC is $6,600 because we use equation 8 above. Thus, we always compare costs for EOQ (ignoring container costs) with costs for the next lowest size container when it is used to capacity.

V. THE ECONOMIC LOT SIZE

So far, we have discussed raw material inventories, but what about goods-in-process inventories or finished goods inventories? Many manufacturing organizations have the problem of deciding how many goods to produce for inventory. In this environment, it costs money to set up the production apparatus each time a good or component is produced. Consequently, as the size of the production run (lot size) decreases, the *annual* cost of setup increases. Therefore the setup costs are analogous to ordering costs, and

$$C_s = \frac{D}{Z} C_7$$

where C_s is the annual setup costs, D is the annual demand, C_7 is the setup costs per run, and Z is the lot size. For example, assume we are producing a stable textile product such as a T-shirt, and that carrying costs can be expressed as:

$$C_c = \frac{Z}{2} C_2 p$$

where Z is the lot size, C_2 is the annual carrying cost per dollar, and p is the value of the shirt.

Assume that $p = 1$, $C_2 = 0.2$, $C_7 = \$250$, and $D = 100,000$. Then:

$$TVC = \frac{D}{Z} C_7 + \frac{Z}{2} C_2 p$$

Using calculus, we find:

$$Z = \sqrt{\frac{DC_7}{\frac{1}{2}PC_2}}$$

$$= \sqrt{\frac{100,000(250)}{0.1}}$$

$$= \sqrt{250,000,000}$$

$$\cong 15,800$$

The components of carrying cost are subject to the same criticisms discussed earlier. Assume that the components of carrying cost include

(1) cost of capital, (2) warehousing costs, and (3) deterioration. The above equation assumes that warehousing space released as the size of the inventory decreases can be used for another use. Such an assumption does not appear reasonable. Let us assume that warehousing costs are dependent upon the size of the production run. Hence:

$$TVC = \frac{D}{Z} C_1 + \frac{Z}{2} C_2 P + ZC_3$$

where C_1 is the setup cost, C_2 is the annual cost of deterioration and capital per dollar, and C_3 is the annual cost of warehousing per item in inventory. The economic lot size is then:

$$Z = \sqrt{\frac{DC_1}{\frac{1}{2}C_2P + C_3}}$$

Note that C_3 is the cost per item, whereas C_2 is the cost per dollar.

VI. BUFFER STOCKS (SAFETY STOCKS)

The 2,000 tons of asphalt in safety stock are maintained to provide a buffer against increases in usage, delays in delivery, and waste and spoilage. If the firm could be assured that it would have no spoilage or waste, or delays in delivery, or changes in usage, it would not need to maintain a

Figure 13–4

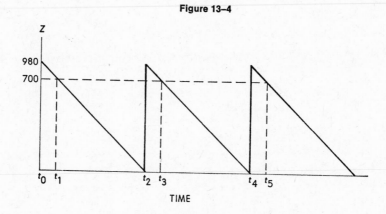

TIME

buffer stock. If the firm does not maintain a buffer stock, and if it takes seven working days from the time the order is placed to delivery, the company orders at the time it has seven days' inventory on hand. Thus the *reorder point* occurs when the firm has 700 tons on hand, and the re-order amount is 980 tons. This is shown in Figure 13–4. At time t_1 the firm has 700 units on hand, and an order for 980 tons is placed. At time t_2

(seven days later) the firm receives the order for 980 tons, and the cycle begins again. The seven-day lead time from placing the order to its receipt is called the *reorder period*.

Obviously, various factors will intervene so that the firm does not receive goods just as it runs out. Consequently, the buffer stock must be maintained. The following pages demonstrate a method of finding an optimum buffer stock.

The Asphalt Pavement Company, discussed earlier, has maintained sufficient inventory so that it has never been out of stock. Its experience on deliveries is shown in Table 13–6. A distribution of usage for the last 100 seven-day periods is given in Table 13–7. Assuming that the economic

Table 13–6

Time between placing order and receipt of goods	Frequency
6 days	20
7 days	60
8 days	20
Total	100

Table 13–7

Usage (in tons)	Probability
600	0.1
650	0.2
700	0.4
750	0.2
800	0.1

order quantity is 980, as found on page 206, this results in an order being placed every 9.8 days. Management would prefer to place an order every 10 days and has found almost no cost differential; i.e., when order quantity is 1,000:

$$TVC = \frac{24,000}{1,000}(80) + \frac{1,000}{2}0.2(20)$$
$$= 1,920 + 2,000$$
$$= 3,920$$

Earlier (on page 209), we found TVC when order quantity is 980 to be approximately $3,919. This $1 cost differential is slight enough to use a 10-day or 1,000-ton reorder quantity.

Buffer stock for variances in demand

The role of the buffer stock is to provide (1) a cushion for variances in demand and (2) a cushion for variances in delivery time. For the moment, let us find the optimal safety stock when only variances in demand occur. Table 13–7 shows that if the Asphalt Paving Company plans no safety stock, it will run out of stock in 30 percent of the reorder periods, because 30 percent of the time over 700 tons are used.

Assume that if APC is out of stock, it must rent tank trucks and pick up the liquid asphalt. Cost of the trucks and a higher price per ton on the asphalt so purchased result in a differential of $200 over the normal delivered price for 50 tons of asphalt. Assume that this is the only relevant cost of being out of stock. Assume further that only a fully loaded truck can be picked up. Since 700 tons must be on hand at the time this order is placed, the only events of interest are the occurrence of demand in excess of 700 tons.

Table 13–8

TABLE OF TOTAL COSTS, GIVEN THE SAFETY STOCK
POLICY AND SHORTAGE CONDITION

	Shortage condition		
Safety stock policy	*None*	*50 tons*	*100 tons*
None................	None	$200.00	$400.00
50 tons..............	$ 5.82	5.82	205.82
100 tons.............	11.64	11.64	11.64

Table 13–8 shows stock shortage situations and policies that could be taken to anticipate the situation. Each cell in the table identifies the total cost, assuming that the policy indicated and the demand indicated took place. Accordingly, if our policy is to keep a safety stock of 50 tons, the cost per seven-day period is 7/240 of the cost per year.[2] Carrying cost per year is:

$$50(0.2)20 = \$200$$

Thus:

$$\frac{7}{240}(200) = \$5.82$$

The best safety stock policy is found by calculating the cost over a very large number of reorder periods and choosing the lowest cost. Over 100 periods the total cost of no safety stock would be calculated by recog-

---

[2] It is assumed that there are 240 working days per year.

nizing that in 70 times, no cost would be incurred; in 20 times, $200 would be incurred; and in 10 times, $400 would be incurred; or:

$$70(0) + 20(200) + 10(400) = \$8,000$$

Dividing this by 100, we find that the average cost per period *over the long run* is $80. We denote this as

$$EC_{\text{None}} = \$80$$

which means that the expected cost (over the long run) of no buffer stock is $80. We can immediately observe that stocking 100 tons costs only $11.64:

$$EC_{100} = \$11.64$$

and is therefore preferable. It now remains to check the 50-ton alternative:

$$
\begin{aligned}
EC_{50} &= \frac{70(5.82) + 20(5.82) + 10(205.82)}{100} \\
&= \frac{407.40 + 116.40 + 2058.20}{100} \\
&= \frac{2,582}{100} \\
&= 25.82
\end{aligned}
$$

which is more than the 100-ton alternative.

Buffer stock for variances in delivery time

It should also be observed that this safety stock still ignores the variation in delivery time. We shall now proceed to calculate the safety stock required to cover the variation in delivery time. However, we shall first assume no variation in demand. In that case the delivery experience on page 215 shows that we shall need either 600, 700, or 800 tons during the reorder period.[3] This yields the table of total costs, given the safety stock policy and shortage condition (Table 13–9). Since the de-

Table 13–9

	Shortage condition	
Safety stock policy	None	100 tons
None......................	None	$400.00
100 tons...................	$11.64	11.64

---

[3] Since usage is assumed to be always 100 tons per day if delivery time is six days, APC will need 600 tons, etc.

livery experience on page 000 indicates that late delivery (i.e., eight days) takes place 20 percent of the time:

$$EC_{None} = 0.2(400) = \$80$$

and

$$EC_{100} = \$11.64$$

Thus, we stock 100 tons for delivery variance.

Buffer stock when usage and delivery time vary

Let us now ascertain what total usage will be when *both* usage and delivery time vary. This is accomplished by calculating the joint probability of each usage rate and each delivery time. Since there are three delivery times and five usage rates, we shall find 15 joint probabilities. This analysis requires an assumption that delivery time and demand are independent. If we further assume that in six days the usage rates are proportionate to those used in seven days, the usage conditions and their probabilities are as shown in Table 13–10.[4]

By the same method of calculation, the usage rates for eight days are as given in Table 13–11.

Table 13–10

Usage	Probability of six-day delivery	Probability of usage	Joint probability
513.6	0.2	0.1	0.02
556.8	0.2	0.2	0.04
600.0	0.2	0.4	0.08
643.2	0.2	0.2	0.04
686.4	0.2	0.1	0.02

Table 13–11

Usage	Probability of Eight-day delivery	Probability of usage	Joint probability
684.8	0.2	0.1	0.02
742.4	0.2	0.2	0.04
800.0	0.2	0.4	0.08
857.6	0.2	0.2	0.04
915.2	0.2	0.1	0.02

---

[4] In this case, we calculate the actual usage as $Z/7 = x/y$, where x *is* the usage rate for y days, y is the number of days of concern, 7 is the number of days for normal delivery time, and Z is the seven-day usage rate of interest. Thus, to find the six-day usage rate for the 600 usage rate in seven days, $Z = 600$, $y = 6$, and $600/7 = x/6$, or $x = y(6)/7 = 513.6$.

The joint probability for seven-day delivery and each usage condition are shown in Table 13–12.

Table 13–13 summarizes the possible usage conditions from reorder point of delivery. In this case, we need more information on the costs of obtaining additional asphalt. Let us assume that it can be purchased in lots of 10 tons and that each lot costs $40 more if purchased on an emergency basis than if ordered through regular channels. Therefore the safety stock policies and costs are as given in Table 13–14:[5]

Table 13–12

Usage	Probability of Seven-day delivery	Probability of usage	Joint probability
600	0.6	0.1	0.06
650	0.6	0.2	0.12
700	0.6	0.4	0.24
750	0.6	0.2	0.12
800	0.6	0.1	0.06

Table 13–13

Usage	Probability of usage
513.6	0.02
556.8	0.04
600.0	0.08 + 0.06
643.2	0.04
650.0	0.12
684.8	0.02
686.4	0.02
700.0	0.24
742.4	0.04
750.0	0.12
800.0	0.08 + 0.06
857.6	0.04
915.2	0.02

Table 13–14

Safety stock policy	Shortage condition				
	None	50 tons	100 tons	160 tons	220 tons
None	None	$200.00	$400.00	$640.00	$880.00
50 tons	$ 5.82	5.82	205.82	445.82	685.82
100 tons	11.64	11.64	11.64	251.64	491.64
160 tons	18.52	18.52	18.52	18.52	258.52
220 tons	25.61	25.61	25.61	25.61	25.61
Probability	0.62	0.16	0.14	0.04	0.02

[5] Note that the company is 50 tons short when usage is either 742.4 tons or 750 tons. This is so because partial lots cannot be purchased.

$$EC_{50} = 0.78(5.82) + 0.14(205.82) + 0.04(445.82)$$
$$+ 0.02(685.82) = \$65.02$$
$$EC_{100} = 0.92(11.64) + 0.04(251.64) + 0.02(491.64) = \$30.60$$
$$EC_{160} = 0.98(18.52) + 0.02(258.52) = \$23.32$$

which is less than \$25.61 (i.e., EC_{220}). Hence the optimum safety stock considering both variances together is less than the sum of each considered separately. It should be remembered that the usage condition found here assumes independence between delivery time and demand. In fact, the distribution of usage during the reorder period and the probability of that usage will normally be obtained from records rather than as computed here. Note that the average cost per reorder period is also called the expected cost. The notation EC_i refers to the expected cost of the ith alternative.

It is unlikely that the costs of shortages used here include all shortage costs. It would seem that such shortages would cause construction delays and idle time, plus potential loss of customers.

Also, it is unlikely that demand in one week is independent of demand in the previous week. We shall deal with problems of this form in later chapters.

VII. REVIEW OF EOQ AND SAFETY STOCK CALCULATIONS

If $TVC = \dfrac{D}{Z} C_1 + ZC_2p$ when $D = 24,000$, $C_1 = \$80$, $C_2 = 0.2$, $p = \$20$, then:

$$Z = \sqrt{\frac{DC_1}{1/2C_2p}} \cong 980$$

Thus the order quantity is 980. Normal delivery time (lead time) is seven days; consequently, the reorder period is seven days' supply. A seven-day supply is 700 tons, and safety stock is 160 tons; hence the re-order point is 860 tons.

It should be noted that the inventory system discussed so far is operated with a flexible ordering policy; i.e., the order is placed when the inventory contains seven days' supply (the reorder period) plus safety stock. Therefore the length of time between orders may vary. However, it is possible that the amount ordered may vary rather than the time between orders. Accordingly, if EOQ is 10 days' supply, the order is placed every 10 days to cover the actual amount used in the previous 10 days. It can readily be seen under this arrangement that in periods of greater than normal usage, a firm takes a higher risk of being out of inventory unless a larger buffer stock is carried. On the other hand, the convenience of ordering at a regular time may more than offset the costs of added buffer stock.

VIII. THE DEPENDENCE BETWEEN ITEMS IN INVENTORY

So far, we have assumed that the inventory policy for each item was independent of every other item. However, this may not be the case.

For example, the inventory data are shown for the major items in the inventory of APC in Table 13–15. Based upon the EOQ model, the order size is:

Coarse aggregate................................5,000 tons
Intermediate aggregate.........................4,714 tons
Fine aggregate................................4,472 tons

This is between 30 and 34 orders per year for each grade of aggregate. It is possible that joint preparation of the orders for these goods might reduce order costs enough to more than offset the increased carrying costs. If

Table 13–15

Item	Annual demand (in tons)	Cost per ton	Order cost	Carrying cost per dollar
Coarse aggregate.............	150,000	$ 4.00	$50	$0.15
Intermediate aggregate........	150,000	4.50	50	0.15
Fine aggregate..............	150,000	5.00	50	0.15
Sand......................	25,000	2.50	50	0.15
Asphalt....................	24,000	20.00	80	0.20

usage of the aggregate is approximately one third for each grade, it might be reasonable to consider all aggregate (ie., coarse, intermediate, and fine together) as a single item, with an average value per ton of $4.50, and find the EOQ. When all three are ordered at the same time, let us assume that a joint order costs $120. Then:

$$D = 450,000$$
$$C_1 = 120$$
$$C_2 = 0.15$$
$$P = \$4.50$$

$$Z = \sqrt{\frac{450,000(120)}{1/2(0.15)(4.50)}}$$
$$= \sqrt{160,000,000}$$
$$= 12,649$$

Dividing this by 3 to get the number of tons of each kind of aggregate, we find that the joint order is for 4,216 tons of coarse, intermediate, and fine. Each type of aggregate must share order costs. Thus, order costs are $40. Comparing total costs with and without joint orders, we find:

Coarse: $\dfrac{150,000}{5,000}(50) + \dfrac{5,000}{2}(0.15)4 \cong \$3,000.00$

$\dfrac{150,000}{4,216}(40) + \dfrac{4,216}{2}(0.15)4 \cong \$2,604.80$

Intermediate: $\dfrac{150,000}{4,714}(50) + \dfrac{4,714}{2}(0.15)4.5 \cong \$3,182.00$

$\dfrac{150,000}{4,216}(40) + \dfrac{4,216}{2}(0.15)4.5 \cong \$2,846.10$

Fine: $\dfrac{150,000}{4,472}(50) + \dfrac{4,472}{2}(0.15)5 \cong \$3,354.00$

$\dfrac{150,000}{4,216}(40) + \dfrac{4,216}{2}(0.15)5 \cong \$3,003.80$

Thus the joint order is substantially less.

IX. OTHER CONSIDERATIONS

The analysis could have assumed that a year consists of 365 days, and that usage occurs on each day and orders can be placed on any day. However, the analysis could, and most frequently does, ignore the weekend from consideration, thus assuming that time stops during the weekend and resumes at the beginning of the next week. Such an assumption cannot affect ordering costs, since ordering costs are strictly dependent upon annual usage. Any capital or warehouse space released because of inventory usage over the weekend probably cannot be put to production use; hence the weekend need not be considered. It is hard to believe that deterioriation or obsolescence can be important over such a short period of time. Consequently, days of nonusage are normally subtracted from 365 to yield the net working days per year, and all calculations proceed from there.

Most manufacturing companies find that a large percentage of their items account for only a small percentage of their inventory investment. For example, 70 percent of the items in an inventory may account for only 10 percent of the value of the total inventory. Thus, the cost of an elaborate inventory control system on these items may well exceed the benefits of such a system.

DISCUSSION TOPICS AND PROBLEMS

1. Derive the EOQ formula when:

Z = Number of units ordered
p = Cost of part
C_1 = Order cost
C_2 = Carrying cost per dollar of inventory investment per year
D = Yearly demand

2. Derive the optimal number of orders to place per year when:

C_1 = Order cost
C_2 = Carrying cost per dollar of inventory per year
D = Yearly demand
p = Cost per part
O = Number of orders placed per year

3. The following questions pertain to the simple EOQ formula.

a) Derive the EOQ formula when:

n = Number of units ordered
p = Cost of part
C_1 = Carrying cost per dollar of inventory investment *per year*
C_2 = Order cost
M = Monthly demand

b) What is included in the inventory-carrying costs?

c) Is the EOQ model independent of time? Explain why or why not.

4. The XYZ Department store has installed an inventory control system on staple merchandise. Staple merchandise must:

a) Be that merchandise which the average customer expects the store to have in stock at all times.

b) Be that merchandise for which the potential loss due to markdowns is nominal.

c) Be that merchandise which the manufacturer or distributor will deliver on a regular basis.

d) Be that merchandise on which the lead time from vendor to warehouse is reasonably constant.

e) Be that merchandise which is not perishable.

f) Be that merchandise which can be stored with ease.

Those items which come in sizes and/or colors are forecast every two months by the departmental buyer. The buyer forecasts only gross sales; i.e., he forecasts, for example, the number of T-shirts needed. The size breakdown is made by the model, which uses the size experience of the last year.

Actual sales are charged against the inventory records weekly. The buffer stock level is two weeks' supply. The economic order quantity is computed based upon the latest forecast. (*Note:* A month is four weeks.)

At the time of installation the store had 150 size 36 Hanes T-shirts on hand. The buyer has forecast sales of 8,000 Hanes T-shirts during the next two months, and experience shows that 5 percent of all Hanes T-shirts sold are size 36.

The model used to determine the economic order quantity is the standard EOQ model. Cost of the T-shirt is $1, carrying cost per dollar of inventory investment per year is 26 cents, and ordering cost is $8 per order. Lead time is one week.

a) What is the initial order for size 36 Hanes T-shirts, and when is it placed?

Weekly sales are:

Week	Sales
1	45
2	55
3	60
4	45
5	50
6	55
7	45
8	40

b) When are subsequent orders placed:

   1) If the reorder point is fixed?
   2) If the reorder amount is fixed?

c) Discuss the possibilities for joint ordering here.

d) On the basis of the information available here, evaluate this application. Make and state any assumptions necessary to complete this evaluation.

5. A manufacturing company which uses only one item of raw material finds that the costs of warehousing are:

$$TWC = \$20 \frac{D}{Z} + \$0.04Z + \$0.05D + \$150$$

Indicate where each term in the equation belongs in the EOQ equation.

6. How does the first example in this chapter handle the cost of being out of inventory?

7. A manufacturing company produces four products (*A*, *B*, *C*, and *D*) from raw materials 1, 2, and 3.

a) Setup cost for product *A* is $150. Annual demand is 1,600, value per part is $40, carrying cost per dollar are 20 cents. What is the economic lot size?

b) An executive of the company maintains that the value per part should be based upon its selling price of $44 rather than its allocated cost value of $40. Do you agree? If so, why? If not, why? Indicate the difference in the economic lot size between each assumption.

c) Order cost for raw material 1 is $50, annual demand is 3,000 units, value per part is $6, and carrying cost per dollar is 24 cents. What is the economic order quantity?

d) Product *A*, discussed in part (*a*) above, is in greater demand in the second half of the year than the first. In fact, 60 percent of its sales are in the second half of the year. Compute the economic lot size for the first and second halves of the year in part (*a*) of this question.

e) In part (*c*) of this question, delivery time takes five working days, and buffer stock is 100 units. The company works 300 days per year. Indicate the reorder point and the reorder period.

8. How does the model take into account differences in the size of the items in inventory?

SELECTED REFERENCES

Brown, Robert G. *Decision Rules for Inventory Management.* New York: Holt, Rinehart & Winston, Inc., 1967.

Buffa, Elwood S. *Models for Production and Operations Management.* New York: John Wiley & Sons, Inc., 1963.

Buffa, Elwood S. *Production-Inventory Systems: Planning and Control.* Homewood, Ill.: Richard D. Irwin, Inc., 1968.

Hadley, G., and Whitin, T. M. *Analysis of Inventory Systems.* Englewood Cliffs, N.J.: Prentice-Hall, Inc., 1963.

Magee, J. D. *Production Planning and Inventory Control.* New York: McGraw-Hill Book Co., Inc., 1958.

Whitin, T. M. *Theory of Inventory Management.* Princeton: Princeton University Press, 1953.

14

Queuing and other
probabilistic
models

I. INTRODUCTION

The models discussed in this chapter are related because they represent conditons of data uncertainty. In each of these models the condition which occurs is assumed to occur by chance. Since the events can be characterized by a probability, all of the models rely upon probability theory.

The three models to be discussed are (1) queuing theory, (2) revision of prior probabilities, and (3) the brand-share model (Markov chain). Each of these models will be presented in its most elementary form and will thus rely upon the probability concepts shown in Chapter 11.

II. INTRODUCTION TO QUEUING MODELS

Queuing models, also called waiting-line models, are models where a facility performs a service. The most common queue is that of a consumer service such as a bank teller or grocery check-out counter. In these instances, each customer must receive a service, and the length of that service varies from customer to customer. At the same time, the number of customers demanding the service varies. The line that forms in front of these service facilities is called a queue or channel. Thus a grocery store with one check-out counter is a single-channel facility. A grocery store with more than one check-out counter is a multichannel facility. If the service facility is capable of servicing the customer when he arrives, no bottlenecks will occur. If it takes 12 minutes to service a customer and one arrives every 10 minutes, a queue will build up and, in fact, build up to infinite length. The 10 minutes are known as the arrival rate. In this case, only a reduction in arrivals (demand) or an increase in the number of service facilities or speedier processing will reduce the queue and eliminate the bottleneck. When there are variations in arrival time and/or service time, the queue will fluctuate in size.

Purpose

There are basically two opposing costs in waiting-line problems: (1) the service or facility cost and (2) the waiting-time cost. The general approach to waiting-line problems is to minimize costs knowing the average cost of operating a facility and the cost per unit of waiting time. Total and incremental cost analysis is also essential. For example, the cost of additional facilities, costs of maintaining different queue lengths, and the queue discipline chosen must be considered.

An optimum solution occurs when the sum of the facility and waiting-line costs are minimum. The service or facility cost can readily be obtained from historical accounting data. However, the waiting-time cost can be very difficult to ascertain and quantify. It is extremely difficult to predict when a prospective service user will become impatient and leave the queue. For example, the loss of customer goodwill in a department store can only be estimated. When waiting-time costs cannot be readily determined the decision maker may utilize some other basis, such as the calculated average waiting time in the queue, as a basis for decision making.

It is important to note that existing waiting-line models are not directly applicable to all business situations. The user of waiting-line theory will in many cases have to develop a new model that will be descriptive of the particular flow system under study. For instance, the flow of customers differs between a supermarket and an airline terminal. In a supermarket the arrival of customers may be constant during the entire day, whereas customers at an airline terminal arrive in bunches just prior to the scheduled flight departure. In order effectively to evaluate different levels of service, indexes of performance are needed to evaluate system alternatives. Some of these indexes are (1) the average arrival rate, (2) the average service rate, (3) the average length of the queue, and (4) the average time spent in the queue.

Elements of the system

The major variables in a waiting-line system may be classified into five distinct areas, which will now be discussed.

Arrivals. Arrivals into the system occur according to a probability distribution that is independent of the service provided by the system. Arrivals may occur at a constant rate or may closely approximate the normal distribution, or may approximate the Poisson distribution. Often an arrival occurs at random and is independent of what has previously occurred. The arrivals into the system may, however, be dependent upon the service facility, as in the case of a flow of automobiles leaving a traffic light.

Service. The service time can be fixed (as in the case of a vending machine), or exponentially distributed (as is frequently true in the service provided by people), or normally distributed. In elementary models, service time is usually independent of arrivals.

Facilities. The system may have various configurations of servicing facilities, some of which will now be discussed.

1. *Single channel.* One queue feeds one service facility (e.g., the box office at a movie theater; see Figure 14–1).

Figure 14–1

REPRESENTATION OF A SINGLE-CHANNEL QUEUE

2. *Multichannel.* Many queues feed many service facilities (e.g., the flow of customers in a supermarket; see Figure 14–2). Some of the facilities in a multichannel system may be segregated for special-purpose customers (e.g., in a supermarket, there is usually one counter for "express service" for small-purchase customers).

Figure 14–2

REPRESENTATION OF A MULTICHANNEL SERVICE FACILITY WITH OVERFLOW

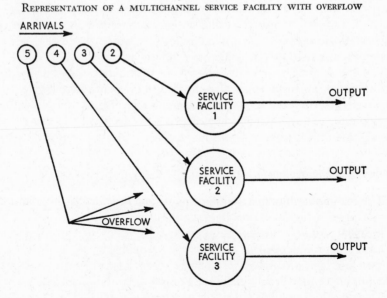

3. *Multistage.* A queue must pass through two service facilities, either in a sequence or in tandem (e.g., enter a queue to purchase an item in a department store, and then enter a second queue to have the item wrapped; see Figure 14–3).

4. *Limited service.* The service facilty may have limited availability, or there may be queue interference. Queue interference may occur when the queues of ships form when opposing traffic can only use one lane of traffic. This is typical of some existing canals.

Figure 14–3

REPRESENTATION OF A MULTISTAGE CHANNEL

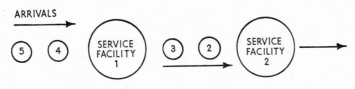

Queue discipline. Queue discipline refers to the order in which the service facility selects the next customer (or unit) to be served. The next customer may be selected on a first-come, first-served basis or may be selected on a random basis, as when a telephone operator selects a waiting call. Some customers may be given a priority basis for service. Preemptive priority occurs when the customer being served is immediately replaced in the service facility by the high-priority customer. Nonpreemptive priority occurs when the high-priority customer moves to the head of the queue but does not disturb the customer being served.

Another aspect of queue discipline is whether a customer in a queue can move to a shorter queue in the multichannel system. Customer behavior is such that a customer may refuse to join a queue because of the size of the present queue. Also, consideration must be given to customer collusion and jockeying from one queue to another. A customer in a queue may become impatient and leave the queue. An impatient customer at a restaurant may leave the queue and the restaurant, resulting in a lost sale. Queue control specifies that a limit has been established on the size of the queue.

Output of the Queue. The output of a queue is important when the system is multistaged because the possibility of a service facility breakdown can have repercussions on the queues. The line before the breakdown will lengthen, and the line following the breakdown will diminish.

III. FIXED ARRIVAL, FIXED SERVICE TIME

The simplest situation occurs when arrivals occur at regular specified intervals (such as every 10 minutes) and service is the same length of time for each arrival (such as 10 minutes). When the arrival time and service time are fixed *and the same,* no backlog occurs. A typical example is a job shop fabrication company which maintains a tool crib from which its employees obtain tools, etc. Assume that the crib has an attendant who is paid $2 per hour. Further, assume that the machine operators obtaining tools, etc., from the crib are paid $4 per hour. Hence, if the crib is open six hours, both the attendant and the various operators spend six hours at the crib, and the cost of the crib attendant and the various machine operators represents a total cost of $2(6) + 4(6) = \$36$.

Assume that an improved crib layout can be found so that service time is six minutes. Then the total cost of the service is calculated by figuring the cost per machine operator serviced, times the number of operators serviced, plus the cost of the attendant. Cost per operator serviced is the fraction of an hour required for service times the hourly rate:

$$(6/60)4 = 24/60 = \$0.40$$

The number serviced is six per hour for six hours, or 36. Thus:

$$
\begin{aligned}
TC &= \$2(6) + 36(\$0.40) \\
&= \$12 + \$14.40 \\
&= \$26.40
\end{aligned}
$$

It is worthwhile noting that the workday value of the improved layout is $\$36.00 - \$26.40 = \$9.60$. Using present-value analysis, shown in Chapter 19, a decision as to the desirability of the improved layout could be made. The purpose of showing the above example is to demonstrate how the total costs are calculated for the case when service time is less than the arrival rate.

Assume that an arrival occurs every 9 minutes and service time is 10 minutes. With one attendant, the line will become progressively larger. A machine operator arrives every nine minutes. Let the number arriving per hour be X. Calculating $9X = 60$, $X = 6\frac{2}{3}$. Every hour, therefore, two-thirds of a machine operator buildup occurs. At the end of the six-hour day, $6(\frac{2}{3}) = 4$ machine operators are in the line. The waiting time of the machine operators while not being serviced is no minutes for the first man, one minute for the second man, two minutes for the third, etc. Consequently, excess time in the queue is given by

$$Z = \frac{n(n-1)}{2}$$

where n is the total number serviced and

$$n = \frac{6(60)}{9\ \text{MIN}} = 40$$

The length of time the last machine operator must wait to begin receiving service is $n - 1$ minutes. Given $n = 40$, $Z = 780$. If the machine operators wait until serviced and are not paid overtime, they have waited

$$\frac{780}{60} = 13 \text{ hours at } \$4 = \$52$$

Also, the attendant must work 40 extra minutes, at a cost of $1.33. Accordingly, the *excess time* costs are $53.33. Obviously, the addition of one attendant would eliminate all excess time costs.

Since a six-hour day was used for the crib attendant, we may assume that the other two hours a day he works are maintenance in the crib. However, a second attendant would probably not eliminate any maintenance cost; thus, his entire salary should be charged to the cost of reducing excess operator time.

Table 14–1

Alternative	*Cost of attendants' normal time*	*Cost of excess attendant time*	*Cost of machine operators' normal time*	*Cost of machine operators' excess time*	*Total costs*
One attendant............	$12	$1.33	$24	$52	$89.33
Two attendants..........	28	Zero	24	Zero	52.00

In truth, management is now faced with a choice among alternatives which can be shown as in Table 14–1. Hence, management should have two attendants, despite the presence of idle attendant time.

Queuing models with variable arrival and/or service times are much more complex. The dock facilities model of Chapter 19 will demonstrate a model with fixed service time and random arrival time. The complexity of further queuing models is beyond the scope of this book.

IV. REVISION OF PRIOR PROBABILITIES

Often, management is faced with the problem of making a decision on the basis of insufficient knowledge, and additional knowledge is costly. The following model provides one small approach for dealing with this situation.

Let us assume that we are a ball-bearing manufacturer producing stainless steel ball bearings for use in the space program. These ball bearings come in numerous different sizes and are made in various lot sizes. Presently, we are starting to produce a lot of 500 class *A* ball bearings. A defective bearing requires special handling which costs 50 cents each. Normal machine setup yields 2 percent defective items. However, the machine must be reset for each production run, and sometimes (20 percent of the time) the setting is slightly off, yielding 20 percent defective items. If this conditon is known or suspected, the machine can be reset at a cost of $8. When it is reset, we assume that the resulting defects are 2 percent. Again, we are faced with a familiar opposing-cost problem—it costs money to reset the machine. But if it has a bad setting, that also costs money. The manager must make a choice of either accepting the setup or rejecting it and ordering a new setup. Table 14–2 summarizes the situation facing the manager. The cost of accepting a good setup is 10 defective items specially handled at a cost of 50 cents each, or a total of $5. When any setup is rejected, 2 percent, or 10, are defective, for a $5 special handling cost plus

Table 14–2

Description of machine setting	Probability of setting	Percent defective	Conditional cost of alternatives Accept setup	Conditional cost of alternatives Reject setup
Good........................	0.8	0.02	$ 5	$13
Bad........................	0.2	0.20	50	13

the $8 machine adjustment cost, or a total of $13. Accepting a bad setup results in $0.2(500) = 100$ defective units, each costing 50 cents, for a total cost of $50. We may now calculate the expected cost (EC) of either accepting or rejecting. Thus, 80 percent of the time, we have a good setup costing $5, and 20 percent of the time a bad setup costing $50. Therefore:

$$EC_{\text{accept}} = 0.8(5) + 0.2(50) = \$14$$

and

$$EC_{\text{reject}} = 0.8\ (13) + 0.2(13) = \$13$$

The conclusion based upon existing information is to reject the setup. However, if we had some additional knowledge to indicate a stronger probability of a good setup, we might change our decision.

Let us review the events facing this decision maker. Let:

G_s = Good setup
B_s = Bad setup
G_b = A good bearing being produced
D_b = A defective bearing being produced

Then the joint probabilities are:

$$P(G_sG_b) = (0.8)(0.98) = 0.784$$
$$P(G_sD_b) = (0.8)(0.02) = 0.016$$
$$P(B_sG_b) = (0.2)(0.8\ ) = 0.160$$
$$P(B_sD_b) = (0.2)(0.2\ ) = \underline{0.040}$$
$$1.000$$

The definition of conditional probability tells us:

$$(1) \qquad P(G_s/G_b) = \frac{P(G_sG_b)}{P(G_b)}$$

And, assuming statistical independence, we know that:

$$(2) \qquad P(G_b) = P(G_bG_s) + P(G_bB_s)$$

Substituting equation (2) into equation (1) gives:[1]

$$(3) \qquad P(G_s/G_b) = \frac{P(G_sG_b)}{P(G_bG_s) + P(G_bB_s)}$$

Multiplying $P(G_b/G_s) = \dfrac{P(G_bG_s)}{P(G_s)}$ by $P(G_s)$ gives:

$$(4) \qquad P(G_bG_s) = P(G_b/G_s)\, P(G_s)$$

Also, multiplying $P(G_b/B_s) = \dfrac{P(G_bB_s)}{P(B_s)}$ by $P(B_s)$ gives:

$$(5) \qquad P(G_bB_s) = P(G_b/B_s)P(B_s)$$

Substituting equations (4) and (5) into equation (3) gives:

$$(6) \qquad P(G_s/G_b) = \frac{P(G_s)P(G_b/G_s)}{P(G_b/G_s)P(G_s) + P(G_b/B_s)P(B_s)}$$

This provides us with a means of evaluating the probability of a good setup, given that we have a good ball bearing.

Let us assume that we take a sample of one and it is good. This may be summarized in the table of symbols (Table 14–3).

Table 14–4 includes values from the previous example. If we knew the

Table 14–3

Machine setting	Probability of one defective item, given setting	Probability of setting	Probability of sample of one good item
Good	$P(D_b/G_s)$	$P(G_s)$	$P(G_b/G_s)$
Bad	$P(D_b/B_s)$	$P(B_s)$	$P(G_b/B_s)$

Table 14–4

Machine setting	Probability of one defective item, given setting	Probability of setting	Probability of sample of one good item
Good	0.02	0.8	0.98
Bad	0.20	0.2	0.80

[1] The reader will recall that $P(G_bG_s) = P(G_sG_b)$.

joint probability of the sample which occurs and the setting, we would then be able to compute the ratio of these events. The probability of the occurrence of one good item for a good setting and the occurrence of one good item for a bad setting yields the overall probability of a good item occurring. Thus, 80 percent of the time, we shall have 98 percent good items; and 20 percent of the time, we shall have 80 percent good items, or:

$$0.8(0.98) + 0.2(0.8) = 0.784 + 0.16 = 0.944$$

Thus each element in the above equation yields the probability that the event will occur. This may be summarized in Table 14–5. We may then

Table 14–5

Machine setting	Probability of one defective, given setting	Probability of setting	Probability of sample (one good)	Probability of sample and setting
Good...........0.02		0.8	0.98	0.784 $P(G_sG_b)$
Bad.............0.20		0.2	0.80	0.16 $P(B_sG_b)$
				0.944

expect that the good setting occurs $\dfrac{0.784}{0.944} = 0.83$, or 83 percent of the time; and the bad setting occurs 0.17, or 17 percent of the time. These are revised probabilities, given that we have a sample of one good item. Please note that this could have been computed directly from equation (6) above. This paragraph provides an alternative approach.

Continuing along this line, suppose that two good items are found. Assuming independence, the probability of two good items for the good setup is:

$$(0.98)(0.98) = 0.9604$$

and the probability of two good items for a bad setup is:

$$(0.8)(0.8) = 0.64$$

Table 14–6 shows the revised probabilities. Does this information modify

Table 14–6

Machine setting	(1) Probability of one defective	(2) Probability of setting	(3) Probability of sample (two good)	(2) × (3) Joint Probability of setting and sample	Revised Probability
Good.......0.02		0.8	0.9604	0.76832	0.8572
Bad.........0.20		0.2	0.64	0.12800	0.1428
				0.89632	1.0000

our original decision to reject the setup? Let us recalculate the expected cost of acceptance now:

$$EC_{accept} = 0.8572(5) + 0.1428(50)$$
$$= 4.286 + 7.14$$
$$= 11.426$$

which is less than the expected cost of rejection. This additional information allows us to reduce the expected costs of the best action by $1.574.

One could now ascertain all of the costs and benefits of drawing a sample of two items. It is only when two good items are found in a sample of two that the revised probability of a good setting increases. Thus the cost of obtaining the sample of two must be less than the value of information on a sample of two good bearings times the frequency that that setting is found. Here the value of information for a sample of two is $1.574(.89632) = 1.40. The cost of sampling must be less than this.[2]

V. THE BRAND-SHARE MODEL[3]

In Chapter 5, we discussed the concern of management with market share and the desire to maintain market share. We have also talked about the difficulty of identifying the effects on future sales and profits of actions taken now. The cost of stock shortages becomes difficult to identify because of its effect on future sales. One of the prime ingredients in determination of present and future share is customer loyalty. The brand-share model offers a way of looking at market shares over time based upon customer propensity to repurchase the company's product or switch to products of competing companies. Repurchase propensities are not loyalties. However, the willingness to change purchase patterns may be close to loyalty.

The brand-share model may be understood via the following example. Assume that the United States has three brands of cigarettes: Ace cigarettes (A), Better cigarettes (B), and Continental cigarettes (C). A market survey shows that 60 percent of Ace customers repurchase Ace cigarettes, 20 percent purchase Better cigarettes, and 20 percent purchase Continental cigarettes. The matrix in Table 14–7 of purchase probabilities will summarize the data. This is also called a matrix of transition probabilities or switching matrix. Thus, 70 percent of B's customers repurchased B's cigarettes, 20 percent purchased C's cigarettes, and 10 percent purchased A's cigarettes. Further, of the 1 million packs purchased last week, 300,000 were Ace, 400,000 were Better, and 300,000 were Continental. Hence, last

---

[2] For further information, see R. Schlaifer, *Probability and Statistics for Business Decisions* (New York: McGraw-Hill Book Co., Inc., 1959).

[3] The generalized title for the material in this section is *Markov processes*. In searching mathematical or other quantitative literature, one should look under the title *Markov processes* or *Markov chains*.

Table 14–7

MOST RECENT PURCHASE
(TO)

		A	B	C
PREVIOUS PURCHASE (FROM)	A	0.60	0.20	0.20
	B	0.10	0.70	0.20
	C	0.10	0.10	0.80

week's market shares were 0.3, 0.4, and 0.3 for *A, B,* and *C,* respectively.

Since our average cigarette smoker smokes a package a week, this week we expect all smokers to purchase cigarettes in the fashion shown in Table 14–7. Therefore, of the 300,000 Ace customers, 0.6(300,000), or 180,000, will purchase Ace; 60,000 will purchase Better; and 60,000 will purchase Continental. These purchases for all customers and companies are shown in Table 14–8.

Table 14–8

	Purchase of:		
Purchase by:	A	B	C
A	180,000	60,000	60,000
B	40,000	280,000	80,000
C	30,000	30,000	240,000
Total	250,000	370,000	380,000

The market share is now 25 percent, 37 percent, and 38 percent, respectively, for *A, B,* and *C.* Since this information has predicted sales for the coming week, we may now go on and make a prediction for the week following. Our analysis assumes that the switching behavior shown in Table 14–7 does not change. Now, *A* has only 250,000 customers, 60 percent of whom will repurchase *A.* This is summarized in Table 14–9. It

Table 14–9

	Purchase of:		
Purchase by:	A	B	C
A	150,000	50,000	50,000
B	37,000	259,000	74,000
C	38,000	38,000	304,000
Total	225,000	347,000	428,000

should be noted that the brand share of any brand can be calculated by looking at the percentage of the total market each company possesses. Let S_i represent the last brand share of firm i, and let a_{ij} represent the repurchase probability of the jth brand by customers of the ith brand. Thus, a_{21} is the probability of brand B customers purchasing brand A cigarettes. Let S_i^1 represent the new brand share. Then:

$$S_1^1 = a_{11}S_1 + a_{21}S_2 + a_{31}S_3$$

Checking against the 22.5 percent brand share for A shown in Table 14–7:

$$\begin{aligned} S_1^1 &= 0.6(0.25) + 0.1(0.37) + 0.1(0.38) \\ &= 0.15 + 0.037 + 0.038 \\ &= 0.225 \end{aligned}$$

which checks.

The end may seem near for Ace cigarettes. However, one can observe that the drop in market share was not so great in Table 14–9 as in Table 14–8. Also, as long as B and C have customers, Ace will sell to those dissatisfied customers of B and C. Consequently, one might intuitively feel that at some point the market share will remain the same because losses will be exactly offset by gains. This is just what happens. Let S_i represent the brand share of brand i in period j, and let S_i^1 represent the brand share of brand i in period $j + 1$. The condition that losses will exactly offset gains is called an equilibrium. When this condition occurs, $S_i = S_i^1$. Thus, at equilibrium:

$$S_1^1 = a_{11}S_1 + a_{21}S_2 + a_{31}S_3 = S_1$$

$$S_2^1 = a_{12}S_1 + a_{22}S_2 + a_{32}S_3 = S_2$$

$$S_3^1 = a_{13}S_1 + a_{23}S_2 + a_{33}S_3 = S_3$$

Since a_{ij} is by definition between zero and one (including zero and one), we may subtract S_i from each side to get the following actual system:

(1)
(2)
(3)

$$-0.4S_1 + 0.1S_2 + 0.1S_3 = 0$$
$$0.2S_1 - 0.3S_2 + 0.1S_3 = 0$$
$$0.2S_1 + 0.2S_2 - 0.2S_3 = 0$$

We know further that:

(4)

$$S_1 + S_2 + S_3 = 1.0$$

From our knowledge of matrix algebra, we know that we can evaluate the column vector S when we have the following system $As = b$, by:

$$A^{-1}As = A^{-1}b$$
$$s = A^{-1}b$$

Thus, if we can find the inverse of A, we can evaluate S. Let A include equations 1, 2, and 4 giving:[4]

$$\begin{pmatrix} -0.4 & 0.1 & 0.1 \\ 0.2 & -0.3 & 0.1 \\ 1.0 & 1.0 & 1.0 \end{pmatrix} \begin{pmatrix} S_1 \\ S_2 \\ S_3 \end{pmatrix} = \begin{pmatrix} 0 \\ 0 \\ 1 \end{pmatrix}$$

Using the matrix methods discussed above, we find that at:

$$S_1 = 0.20, \quad S_2 = 0.3, \quad \text{and } S_3 = 0.5$$
$$S_1^1 = S_1, \quad S_2^1 = S_2, \quad \text{and } S_3^1 = S_3$$

which is demonstrated below:

$$0.2(0.6) + 0.3(0.1) + 0.5(0.1) = 0.2$$
$$0.2(0.2) + 0.3(0.7) + 0.5(0.1) = 0.3$$
$$0.2(0.2) + 0.3(0.2) + 0.5(0.8) = 0.5$$

This is the long-run outlook for brand shares under present circumstances.

In view of the expected drop in the market share of Ace brand, the company may wish to take action to rectify the situation. Suppose the company has test-marketed a modified product in a local market and the modified matrix of switching probabilities is as shown in Table 14–10. As

Table 14–10

To:

		A	B	C
	A	0.8	0.1	0.1
FROM:	B	0.1	0.8	0.1
	C	0.1	0.1	0.8

one might have guessed, the equilibrium or long-run market share is one third for all firms. Note that this conclusion is independent of the starting market shares. However, the length of time to attain the equilibrium (long-run) shares does depend upon the starting shares.

This model makes a number of assumptions which delimit its use. It assumes that the switching behavior is permanent. The product change made by Ace may have appeared so successful because the product was new, and the high repurchase probability may be only temporary. The model further assumes that the customers repurchase once and once only during the time period represented. Multiple purchases in a short time period are not likely to distort the results. However, the existence of a different group of customers in each period may so weaken the model as to render it useless. For example, the purchase of automobiles is so infre-

---

[4] Note that the b vector must contain at least one nonzero number in order to derive a solution. Thus, equation 4 and any two others must be included.

quent that market share in the sense meant here is meaningless. In order to get the true market share, the automobile company would have to identify the present car ownership of those customers who plan to purchase in the current period (say a year). Next the automobile company would need to know not only present ownership, but also previous ownership. Since average car life is seven years or so, the switching behavior is almost ancient history and hardly seems useful as a reasonable prediction of present behavior. Thus, this model is most useful for products of high purchase frequency.

The model also assumes either that there is a fixed market potential or that new entrants are distributed according to the then prevailing market share and have the same switching patterns as existing customers.

The switching matrix is an example of a Markov chain, which is a way of representing the probability of any outcome as being dependent upon its position now and the distribution of its possible movements.

VI. TREE DIAGRAMS

Consider the smoker in the brand-share model a piece of protoplasm which chooses a cigarette based upon where it is, and which switches readily. Thus a smoker now smoking *A* may either stay with *A* or go to *B* or go to *C*. Once at *B*, he may stay with *B* or go to *C* or go to *A*. In effect, he should eventually bounce completely around the system. (Not very loyal, is he?) The tree diagram (Figure 14–4) will show what hap-

Figure 14–4

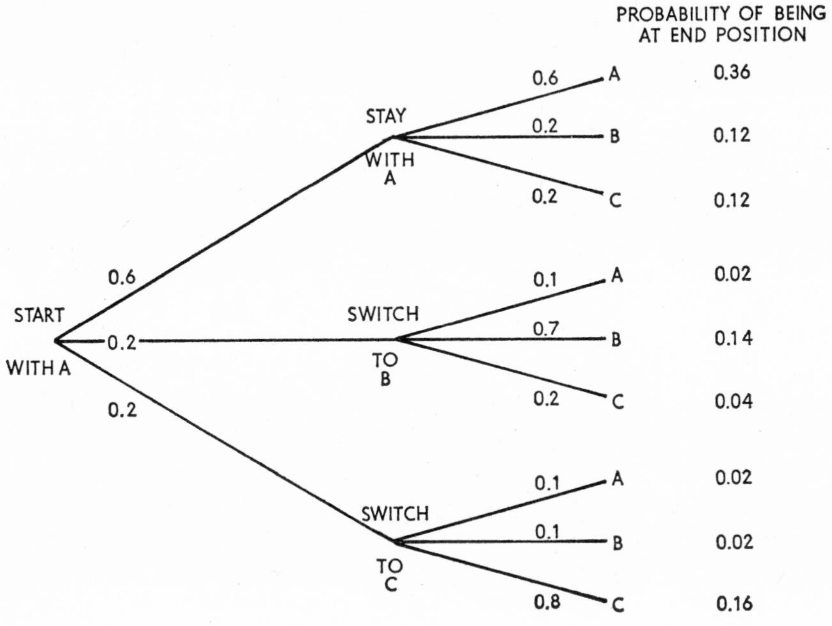
PROBABILITY OF BEING AT END POSITION
START WITH A
0.6
0.2
0.2
STAY WITH A
SWITCH TO B
SWITCH TO C
0.6
A
0.36
0.2
B
0.12
0.2
C
0.12
0.1
A
0.02
0.7
B
0.14
0.2
C
0.04
0.1
A
0.02
0.1
B
0.02
0.8
C
0.16

pens. Thus, at the end of two weeks, he has a 0.36 chance that he is still purchasing *A*, having purchased *A* the first week. Of course, the same kind of diagram may be constructed for someone starting at *B* or *C*.

DISCUSSION TOPICS AND PROBLEMS

1. Describe a specific example of each of the following queuing situations:
a) Fixed arrival, random service time
b) Random arrival, fixed service time
c) Random arrival, random service time
d) Random arrival, neither fixed nor random service time

2. Many queuing models assume that arrivals and service time are independent. Discuss a case in which this is not true. In this case, what is the direction of dependence? Can you cite another case with the direction reversed?

3. In the queuing example(s) cited in this chapter, waiting time could be readily computed. Frequently, it is a customer who is waiting. Discuss the problems of establishing waiting-time costs for customers. Suggest a method for dealing with this problem.

4. A new supermarket is trying to decide how many check-out registers to install. However, none of the people connected with planning the store has had any more training in queuing theory than shown in this chapter. They know that each day has two different customer arrival patterns. During the first five hours of the day, customers arrive randomly. However, a customer arrives every five minutes on the average. During the second five hours of the day, customers arrive randomly. However, one arrives every three minutes on the average. Service time is random but takes 10 minutes on the average, regardless of the time of day. Assume that the daily fixed cost of each check-out counter is $8. This fixed cost includes cost of capital and allocated operating expenses. Further, assume that each check-out operator costs $3 per hour. The company has decided to value customer waiting time at $4 per hour. Assume that check-out operators may be hired for five hours at a time and are readily available. Since the planners do not know how to deal with random arrivals and service time, assume that the average time represents a fixed arrival and service time (ignore any error this assumption causes).

a) How many check-out counters are necessary during the peak period? (Use the $8 fixed cost.) What kind of error is caused by assuming that average arrival and service time is a fixed time?
b) Compare the cost of three and four registers during the peak period.
c) The manager shows you the following table from the *Supermarket Journal*:

SURVEY OF CASH REGISTERS AND AVERAGE DAILY
SALES VOLUME

Sales volume	Average number of operating cash registers
$ 500–$1,499	2.0
1,500–2,499	3.2
2,500–3,499	4.4
3,500–4,499	5.6
4,500 or more	7.2

The manager informs you that the average customer spends $17, and store services 150 customers daily, sales volume is $2,550. Further, he has used the two-point formula for a line and found the following equation: $R = 1.2V + 0.8$, where R is the number of operating cash registers and V is sales volume (in thousands of dollars). He thus concludes that his store requires 3.86 registers and that four is enough.

Evaluate his methodology, logic, and conclusion.

d) Assume that all of the information provided thus far is correct. How many registers would you recommend?

5. You are a manufacturer who has an automatic machine which produces ball bearings. If the machine is set up correctly, it will produce 90 percent acceptable parts. If it is set up partially correct, it will produce 80 percent acceptable parts. If it is set up incorrectly, it will produce 50 percent acceptable parts. Past experience indicates that a correct setup is attained 60 percent of the time; a partially correct setup, 20 percent of the time; and an incorrect setup, 20 percent of the time. The setup event occurs randomly.

a) Compute the revised probability of each setup event if one acceptable part is produced in a sample of one part (show your work in table form, as in the text).

b) Compute the revised probability of each setup event if one acceptable part and one unacceptable part are produced in a sample of two parts (show a table).

6. The Nil Company produces 10 types of widgets on a widget-producing machine. This machine produces some defective items, depending upon the effectiveness of the setup for the production run. For class *A* widgets, experience has shown that the percent defective is either 0.2 or 0.4. The probability of a good setup is 0.7, and the probability of a bad setup is 0.3.

When the machine was first set up, a sample of three items was taken, and no defectives were found in the sample.

a) What are the revised probabilities of a good and a bad setup for class *A* widgets?

b) Assume that the probability of a good setup is 0.5 and the probability of a bad setup is 0.5. Further, assume that when the machine was set up, a sample of one item was taken, and it was defective. The percent defective remains the same as indicated above. What are the revised probabilities of a good and a bad setup for class *A* widgets?

7. The C and B toothpaste companies are faced with the following matrix of transition probabilities:

To:

		B	C
FROM:	B	0.7	0.3
	C	0.4	0.6

a) Assume that company *B* now holds 60 percent of the market. What do you predict its market share will be at the end of this period? At the end of two periods?

b) Set up the equation system to find the equilibrium for this situation.

c) If the matrix of transition probability looks as follows, what is the equilibrium condition?

To:

		B	C
FROM:	B	0.7	0.3
	C	0.0	1.0

d) If the matrix of transition probabilities looks as follows, what is the equilibrium condition?

To:

		B	C
FROM:	B	0.6	0.4
	C	0.4	0.6

8. The Astor Candy Company of Falls Church, Virginia, is in competition with two firms (Basto and Chocko) for the market located in the northeastern part of the United States. A recent independent market survey has shown the following switching behavior for the customers of these candy producers:

		LAST PURCHASE		
		A	B	C
PREVIOUS PURCHASE	A (Astor)	0.7	0.1	0.2
	B (Basto)	0.2	0.5	0.3
	C (Chocko)	0.1	0.3	0.6

Your own marketing research department has done a fairly extensive survey of the market, and it has arrived at a total market figure of 1.5 million boxes of candy. It has also been pointed out to you that the market shares for each company during the last week were as follows: 0.30 for *A*, 0.28 for *B*, and 0.42 for *C*.

Given these data, you are asked to find the long-run outlook for the brand shares (assuming that none of the companies modify their behavior in any way).

9. Assume that the only makes of American cars are Fords and General Motors and that the following matrix of transition probabilities holds:

To:

		GM	Ford
FROM:	GM	0.8	0.2
	Ford	0.4	0.6

Assume that the relevant period of time for the transition probabilities is one year. Further, assume that GM sold 6 million cars last year and Ford sold 4 million.

a) What do you predict will be each company's sales this year? Next year?
b) If the market is expanding so that 100,000 new customers are purchasing cars each year, what is your prediction of sales for each company this year? Next year?
c) If the market is expanding but new customers are purchasing 50 percent GM and 50 percent Ford, what is your prediction of sales for each company this year? Next year?

SELECTED REFERENCES

Ackoff, Russell L., and Sasieni, Maurice W. *Fundamentals of Operations Research.* New York: John Wiley & Sons, Inc., 1968.

Churchman, C. West; Ackoff, Russell L.; and Arnoff, E. Leonard. *Introduction to Operations Research.* New York: John Wiley & Sons, Inc., 1957.

Cox, D. R., and Smith, W. *Queues.* London: Methuen & Co., Ltd.; and New York: John Wiley & Sons, Inc., 1961.

Hillier, Frederick S., and Lieberman, Gerald J. *Introduction to Operations Research.* San Francisco: Holden-Day, Inc., 1967.

Levin, Richard I., and Kirkpatrick, C. A. *Quantitative Approaches to Management.* New York: McGraw-Hill Book Co., Inc., 1965.

Morse, P. M. *Queues, Inventories and Maintenance.* New York: John Wiley & Sons, Inc., 1958.

Prabhu, N. U. *Queues and Inventories.* New York: John Wiley & Sons, Inc., 1965.

Saaty, Thomas L. *Elements of Queuing Theory.* New York: McGraw-Hill Book Co., Inc., 1961.

Schlaifer, R. *Probability and Statistics for Business Decisions.* New York: McGraw-Hill Book Co., Inc., 1959.

15

Models of linear
systems, I[1]

I. INTRODUCTION

In previous chapters, most of the models have been reducible to one equation. The classical economic model and the economic order quantity model begin with separate equations for the various elements. In many instances the final model cannot be reduced to one equation. A common type of situation which cannot be reduced to a single equation is when the measurable objective is to be maximized or minimized subject to certain conditions which impede or constrain that objective. When the constraining conditions are linear and the function describing the objective is linear, the solution may be found using linear programming, which is the subject of this and the next chapter.

The linear programming model is often called an allocation model because it allocates resources to alternative uses. The linear programming model is best discussed after looking at an example. We shall begin by using the graphical method for optimizing the objective and then look at the algebraic process implied by the graphical method. In Chapter 16, we shall look at an analytic method called the simplex algorithm.

The graphical method is not generally used to solve real-world problems but is very effective in providing a conceptual understanding of the solution method. Familiarity with the problems involving only a few variables provides a great deal of insight into what can happen in a more realistic case.

---

[1] This entire chapter is adapted by permission from chapter 2 of Richard I. Levin and Rudolph P. Lamone, *Linear Programming for Management Decisions* (Homewood, Ill.: Richard D. Irwin, Inc., 1969).

II. THE SAMPLE PROBLEM

The graphical method is best demonstrated when applied to a manufacturer who wants to determine the most profitable combination of products to make and sell.

Assume that our manufacturer produces chairs and tables. Production of each product requires processing in two departments, the machinery department (1), and the finishing department (2). Department 1 has up to 32 hours available. Department 2 can handle up to 36 hours of work. Manufacturing one chair requires four hours in department 1 and three hours in department 2. Each table requires two hours in department 1 and six hours in department 2.

Table 15–1

Product	Time to complete each unit	
	Department 1	*Department 2*
Chair...........................	4 hours	3 hours
Table...........................	2 hours	6 hours
Total time available............	32 hours	36 hours

The profit contribution is $4 per chair and $5 per table. The company has no difficulty selling all the chairs and tables it can produce. The manufacturer's problem is to determine the best possible combination of chairs and tables to produce in order to maximize profits. The possible profit, however, is limited by the time constraints in each department, since there are only 32 hours available in department 1 and 36 hours available in department 2. Thus, in choosing the best combination of products, the manufacturer must allocate the limited resources of each department in a way which will yield the highest possible profit.

Let us use X_1 to represent the number of chairs to be produced and X_2 to represent the number of tables to be made. The information used to solve the problem is summarized in Table 15–1.

Formulating the problem

To begin solving the problem, we must restate the information in mathematical form. Our manufacturer realizes a profit contribution of $4 per chair and $5 per table. His objective is to make as much profit as possible on all the tables and chairs produced. The manufacturer can express his objective as an equation:

$$P = 4X_1 + 5X_2$$

where:

$$P = \text{Profit}$$
$$4X_1 = \text{Total profit from sale of chairs}$$
$$5X_2 = \text{Total profit from sale of tables}$$

This equation is referred to as the objective function, which shows the relationship of output to profit.

The manufacturer has two conditions which will limit the extent to which profit can be maximized: (1) the time available in department 1 and (2) the time available in department 2. The time used in producing chairs and tables must not exceed the total time available in the respective departments. In other words, the hours required to make one chair times the number of chairs produced, plus the hours necessary to make one table times the number of tables produced, must be equal to or less than the time available in each department. From the data given in Table 15–1, we can express these constraints as inequalities:

$$4X_1 + 2X_2 \le 32 \text{ (department 1)}$$
$$3X_1 + 6X_2 \le 36 \text{ (department 2)}$$

The first inequality above states that the hours required to produce one chair (four hours) times the number of chairs produced (X_1), plus the hours necessary to make one table (two hours) times the number of tables made (X_2), must be equal to or less than the 32 hours available in department 1. A similar explanation applies to the second inequality.

Since negative production has no meaning, all values of the variables in the solution of any linear programming problem must be positive. This will be true for all linear programming problems. In our problem, this means that the variables must be greater than or equal to zero $(X_1 \ge 0, X_2 \ge 0)$.

The mathematical formulation of the problem can now be summarized:

$$\text{Maximize:} \quad P = 4X_1 + 5X_2$$

subject to these limiting conditions (hereafter referred to as constraints):

$$4X_1 + 2X_2 \le 32$$
$$3X_1 + 6X_2 \le 36$$
$$X_1 \ge 0$$
$$X_2 \ge 0$$

Graphing the constraints

Our next step is to plot the constraints in the problem on a graph, with X_1 shown on the X-axis and X_2 shown on the Y-axis.

Before graphing the first inequality, $4X_1 + 2X_2 \le 32$, let us note that it consists of two parts: an equality part and an inequality part. Thus the possible combinations of chairs and tables that can be processed in department 1 will be all points which satisfy either

$$4X_1 + 2X_2 = 32$$

or

$$4X_1 + 2X_2 < 32$$

Now the equality $4X_1 + 2X_2 = 32$ may be plotted on the graph by first locating its two terminal points and joining these points by a straight line. To locate these points, we proceed as follows:

1. If we assume that all the time available in department 1 is used in processing tables—that production of chairs is zero—16 tables could be made. Accordingly, if we let $X_1 = 0$, then $X_2 = 16$. Proof:

$$4X_1 + 2X_2 = 32$$
$$4(0) + 2X_2 = 32$$
$$X_2 = 16 \text{ tables}$$

Our first point, then, is (0, 16), meaning the production of no chairs and 16 tables.

2. To find the second point, we now assume that all the time available in department 1 is used in making chairs. Under this assumption, we could produce eight chairs. Hence, if we let $X_2 = 0$, then $X_1 = 8$.

Our second point, therefore, is (8, 0), meaning the production of eight chairs and no tables. Locating these two points, (0, 16) and (8, 0), and joining them, gives us the straight line shown in Figure 15–1.

Figure 15–1

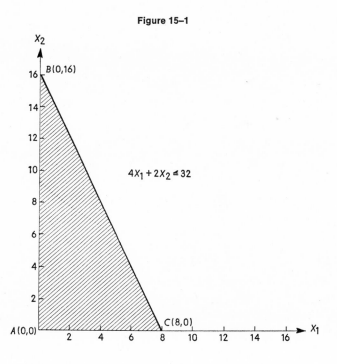

The inequality part of our first constraint, $4X_1 + 2X_2 < 32$, is the entire shaded area to the left of the line BC. Consequently, the graph of the inequality $4X_1 + 2X_2 \leq 32$, including both parts, is the entire area ABC, which lies *on* or *to the left* of the line BC. Note that the condition X_1, $X_2 \geq 0$ is also assumed. To graph the inequality, therefore, we simply graph the equality. The resulting line forms the upper boundary of the area represented by the inequality.

Figure 15–2

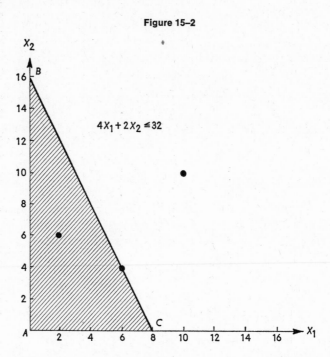

Let us now examine several combinations of chairs and tables shown as points in Figure 15–2. *Any* combination of chairs and tables on line BC will use up all the 32 hours available in department 1. For example, producing six chairs and four tables [point (6, 4) on the graph] will require all of the available 32 hours:

$$6(4 \text{ hours}) + 4(2 \text{ hours}) = 32 \text{ hours}$$

Any point to the left of the line will result in unused capacity; i.e., all the hours will not be used. If, for example, we produced two chairs and six tables [point (2, 6)], the total required time would be 20 hours, which is less than the total available time of 32 hours. Likewise, any point to the right of the line, such as producing 10 chairs and 10 tables, would require 60 hours, which is 28 hours in excess of the total available hours.

Indeed, *any* combination of chairs and tables which lies to the right of the line *BC cannot* be produced without violating the constraint, i.e., exceeding the 32 hours available. We can produce *only* those combinations of chairs and tables which lie within the area *ABC* or on the boundaries of the area *ABC*.

A similar explanation applies to the graph of the second constraint for department 2, represented by the inequality $3X_1 + 6X_2 \leq 36$. Using the same procedure explained above, the terminal points are located as follows:

1. Let $X_1 = 0$. Then:

$$X_2 = 36/6 = 6$$

First point: (0, 6)

2. Let $X_2 = 0$. Then:

$$X_1 = 36/3 = 12$$

Second point: (12, 0)

Joining these two points gives the line *EF* in Figure 15–3, representing all combinations of chairs and tables which use up exactly 36 hours, i.e.,

$$3X_1 + 6X_2 = 36$$

The area *AEF* contains *all* possible combinations which use less than or including the 36 hours available ($3X_1 + 6X_2 \leq 36$). Thus, any point—any

Table 15–3

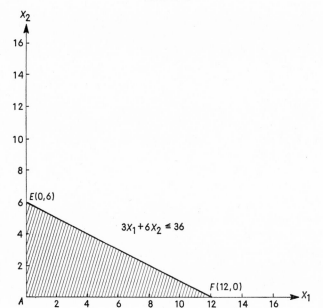

combination of chairs and tables falling within the area *AEF*—will satisfy the time restriction in department 2. Conversely, any point outside the shaded area will violate the time restriction in department 2.

In graphing the two constraints, we have found the combinations of chairs and tables which may be processed in each department without violating the time restrictions. However, in order to complete a chair or table, both departments must be used. The next step, then, is to find an area which is common to both areas described by the separate graphs for

Figure 15–4

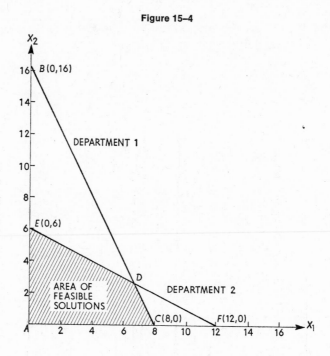

each department so that the best combination of completed chairs and tables will not exceed the available time in either department. To find this common area, we simply plot the two original inequalities (see Figures 15–1 and 15–3) on the same X_1- and X_2-axes. This we have done in Figure 15–4. The area that does not exceed the time constraints in either department—the shaded area *AEDC* in Figure 15–4—contains all possible combinations of chairs and tables satisfying both inequalities together. This area is referred to as the area of feasible solutions because it never violates the inequalities when taken together.

To illustrate, three combinations have been located as points in Figure 15–5.

Figure 15–5

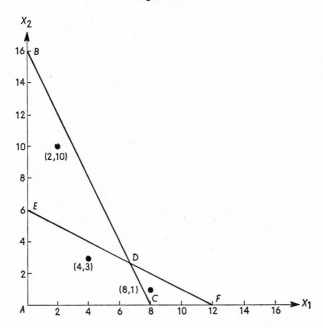

Example 1.   Four chairs and three tables:

Department 1: $4X_1 + 2X_2 \leq 32$ hours available
$4(4) + 2(3) = 22$ hours required

Department 2: $3X_1 + 6X_2 \leq 36$ hours available
$3(4) + 6(3) = 30$ hours required

The time required to make four chairs and three tables falls within the time available in both departments. The reader may verify that any point within the common area *AEDC*, referred to as the area of feasible solutions, will use less than or up to the time available in both departments.

Example 2. Two chairs and 10 tables:

Department 1: $4X_1 + 2X_2 \leq 32$ hours available
$4(2) + 2(10) = 28$ hours required

Department 2: $3X_1 + 6X_2 \leq 36$ hours available
$3(2) + 6(10) = 66$ hours required

In the above example, we find that the time required to make 2 chairs and 10 tables falls within the time available in department 1 but *exceeds* the time available in department 2. Thus, this combination is not possible, since it falls outside the area of feasible solutions.

Example 3. Eight chairs and one table:

Department 1 : $4X_1 + 2X_2 \leq 32$ hours available
$4(8) + 2(1) = 34$ hours required
Department 2 : $3X_1 + 6X_2 \leq 36$ hours available
$3(8) + 6(1) = 30$ hours required

In this example the time required to make eight chairs and one table falls within the time available in department 2 but *exceeds* the time available in department 1. Accordingly, it would be impossible to produce this combination, given the present time constraints.

Testing the corner points of the feasible solutions area

Our goal is to choose that combination of chairs and tables which will maximize profit, given the time restrictions in each department. For reasons to be explained later, the optimum combination in the graphical solution to *any* linear programming problem will be found at one of the corner points of the area of feasible solutions; in our problem, this is the area *AEDC*. We already have found three of the four corner points (see Figure 15–4); they are:

$$A............(0, 0)$$
$$E............(0, 6)$$
$$C............(8, 0)$$

How can we locate point *D?* Reading its location from a precisely drawn graph is one possibility. Another method is to solve simultaneously the equations of the two lines which intersect at point *D,* the only point common to both equations. To solve these two equations:

$$4X_1 + 2X_2 = 32$$
$$3X_1 + 6X_2 = 36$$

we proceed as follows:

1. Multiply the first equation by -3 and add the second equation to it:

$$-3(4X_1 + 2X_2 = 32) = -12X_1 - 6X_2 = -96$$
$$3X_1 + 6X_2 = 36$$

$$-9X_1 = -60$$
$$X_1 = 60/9 = 6\tfrac{2}{3}$$

2. Now, substitute $6\tfrac{2}{3}$ for X_1 in the second equation:

$$3X_1 + 6X_2 = 36$$
$$20 + 6X_2 = 36$$
$$6X_2 = 16$$
$$X_2 = 2\tfrac{2}{3}$$

Point *D* thus is $(6\tfrac{2}{3}, 2\tfrac{2}{3})$.

We can now test the four corner points of the area of feasible solutions by substituting the values of each point in the objective function $(P = 4X_1 + 5X_2)$:

Point A $(0, 0)$: $4(0) + 5(0) = \$ 0$
Point E $(0, 6)$: $4(0) + 5(6) = 30$
Point C $(8, 0)$: $4(8) + 5(0) = 32$
Point D $(6\tfrac{2}{3}, 2\tfrac{2}{3})$: $4(6\tfrac{2}{3}) + 5(2\tfrac{2}{3}) = 40$

The optimum combination, $6\tfrac{2}{3}$ chairs and $2\tfrac{2}{3}$ tables, located at point D, yields a maximum profit of \$40. Substituting $6\tfrac{2}{3}$ for X_1 and $2\tfrac{2}{3}$ for X_2 in the constraints, we find that the optimum solution uses up the time available in each department:

Department 1: $4X_1 + 2X_2 \leq 32$ hours available
$4(6\tfrac{2}{3}) + 2(2\tfrac{2}{3}) = 32$ hours required
Department 2: $3X_1 + 6X_2 \leq 36$ hours available
$3(6\tfrac{2}{3}) + 6(2\tfrac{2}{3}) = 36$ hours required

As will be shown in another section, there may be cases in which the optimum solution will result in unused capacity.

Exchange rates

The fact that the candidates for the maximum profit condition are found at the corner points can be understood with the concept of exchange rates. Let us arbitrarily offer the point $X_1 = 4$, $X_2 = 2$ as a candidate for the maximum profit condition. Since we earlier showed that the point $X_1 = 4$, $X_2 = 3$ did not violate the constraints, we know this point is an acceptable candidate. It is shown in Figure 15–6 as point G.

Figure 15–6

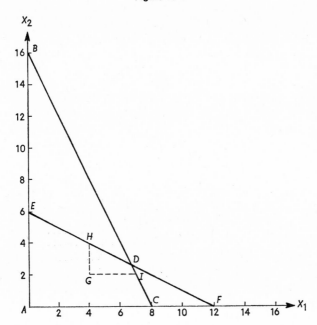

At point G, profit is $4(4) + 5(2) = \$26$. However, the reader can easily see that more tables could be produced up to point H. Since each table produced in addition to the present two yields $5 to profit and overhead, it is desirable to increase the production of tables to the maximum. The factor which limits the production of tables is the 36 hours of available capacity in department 2; i.e., $3X_1 + 6X_2 \leq 36$. In this case, we shall use all of the available capacity, thus transforming the inequality to an equality: $3X_1 + 6X_2 = 36$. Since we are producing four chairs, the maximum number of tables is $3(4) + 6X_2 = 36$ and $X_2 = 4$. The resulting profit is $4(4) + 5(4) = \$36$, or an increase of $10 over point G.

Since it is desirable to increase the production of tables while holding the production of chairs constant, a like analysis will conclude that it is also desirable to increase the production of chairs while holding the production of tables constant. This is shown by point I in Figure 15–6. The resulting production of chairs is 7 chairs, and profit is then $38. In this instance the latter move yields a higher profit. However, the analysis clearly demonstrates that regardless of the choice of points in the area of feasible solutions, it is always desirable to move to the outer boundaries of the feasible solutions area. In other words, we have narrowed the candidates for the optimum solution to the lines ED and DC in Figure 15–6.

We shall now demonstrate that the point H (or I) is not the optimum profit point, because a movement either to the right or to the left will increase profits.[2] If we are at point H in Figure 15–6, what happens to profits if we reduce the production of chairs by one unit? Such a reduction represents a shift of point H upward and to the left. The original and modified point H can be expressed:

Original: $3(X_1) + 6(X_2) = 36$, where $X_1 = 4$, $X_2 = 4$
Modified: $3(X_1) + 6(X_2) = 36$, where $X_1 = 3$, X_2 is unknown

Solving for X_2, we find:

$$3(3) + 6X_2 = 36$$
$$X_2 = 4\tfrac{1}{2}$$

Thus, when we reduce the production of X_1 by one unit, we can increase the production of X_2 by one-half unit. This is to be expected because the three hours required to process one unit of X_1 is one half of the six hours required to process one unit of X_2.

We can now investigate the effect of this change in production mix on profits by remembering that the profit contribution is $4 for X_1 and $5 for X_2. The net effect of giving up one chair to make one-half table is:

Profit gained by making one-half table: $\tfrac{1}{2}(\$5)$	$2.50
Profit lost by giving up one chair: $1(\$4)$	$4.00
Net change in profit (gain minus loss)	$-\$1.50$

[2] In rare instances, profits will neither increase or decrease. This condition will be discussed later.

If the exchange rate is the same for all of line *EF*, it is desirable to exchange tables for chairs (i.e., the opposite direction). Since we know that the line *EF* is linear and that it has a constant slope, we know the exchange is proportional throughout the line. However, if we make the exchange so that the point is found on line *EF* but to the right of point *D*, we shall be violating the constraints of department 1. Accordingly, we can only exchange to point *D*, which we earlier said was the maximum. A similar analysis at point *I* would force us to move to point *D*.

The purpose of this discussion is to prove that because of the existence of desirable or undesirable exchange rates, the optimum solution cannot exist on the line segment but must exist at a corner point. However, all three corner points *E*, *D*, and *C* are valid candidates for the optimum.

Isoprofit lines

Let us now examine another method of demonstrating why the most profitable combination of chairs and tables occurs at corner point *D*. To do this, we must plot the objective function ($P = 4X_1 + 5X_2$) directly on the graph of the feasible solutions area.

In order to graph the objective function, we first let profit equal some dollar figure that we can attain without violating a restriction. We have arbitrarily chosen to let profit equal \$20, a profit easily attainable. Then the objective function is $20 = 4X_1 + 5X_2$. We now locate the two terminal points. When $X_1 = 0$:

$$20 = 4(0) + 5X_2$$
$$X_2 = 4$$

and when $X_2 = 0$:

$$20 = 4X_1 + 5(0)$$
$$X_1 = 5$$

Joining these two points gives the line shown in Figure 15–7.

The objective function ($20 = 4X_1 + 5X_2$) graphed in Figure 15–7 represents all the possible combinations of chairs and tables which would yield a total profit of \$20 and is called an isoprofit. For example, the point ($2\frac{1}{2}$, 2) is located on this line:

$$4(2\frac{1}{2}) + 5(2) = 20$$

Suppose we graph another isoprofit line representing all combinations of chairs and tables which would result in a profit of \$35. In other words, we shall graph a line represented by the profit equation, $35 = 4X_1 + 5X_2$. This line is illustrated in Figure 15–8, together with the line of the previous profit equation, $20 = 4X_1 + 5X_2$.

Let us examine the significance of these parallel profit lines. The second profit line ($35 = 4X_1 + 5X_2$) represents all combinations which would

Figure 15–7

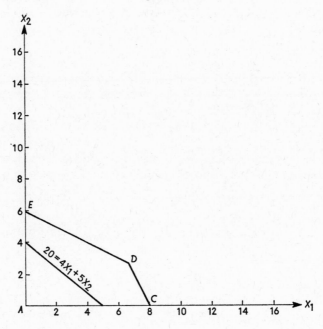

Figure 15–8

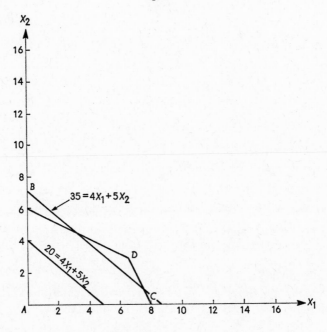

yield a $35 profit. The second profit line, then, generates more profit than the first line ($35 versus $20). However, if we produce all X_2:

$$35 = 4(0) + 5X_2$$
$$X_2 = 7$$

But as shown in Figure 15–4, this violates the department 2 constraint. If we produce $5X_2$, then $X_1 = 2.5$, and no constraints are violated. The second line is parallel to the first line, but farther from the origin, point A $(0, 0)$. Thus, as long as no constraints are violated, it is preferable to the

Figure 15–9

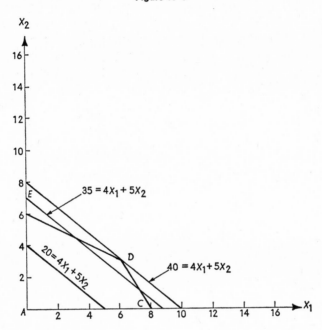

first line. In order to maximize profit, we need to find a profit line which is as far as possible from the original but has at least one point in common with the area of feasible solutions. This line, represented by the profit equation $40 = 4X_1 + 5X_2$, is shown in Figure 15–9, together with the first two profit lines.

III. SOME ADDITIONAL CONSIDERATIONS

Do not be misled into believing that the intersection of department 1 and department 2 (point D) is always the optimum. The optimum is dependent upon the nature of the objective function.

Alternate optima

By delineating the feasible solutions area, we have solved the manufacturer's problem. What effect would a change in the profit contribution of each product have on the feasible solutions area? Since the objective function played no part in defining the area of feasible solutions, the answer is that a change in the objective function will have no effect on the feasible solutions area. It may, however, result in a new optimum combination of chairs and tables.

For example, suppose the profit contribution is $10 per chair and $5 per table. In this case the profit at each corner point may be calculated as follows:

$$
\begin{array}{lll}
\text{Point } A\ (0,0): & 10(0) + 5(0) = & \$\ 0 \\
\text{Point } E\ (0,6): & 10(0) + 5(6) = & 30 \\
\text{Point } C\ (8,0): & 10(8) + 5(0) = & 80 \\
\text{Point } D\ (6\tfrac{2}{3}, 2\tfrac{2}{3}): & 10(6\tfrac{2}{3}) + 5(2\tfrac{2}{3}) = & 80
\end{array}
$$

We now have *two* different combinations of chairs and tables that yield a maximum profit of $80, points D and C. In fact, if we plot the new objective function on the graph of the original feasible solutions area, we shall find that there are not two but many different combinations of chairs and tables which yield the *same* maximum profit; hence the term *alternate optima*. Using the same procedure previously explained, we have plotted two profit lines in Figure 15–10.

Figure 15–10

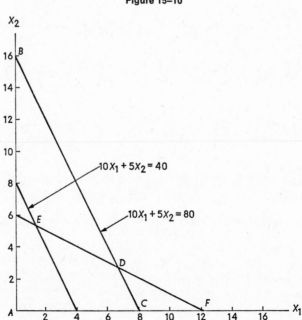

Note that the profit lines are parallel to the line DC, which forms part of the boundary of the feasible solutions area. Hence, as we shift the profit line away from the origin, it will coincide with the line segment DC. Each point on this line DC, including the corner points D and C, represents a different combination of chairs and tables which can be produced giving the same profit of $80. If we were to shift the second profit line further from the origin, there would be no point in common with the area of feasible solutions.

Previously, we stated that the optimum solution to *any* linear programming problem would be found at one of the corner points of the feasible solutions area. In some cases, as the example above shows, the solution may consist of a whole line segment; but even then, there is at least one corner point solution, i.e., points D and C.

Optimum solution with unused capacity

In the solution to the sample problem, we used all of the hours available in each department. However, the desirability of point D (production of $6\frac{2}{3}$ chairs and $2\frac{2}{3}$ tables) results because of the nature of the objective function and not because this is the only combination which uses all available capacity. If the objective function is:

$$P = 12X_1 + 5X_2$$

then, testing each corner point:

At $X_1 = 8$, $X_2 = 0$ $P = 12(8) + 5(0) = 96$
At $X_1 = 0$, $X_2 = 6$ $P = 12(0) + 5(6) = 30$
At $X_1 = 6\frac{2}{3}$, $X_2 = 2\frac{2}{3}$ $P = 12(6\frac{2}{3}) + 5(2\frac{2}{3}) = 93.33$

Thus the optimum occurs when eight chairs and no tables are produced. In department 2, only 24 of the 36 hours are used because it takes 3 hours to process each of the eight units, for a total of 24 hours. This means that department 2 is idle 12 hours. However, full utilization of department 2 will result in lower profits.

IV. ASSUMPTIONS OF THE LINEAR PROGRAM MODEL

Linearity in the objective function

As indicated earlier, this model is a linear representation of the environment. Linearity in the objective function means that each chair or table sold contributes $4 and $5, respectively, to overhead and profit. This means that all units offered for sale are sold; and within the relevant range the demand curve is horizontal, as shown in Figure 15–11. The relevant

Figure 15–11

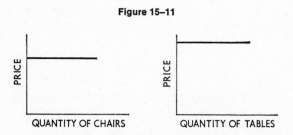

range is from zero to eight chairs and zero to six tables. This relevant range results from the values assigned the constraints rather than being a preestablished figure. The demand restriction can be relaxed by segmenting the demand curves in the fashion illustrated in the last section of Chapter 12. Once segmented, a number of alternative situations can be compared. For example, assume that when more than four chairs are produced, the profit contribution on all chairs (including the first four) drops to $3. Then we have two problems:

1. Maximize: $P = 4X_1 + 5X_2$
   Subject to: $X_1 \leq 4$
   $$4X_1 + 2X_2 \leq 32$$
   $$3X_1 + 6X_2 \leq 36$$
2. Maximize: $P = 3X_1 + 5X_2$
   Subject to: $X_1 > 4$
   $$4X_1 + 2X_2 \leq 32$$
   $$3X_1 + 6X_2 \leq 36$$

Given these two problems, we maximize P for each and choose the highest value of P. Problem 2 can be simplified by recognizing that at least four chairs must be made before any decision problem exists. Hence the profitability on those four chairs may be added to the objective function as a constant and the capacity in each department reduced by the time required to produce those four chairs, thus reducing the available capacity. The system for problem 2 is then:

Maximize: $P = 3X_3 + 5X_2 + 12$
Subject to: $4X_3 + 2X_2 \leq 16$
$$3X_3 + 6X_2 \leq 24$$

It should be remembered that $X_1 = X_3 + 4$ and $X_3 > 0$. The reader is now in a position to solve this problem.

The linearity of the objective function also implies that production costs are linear. For example, assume that a chair sells for $24 and that costs attributable to the chair include labor of $10 per chair and materials of $10 per chair—thus the conclusion that the contribution is $4. Likewise, the table might sell for $30, with material costing $15 per table and labor $10 per table. If the material is subject to a quantity discount, we may need to segment the problem as suggested above.

Products are identified by processing and raw material requirements

The model shown assumes that all products must be processed in all departments. Although this is not an assumption of the linear programming model, we must recognize that the mathematical setup must be different when processing is not required in all departments. For example, assume that tables may be made by processing in department 1 and department 2, as shown, or they may be processed in department 2 only. If processed in department 2, they require nine hours and contribute \$3 to profit and overhead. This can be considered a different product, resulting in the following system:

$$\text{Maximize:} \quad P = 4X_1 + 5X_2 + 3X_3$$
$$\text{Subject to:} \quad 4X_1 + 2X_2 + 0X_3 \leq 32$$
$$3X_1 + 6X_2 + 9X_3 \leq 36$$

The graphical method just shown is not powerful enough to yield an answer, but the simplex method shown in the next chapter will give a solution to this problem.

This discussion demonstrates that it is not the characteristics of the final product but the inputs which distinguish one product from another.

Linearity in the constraints

Linearity in the constraints implies that the amount of time required to process each product is the same regardless of the number processed. Thus, it takes four hours to process a chair in department 1, regardless of whether it is the first or the sixth chair, or regardless of whether the department processes only chairs or both chairs and tables. It is possible that fatigue or boredom may result in a longer processing time for later chairs. Conversely, a learning curve may exist, so that later chairs are processed faster. In the sample problem the assumption of linearity seems reasonable. However, the segmentation process may be used if non-linearities exist. When more than three chairs are processed in department 1, efficiency increases so that it takes only $3\frac{1}{2}$ hours to produce all chairs over three. This saves \$1 on labor costs. Hence, up to three, the chairs' contribution is \$4; but over three, it is \$5. The following two systems result:

$$1. \quad \text{Maximize:} \quad P = 4X_1 + 5X_2$$
$$\text{Subject to:} \quad X_1 \leq 3$$
$$4X_1 + 2X_2 \leq 32$$
$$3X_1 + 6X_2 \leq 36$$
$$2. \quad \text{Maximize:} \quad P = 5X_3 + 5X_2 + 12$$
$$\text{Subject to:} \quad 3.5X_3 + 2X_2 \leq 20$$
$$3X_3 + 6X_2 \leq 27$$

It should be remembered that $X_1 = X_3 + 3$. Accordingly, system 2 merely recognizes the conditions which exist when more than three chairs are produced. Therefore, when $X_1 \leq 3$, $X_3 \leq 0$, and the conditions in system 2 are violated and system 1 is in operation. When $X_1 \succ 3$, the conditions of system 2 are recognized, because the three units already produced generate $12 profit but use:

$$3 \times 4 = 12 \text{ hours of capacity in department 1}$$

and

$$3 \times 3 = 9 \text{ hours of capacity in department 2}$$

Assumption of static time period

The linear programming model operates within a specified length of time. This may ignore the impact of past and future decisions except as the constraints may be capable of reflecting these considerations. For example, the availability of raw materials may be included as a constraint. Consequently, if only raw materials for six chairs are on hand, a third constraint, $X_1 \leq 6$, may be added. The time limitation places a more severe restriction on future decisions because it tells us nothing about what to do to prepare for the future.

Assumptions of certainty

The linear programming model also assumes that the relationships occur with certainty. Thus, it assumes that it takes four hours to process each chair in department 1, not an average of four hours. Such an assumption is reasonable if the variance in processing times is slight. Finally, some obvious assumptions are: (1) The system includes all constraints and relevant resources, (2) the measurable objective contributes to the overall objective, and (3) the decision can be implemented.

Requirements of the linear programming model

Conditions or requirements which must exist for the linear programming model to be applicable are:

1. There must be a measurable objective to be maximized or minimized which relates the decision variable to the objective and constraints. Hence, in the sample problem, we are maximizing contribution to overhead and profit as a function of the units produced and the contribution of each unit produced. Implied as a part of this requirement is the presence of alternative courses of action, one of which will achieve the objective.

2. Resources must be limited.

3. The variables in the problem must be interrelated. Accordingly, in

the example, both departments process both goods. At the least, it must be possible to use one department to process two goods.

4. It must be possible to express the objective, limitations, and conditions as a system of linear equations (including inequalities).

V. THE VALUE OF ADDED CAPACITY

Since the available capacity in each department is under the control of management, it is useful to know the value of added capacity. Suppose

Figure 15–12

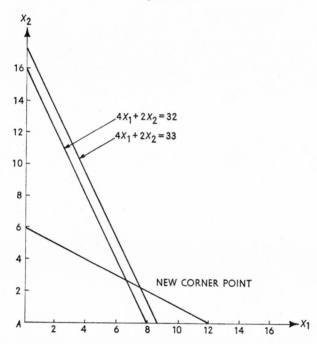

that management adds one hour of capacity to department 1. The resulting area of feasible solutions is increased to the line which represents:

$$4X_1 + 2X_2 = 33$$

as shown in Figure 15–12. There are now two new corner points. One is production of all X_1, or $8\frac{1}{4}$ chairs, at a profit of $4(8\frac{1}{4}) = \$33$, which is less than \$40 and thus not the optimum production. The other new corner point is production of both X_1 and X_2, which is the intersection of:

(1) $4X_1 + 2X_2 = 33$
(2) $3X_1 + 6X_2 = 36$

Multiplying equation (1) by 3 and subtracting equation (2) from that figure gives:

$$12X_1 + 6X_2 = 99$$
$$-3X_1 - 6X_2 = -36$$
$$9X_1 = 63$$
$$X_1 = 7$$

Substituting in equation (1):

$$4(7) + 2X_2 = 33$$
$$2X_2 = 33 - 28$$
$$2X_2 = 5$$
$$X_2 = 2\frac{1}{2}$$

Therefore, at the intersecting point, $X_1 = 7$ and $X_2 = 2\frac{1}{2}$. At this point, profit is:

$$4(7) + 5(2.5) = 28 + 12.50 = 40.50$$

We see that the addition of one unit of capacity increases profit from $40 to $40.50, or by 50 cents. This is the "shadow price" for capacity in department 1. It places a value on the capacity. If the *overhead* cost per period of the next unit of capacity is less than 50 cents, it pays to add that unit of capacity. Obviously, the decision with respect to added capacity must hinge upon conditions in the future as well as conditions now. The 50-cent value is applicable only to present conditions. Also, note that 50 cents is not the value of all subsequent added hours of capacity. If 28 units were added to department 1, the line representing the department 1 restriction would be to the right of the line representing the department 2 restriction, as shown in Figure 15–13. In this case, department 2 is the only limiting factor; consequently, additional capacity in department 1 contributes nothing and has no shadow price. Thus the shadow price is applicable only over a range.

It is left as an exercise for the reader to verify that the shadow price in department 2 is approximately 67 cents.

VI. THE CASE WITH MORE THAN TWO CONSTRAINTS

In the problem thus far, we have had two products and two restrictions. Suppose that we have three restrictions and that the problem can be stated as follows:

Maximize: $P = 4X_1 + 5X_2$
Subject to: $4X_1 + 2X_2 \leq 32$
$$3X_1 + 6X_2 \leq 36$$
$$X_1 + X_2 \leq 8\frac{1}{2}$$

This is graphed in Figure 15–14. The third restriction is shown by the line GH, which eliminates the point D from the area of feasible solutions

Figure 15–13

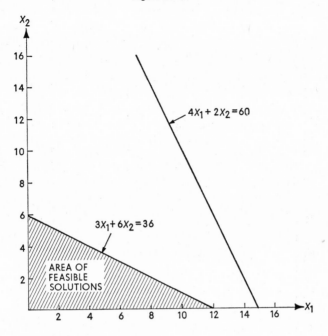

Figure 15–14

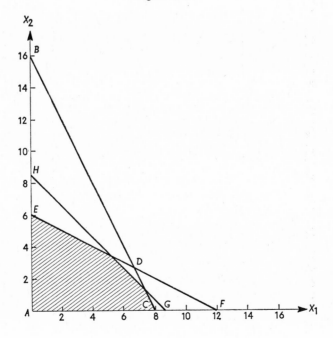

because it violates the constraint represented by this restriction. The result is that we have four candidates for an optimal solution, rather than three.

Assume that the third restriction is $X_1 + X_2 \leq 10$, as shown in Figure 15–15. In this case the restriction falls outside the area of feasible solutions. Hence the original set of feasible solutions is not changed, and the optimum solution is the same as before—point D. If the third restriction were a production department like the other restrictions, the manufacturer would have more than enough time in department 3 to make any of the

Figure 15–15

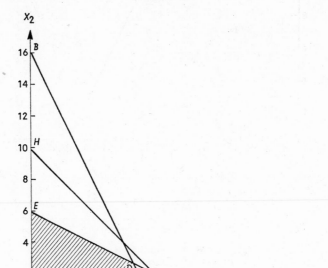

possible combinations in the previously identified area of feasible solutions. In this case, departments 1 and 2 are the limiting departments. Accordingly, the third restraint is redundant (i.e., not functioning as a true constraint) and can be completely ignored.

It is possible that this constraint represents a limitation completely different from the previous ones. If the products being manufactured each required one unit of a key component, the maximum number which could be produced would be limited by the inventory of components. The third restriction might then represent an inventory restriction rather than a capacity restriction.

VII. A MINIMIZATION PROBLEM

We turn now to a different type of problem where the objective is to *minimize* costs subject to certain restraints. Suppose an agricultural feed company has developed a new chicken feed consisting of two ingredients, A and B, which cost 32 cents and 36 cents per pound, respectively. Each pound of ingredient A contains four units of protein and two units of vitamins. Each pound of ingredient B contains three units of protein and six units of vitamins. Each bag of the chicken feed should contain at least four units of protein and five units of vitamins. The company's problem is to find the best combination of ingredients A and B which will meet the minimum requirements of protein and vitamins at the least cost. The problem information is summarized in Table 15–2.

Table 15–2

Nutrients (units)	Ingredients A (32 cents per pound)	B (36 cents per pound)	Minimum requirements
Protein.......................4		3	4 units
Vitamins......................2		6	5 units

To solve this minimization problem, we follow the same procedure used in solving the maximization problem: First, we express the problem in mathematical form. Suppose we let Y_1 equal the number of pounds of ingredient A, and Y_2 the number of pounds of ingredient B. Given the cost per pound for each ingredient, the objective function is:

$$\text{Minimize cost:} \quad C = 0.32Y_1 + 0.36Y_2$$

There are two contraints representing the minimum requirements for each nutrient:

$$4Y_1 + 3Y_2 \geq 4 \text{ (protein)}$$
$$2Y_1 + 6Y_2 \geq 5 \text{ (vitamins)}$$

Note that these constraints represent a different type of inequality ($\geqq$). This type of inequality is used to represent minimum requirements; for example, in this problem, each nutrient must be *at least* a certain value.

The first constraint states that the number of units of protein (four) per pound in ingredient A times the number of pounds (Y_1) of ingredient A, plus the units of protein per pound (three) in ingredient B times the number of pounds (Y_2) of ingredient B, must be greater than or equal to four units of protein. A similar explanation applies to the second constraint.

The next step is to graph the two constraints, using the procedure previously explained. In Figure 15–16, we have graphed the first constraint.

Note that all combinations of X_1 and X_2 which satisfy this type of inequality ($\geqq$) fall on or to the *right* of the line in Figure 15–16. This type of inequality represents a lower boundary for the feasible solutions. Compare this to the "less than or equal to" type which provides the upper boundary for the feasible solutions in a given constraint.

Both constraints are shown in Figure 15–17.

Figure 15–16

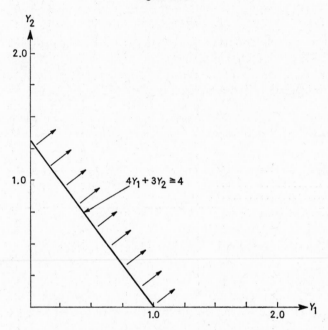

The area of feasible solutions consists of all points falling on and to the right of the line segments AB and BC.

Finally, to find the least-cost combination, we test each corner point of the feasible solutions area. The points for B and C given in Figure 15–17 were obtained by solving simultaneously the equations of the lines which intersect at those points. Given the objective function:

$$C = .32Y_1 + .36Y_2$$

we can find the least-cost combination:

Point A $(0, \frac{4}{3})$: $0.32(0) + 0.36(\frac{4}{3}) = 0.48$
Point B $(\frac{1}{2}, \frac{2}{3})$: $0.32(\frac{1}{2}) + \frac{2}{3}(36) = 0.40$
Point C $(2\frac{1}{2}, 0)$: $0.32(2\frac{1}{2}) + 0.36(0) = 0.80$

The optimum solution is at point ($\frac{1}{2}$, $\frac{2}{3}$). This means that the specified requirement of protein and vitamins will be met at a minimum cost of

Figure 15–17

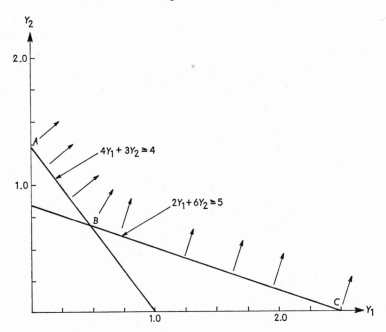

40 cents if we mix one-half pound of ingredient *A* (Y_1) and two thirds of a pound of ingredient *B* (Y_2). Thus, each bag of chicken feed will weigh a total of $1\frac{1}{6}$ pounds. The cost per pound will be 34.5 cents, i.e., $\frac{7}{6}x = 0.40$, where *x* is the cost per pound.

Checking, we find that the minimum requirements have been met:

$$4Y_1 + 3Y_2 \geq 4$$
$$4(\tfrac{1}{2}) + 3(\tfrac{2}{3}) = 4$$
$$2Y_1 + 6Y_2 \geq 5$$
$$2(\tfrac{1}{2}) + 6(\tfrac{2}{3}) = 5$$

Note that this combination provides exactly the minimum requirements. However, if the cost of ingredient *B* had been 18 cents, four thirds of ingredient *B* would have minimized the cost. In this case, we would just fill the requirements for proteins (but would exceed the requirements for vitamins):

$$4Y_1 + 3Y_2 \geq 4$$
$$4(0) + 3(\tfrac{4}{3}) = 4$$
$$2Y_1 + 6Y_2 \geq 5$$
$$2(0) + 6(\tfrac{4}{3}) = 8$$

VIII. OTHER GRAPHICAL INTERPRETATIONS

Let us now examine a problem which has both types of inequalities ($\leq$ and $\geq$). The problem is:

$$\text{Maximize:} \quad P = 4X_1 + 3X_2$$
$$\text{Subject to:} \quad (1) \ 2X_1 + 4X_2 \leq 30$$
$$(2) \ 4X_1 + 2X_2 \leq 30$$
$$(3) \ 2X_1 + 3X_2 \geq 18$$

The three constraints are graphed in Figure 15–18.

The shaded area in Figure 15–18 represents the area of feasible solutions, with the optimum solution at point D (5, 5). Note that the lower boundary of the feasible solutions area is represented by the "greater than or equal to" type of inequality. Any point below line segment BA is not a feasible solution. Similarly, the upper boundary of the area of feasible solutions is represented by the "less than or equal to" type. Any point above line segments CD and DA is not a feasible solution. Thus the two types of inequalities are often referred to as lower bound ($\geq$) and upper bound ($\leq$) constraints.

If one of the constraints in a problem is represented by an equality, the optimum solution must lie *on it* rather than *on or to one side of it*. For example, if we add to the above problem the constraint $X_1 + X_2 = 8$, we

Figure 15–18

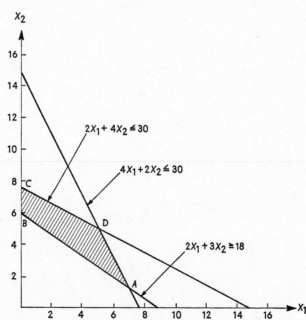

Figure 15–19

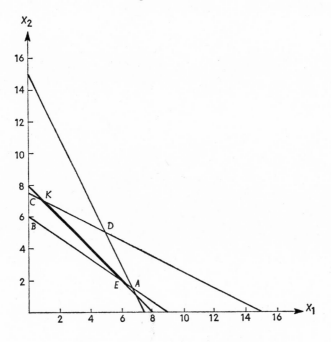

Figure 15–20

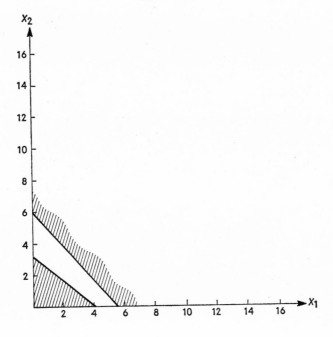

get the new feasible solution area, shown in Figure 15–19. In this case the area of feasible solutions has been reduced to the heavy portion *KE* on the line for the new constraint, the optimum solution being at point (6, 2).

In some cases, there is no feasible solutions area. That is, there are no points that satisfy all of the constraints; hence, no feasible solutions are possible. For example, if we graph the following constraints:

$$3X_1 + 4X_2 \leq 12$$
$$6X_1 + 5X_2 \geq 30$$

we get the configuration of Figure 15–20, where there is no area common to both constraints and therefore no area of feasible solutions.

DISCUSSION TOPICS AND PROBLEMS

1. The XYX Company produces 2 products, both of which are record players. Each record player contains the same turntable and speaker which are both purchased as components (i.e., the company does not make them). The firm must assemble the products and then prepare them for shipping. Assembly of record player 1 takes 20 minutes, and assembly of record player 2 takes 12 minutes. Shipping preparation of record player 1 takes four minutes, and shipping preparation of record player 2 takes five minutes. Record player 1 sells for $50, and record player 2 sells for $55. The turntable costs $12; the speaker, $18. Assembly and shipping preparation time costs $12 per hour for direct labor. The company has 40 hours of assembly time and 10 hours of shipping time available. There are 150 turntables and 130 speakers in stock, and the firm will not receive any more until after this production period.

a) Set up all of the equations to represent the linear programming problem.
b) Can you identify a nonrelevant condition? If so, what would you do about it in finding a solution to this problem?
c) Find out how many units of good 1 and good 2 should be produced.
d) This company has conducted additional demand studies and has found that the return per unit of good 1 drops 80 cents when more than 20 units are placed on the market. How would you proceed to handle this problem?

2. A plant produces two goods. Good 1 uses one unit of process *A*, three units of process *B*, and one unit of process *C*. Good 2 uses four units of process *A*, one unit of process *B*, and one unit of process *C*. Available units for each process are as follows: *A*, 240; *B*, 210; and *C*, 90.

Good 1 contributes $2 to overhead and profits, and good 2 contributes $5 to overhead and profits.

a) Find out how many units of good 1 and good 2 should be produced.
b) This company has conducted additional demand studies and has found that the return per unit of good 1 drops 50 cents when more than 20 units are placed on the market. How would you proceed to handle this problem?

3. The driver of a bakery goods delivery truck can determine the type and

quantity of the bakery products he carries on his truck, within certain limits. The products are divided into two categories, bread and pastry. For each loaf of bread the driver sells, he receives 3 cents; and for each package of pastry, he receives 5 cents. He is always able to sell all of the products he carries; but his route is so long that he can make only one trip per day. Certain customers prefer specified minimum quantities of bread and pastry each day. Because of this, the driver must carry at least 150 loaves of bread and 80 packages of pastry. The delivery truck has 200 square feet of shelf space. Each loaf of bread takes up 0.5 square foot; and each package of pastry, 1 square foot.

Find the load mix which yields the maximum revenue to the driver.

4. A whoesaler distributes two similar products. One is a nationally known brand, and the other carries the distributor's own brand. The branded product costs him $10, including processing and overhead costs; and the other costs $6. The branded product sells for $18; the other, for $16. Each must be processed in the packaging and shipping departments. In addition, the product carrying the distributor's brand must be processed in the labeling department. The branded product requires two man-hours in the packaging department and one man-hour in the shipping department. The other requires three man-hours in the packaging department, one man-hour in the shipping department, and two man-hours in the labeling department. The daily capacity for each department is:

	Capacity
Department	*(in man-hours)*
Packaging	210
Labeling	45
Shipping	88

Completed products are loaded directly onto waiting trucks, so there is no storage problem.

Determine the optimum daily product mix.

5. An airline plans to purchase a new airliner, which can be fitted out to carry either first- or second-class passengers, or a combination of both. Each first-class ticket costs $90, and each second-class ticket costs $50, on the route for which the airliner was purchased. However, each first-class seat takes up as much space as 1.2 second-class seats, and the seating capacity of the airliner is 100 second-class seats. In addition, 10 cubic feet of luggage capacity must be allocated to each first-class passenger, and 6 cubic feet to each second-class passenger. The luggage capacity of the airliner is 960 cubic feet. Finally, the maximum passenger and luggage weight is 20,000 pounds. For planning purposes, it is estimated that the average first-class passenger with luggage will weigh 250 pounds; the average second-class passenger with luggage, 200 pounds.

Determine the optimum passenger seating mix for the airliner.

6. Discuss the assumptions and conditions necessary for a linear programming problem.

7. Use Problem 1 and explain the complete logic which supports your contention that your solution in fact maximizes contribution to overhead and profit.

8. The profit figure generated by linear programming is contribution to overhead and profit.

a) Assume that overhead costs in the example used in this chapter (see page 246) are $OC_2 = 0.5C_2 + 20$, where C_2 is the hours of department 2 capacity used. If the objective function does not include this cost, modify it so that it does include this cost.

b) Assume that the capacity in department 2 of the example used in this chapter is not readily modified but that it is readily modified in department 1. The overhead cost is $OC_1 = 0.02C_1^2 + 10$ where C_1 is the hours used in department 1. Considering only the four corner points, does this modify the optimum found in the text?

9. The Taff Manufacturing Company has three departments and makes two products. The maximum capacity of each department for each product, assuming that the firm makes nothing else, and the profit for each unit of each product are as follows (each product must be processed by each department):

Product	Department 1	2	3	Profit per unit
A...........	333	200	500	$2.00
B...........	400	666	333	1.25

a) Determine the maximum profit and amounts of each product which must be produced to obtain it. (*Hint:* The challenge of this problem is to restructure the data so that the problem is amenable to solution).

b) The firm is offered an additional machine on two of the departments, which will allow additional production. The monthly costs for each machine and added production are:

Product	Department 2	Department 3
A........................	40	30
B........................	80	20
Monthly cost of machine.....$100		$100

Should the firm purchase either or both of these machines?

10. The following processing times are given for the departments of the firm shown in Problem 9 of Chapter 12:

Good	Department A	B	Available units of processing time Department	Time
1....................	4	3	A	600
2....................	2	1	B	450

Can you determine the optimal mix, assuming the profit-maximizing price determined for Chapter 12?

11. Refer to Problem 7 of Chapter 12.

a) Determine the optimal mix of good *A* and *B*, assuming that all units can be sold at the profit-maximizing price determined in Chapter 12. Be sure to use the graphical method and indicate the complete rationale as to why you have an optimal solution. If you cannot compute the coefficients in objective function, set them arbitrarily.

b) Why is the solution found above not a true optimal solution?

12. Refer to Problem 8 in Chapter 12. What is the system of linear equations (including objective function) which reflects this situation as a linear programming problem?

SELECTED REFERENCES

Gass, S. I., *Linear Programming: Methods and Applications.* 2d ed. New York: McGraw-Hill Book Co., Inc., 1966.

Levin, Richard I., and Lamone, Rudolph P. *Linear Programming for Management Decisions.* Homewood, Ill.: Richard D. Irwin, Inc., 1969.

Llewellyn, Robert W. *Linear Programming.* New York: Holt, Rinehart & Winston, Inc., 1964.

Loomba, N. P. *Linear Programming: An Introductory Analysis.* New York: McGraw-Hill Book Co., Inc., 1964.

Naylor, Thomas H., and Byrne, Eugene T. *Linear Programming.* Belmont, Calif.: Wadsworth Publishing Co., Inc., 1963.

Spivey, W. Allen. *Linear Programming: An Introduction.* New York: Macmillan Co., 1963.

16

Models of linear
systems, II: The
simplex algorithm

I. INTRODUCTION[1]

In order to solve the linear programming problem by other than graphic
means, we must convert the problem to a system of linear equations. The
reader will recall the following problem from the previous chapter:

$$\text{Maximize:} \quad P = 4X_1 + 5X_2$$
$$\text{Subject to:} \quad 4X_1 + 2X_2 \leq 32$$
$$3X_1 + 6X_2 \leq 36$$
$$X_1 \geq 0$$
$$X_2 \geq 0$$

Slack variables

If we let X_3 represent unused hours of capacity in department 1 and X_4
represent unused capacity in department 2, we may restructure this system
as follows:

$$\text{Maximize:} \quad P = 4X_1 + 5X_2$$
$$\text{Subject to:} \quad 4X_1 + 2X_2 + X_3 + 0X_4 = 32$$
$$3X_1 + 6X_2 + 0X_3 + X_4 = 36$$
$$X_1, X_2, X_3, X_4 \geq 0$$

You will note that X_4 with a coefficient of zero was included in the equation for department 1. With the coefficient of zero, this term is always

---

[1] This chapter relies upon Chapter 15 and a knowledge of matrix algebra such
as that given in Chapter 11.

zero and thus does not affect the equation. It does, however, serve a purpose which will be demonstrated later.

The introduction of X_3 serves to absorb any difference between $4X_1 + 2X_2$ and 32. We may restate this equation:

$$X_3 = 32 - 4X_1 - 2X_2$$

Consequently, X_3 represents the difference or slack between available capacity and utilized capacity. Thus the terms added to transform the system from a system of linear inequalities to a system of linear equations are called *slack varaibles*. An understanding of slack variables is essential to the linear programming model.

Terminology

The linear programming model is applicable only when the system of linear equations has more unknowns than equations. Since each inequality is transformed to an equality via the use of (at least) a slack variable, this condition is always met if the initial problem has only inequality constraints. The linear programming model provides a solution only when a solution exists which contains m or less positive variables and when satisfying the constraints either maximizes or minimizes the objective function.[2] There are two kinds of constraints. The constraint represented by an equation (or inequality) is known as a *linear structural constraint*. The condition which requires each variable be greater than or equal to zero is a *nonnegativity constraint*.

Generally, the solution will contain m positive variables. However, it is worthwhile understanding that less than m positive variables may result in a solution. If we add the following constraint:

$$8X_1 + 4X_2 \leq 64$$

to the example in the previous chapter, the system of linear inequalities is as shown below:

(1)	$8X_1 + 4X_2 \leq 64$
(2)	$4X_1 + 2X_2 \leq 32$
(3)	$3X_1 + 6X_2 \leq 36$

A casual glance at inequalities 1 and 2 indicates that they reduce to one inequality. In this case the optimal solution may contain only two positive variables. Such a condition appears obvious in a system of three equations and five unknowns. However, in a set of 50 equations and 75 unknowns, it may not be immediately obvious.

Any solution containing exactly m positive variables and satisfying the

---

[2] The m refers to the number of equations, and the n refers to the number of unknowns.

linear structural constraints and the nonnegativity constraints is a *basic feasible solution*. Any solution containing less than m positive variables and satisfying the linear structural constraints and the nonnegativity constraints is a *degenerate basic feasible solution*. Any basic feasible or degenerate basic feasible solution that either maximizes or minimizes the objective function is an optimal solution.

The previous chapter demonstrates that only a finite number of corner points need be considered as candidates for the optimal solution. The simplex algorithm is a systematic search process which assures an optimal solution in an orderly progression of steps in which each step improves the value of the objective function. Thus, in the maximization case, each step increases the value of the objective function.

II. THE VECTOR METHOD

The vector method is a pedagogical device which explains the rationale for all of the manipulations of the complex algorithm. The simplex algorithm merely provides an organized framework for conducting these manipulations.

A set of linear equations can be represented as a set of vectors. Hence the system discussed so far can be represented as follows:

$$X_1 \begin{pmatrix} 4 \\ 3 \end{pmatrix} + X_2 \begin{pmatrix} 2 \\ 6 \end{pmatrix} + X_3 \begin{pmatrix} 1 \\ 0 \end{pmatrix} + X_4 \begin{pmatrix} 0 \\ 1 \end{pmatrix} = \begin{pmatrix} 32 \\ 36 \end{pmatrix}$$

Multiplying by the scalar multiples gives:

$$\begin{pmatrix} 4X_1 \\ 3X_1 \end{pmatrix} + \begin{pmatrix} 2X_2 \\ 6X_2 \end{pmatrix} + \begin{pmatrix} X_3 \\ 0X_3 \end{pmatrix} + \begin{pmatrix} 0X_4 \\ X_4 \end{pmatrix} = \begin{pmatrix} 32 \\ 36 \end{pmatrix}$$

Adding the first four vectors gives:

$$\begin{pmatrix} 4X_1 + 2X_2 + X_3 + 0X_4 \\ 3X_1 + 6X_2 + 0X_3 + X_4 \end{pmatrix} = \begin{pmatrix} 32 \\ 36 \end{pmatrix}$$

or:

$$4X_1 + 2X_2 + X_3 + 0X_4 = 32$$
$$3X_1 + 6X_2 + 0X_3 + X_4 = 36$$

If we let:

$$P_1 = \begin{pmatrix} 4 \\ 3 \end{pmatrix} \quad P_2 = \begin{pmatrix} 2 \\ 6 \end{pmatrix} \quad P_3 = \begin{pmatrix} 1 \\ 0 \end{pmatrix} \quad P_4 = \begin{pmatrix} 0 \\ 1 \end{pmatrix} \quad P_0 = \begin{pmatrix} 32 \\ 36 \end{pmatrix}$$

then:

$$X_1 P_1 + X_2 P_2 + X_3 P_3 + X_4 P_4 = P_0$$

In this case, P_1 and P_2 are known as the *structural vectors*, P_3 and P_4 are known as the *unit vectors*, and P_0 is known as the *requirements vector*.

The unit vectors combine to represent the identity matrix formed by the slack variables. The structural vectors are all other vectors except the requirements vector, which represents the constraints. P_0 is a two-component vector which must be found when the values of the scalar multiples $(X_1, X_2, X_3,$ and $X_4)$ are identified. Consequently, at the optimum, we said that $X_1 = \dfrac{60}{9}, X_2 = \dfrac{24}{9}, X_3 = 0,$ and $X_4 = 0.$ The consistency is proved as follows:

$$\frac{60}{9}\begin{pmatrix}4\\3\end{pmatrix} + \frac{24}{9}\begin{pmatrix}2\\6\end{pmatrix} + 0\begin{pmatrix}1\\0\end{pmatrix} + 0\begin{pmatrix}0\\1\end{pmatrix} = \begin{pmatrix}32\\36\end{pmatrix}$$

$$\begin{pmatrix}\dfrac{240}{9}\\\dfrac{180}{9}\end{pmatrix} + \begin{pmatrix}\dfrac{48}{9}\\\dfrac{144}{9}\end{pmatrix} + \begin{pmatrix}0\\0\end{pmatrix} + \begin{pmatrix}0\\0\end{pmatrix} = \begin{pmatrix}32\\36\end{pmatrix}$$

$$\begin{pmatrix}\dfrac{240}{9} + \dfrac{48}{9} + 0 + 0\\\dfrac{180}{9} + \dfrac{144}{9} + 0 + 0\end{pmatrix} = \begin{pmatrix}32\\36\end{pmatrix}$$

$$\begin{pmatrix}32\\36\end{pmatrix} = \begin{pmatrix}32\\36\end{pmatrix}$$

Conditions for a basic feasible solution

Note also that $m = 2$ and that we have exactly two positive variables, which is one of the conditions for a basic feasible solution. In fact, *a basic feasible solution is attained only when m scalar multiples are positive and the rest are zero.* This means that we only need to investigate a limited number of candidates for the optimum.

For the example being discussed, then, six possible combinations of two positive and two zero variables may be identified, as shown in Table 16–1.

Table 16–1

Positive variables	Zero variables
X_1, X_2	X_3, X_4
X_1, X_3	X_2, X_4
X_1, X_4	X_2, X_3
X_2, X_3	X_1, X_4
X_2, X_4	X_1, X_3
X_3, X_4	X_1, X_2

However, a further condition for a basic feasible solution is that the linear structural constraints must be satisfied. It can be seen that if we let each of the slack variables be positive and the other variables be zero, we shall have a basic feasible solution. For the current example, we produce no units of X_1 and X_2, and all of the hours of capacity are unused; i.e.,

Figure 16–1

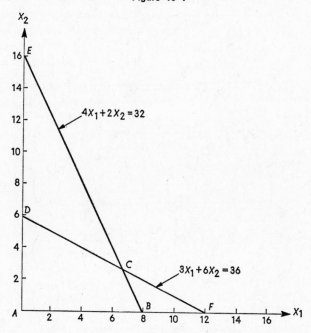

$X_1 = 0$, $X_2 = 0$, $X_3 = 32$, and $X_4 = 36$. In vector form, this is shown below:

$$0 \begin{pmatrix} 4 \\ 3 \end{pmatrix} + 0 \begin{pmatrix} 2 \\ 6 \end{pmatrix} + 32 \begin{pmatrix} 1 \\ 0 \end{pmatrix} + 36 \begin{pmatrix} 0 \\ 1 \end{pmatrix} = \begin{pmatrix} 32 \\ 36 \end{pmatrix}$$

or:

$$\begin{pmatrix} 0 + 0 + 32 + 0 \\ 0 + 0 + 0 + 36 \end{pmatrix} = \begin{pmatrix} 32 \\ 36 \end{pmatrix}$$

Let us graphically represent our problem in Figure 16–1. Each point represents one of the six combinations. A is the combination

$$X_1 = 0$$
$$X_2 = 0$$
$$X_3 = 32$$
$$X_4 = 36$$

just discussed. C is the optimal point $X_1 = \frac{60}{9}$, $X_2 = \frac{24}{9}$, $X_3 = 0$, $X_4 = 0$, discussed earlier. The points B and D are basic feasible solutions. At point B, we can see from Figure 16–1 that $X_1 = 8$ and $X_2 = 0$. Further, X_3 and X_4 can be found by substituting in the equation system. Thus in:

$$4X_1 + 2X_2 + X_3 = 32$$

if $X_1 = 8$ and $X_2 = 0$, then $X_3 = 0$. In:

$$3X_1 + 6X_2 + X_4 = 36$$

if $X_1 = 8$, $X_2 = 0$, then $X_4 = 12$. This is verified in the vector form shown in Figure 16–2. Similarly, at point D, or $X_1 = 0$ and $X_2 = 6$, then $X_3 = 20$ and $X_4 = 0$. However, we are presented with dilemma at point F because at that point, if we let $X_1 = 12$ and $X_4 = 0$, equation 2

$$3X_1 + 6X_2 + X_4 = 36$$

is satisfied only if $X_2 = 0$.

Figure 16–2

$$8 \begin{pmatrix} 4 \\ 3 \end{pmatrix} + 0 \begin{pmatrix} 2 \\ 6 \end{pmatrix} + 0 \begin{pmatrix} 1 \\ 0 \end{pmatrix} + 12 \begin{pmatrix} 0 \\ 1 \end{pmatrix} = \begin{pmatrix} 32 \\ 36 \end{pmatrix}$$

$$\begin{pmatrix} 32 + 0 + 0 + 0 \\ 24 + 0 + 0 + 12 \end{pmatrix} = \begin{pmatrix} 32 \\ 36 \end{pmatrix}$$

$$\begin{pmatrix} 32 \\ 36 \end{pmatrix} = \begin{pmatrix} 32 \\ 36 \end{pmatrix}$$

Substituting this in equation 1, we have:

$$4(12) + 2(0) + X_3 = 32$$
$$X_3 = 32 - 48$$
$$X_3 = -16$$

Thus, we cannot find a combination of positive values for X_1 and X_3 and zero values for X_2 and X_4. Likewise, for point E, we cannot find a combination of positive values for X_2 and X_4 and zero values for X_1 and X_3. Consequently the second and fifth combination in Table 16–1 are non-existent.

Positive scalar multiples must accompany the unit vectors

In review, we have said that if the vector system is structured so that the positive scalar multiples accompany the unit vectors (i.e., those vectors which form the identity matrix), finding the value of the positive variables is a simple matter. Use as an example the following system:

$$X_1 \begin{pmatrix} 4 \\ 3 \end{pmatrix} + X_2 \begin{pmatrix} 2 \\ 6 \end{pmatrix} + X_3 \begin{pmatrix} 1 \\ 0 \end{pmatrix} + X_4 \begin{pmatrix} 0 \\ 1 \end{pmatrix} = \begin{pmatrix} 32 \\ 36 \end{pmatrix}$$

where X_1 and X_2 are zero. It can readily be seen that the system is solved only when $X_3 = 32$ and $X_4 = 36$.

Changing a structural vector to a unit vector

Let us now take the basic system and remember that we may perform row and column manipulations. Suppose we wish to transform the P_2

vector to the unit vector $\begin{pmatrix} 0 \\ 1 \end{pmatrix}$, in the equation system shown in Figure 16–3.

Figure 16–3

(1) $4X_1 + 2X_2 + X_3 + 0X_4 = 32$
(2) $3X_1 + 6X_2 + 0X_3 + X_4 = 36$

If we divided each element in equation (2) by 6, the equation would not be changed, and we would have a 1 in the lower element of the desired unit vector. The new equation (2) is:

$$\tfrac{3}{6}X_1 + X_2 + 0X_3 + \tfrac{1}{6}X_4 = 6$$

We may also express equation (1) by subtracting two times the new equation (2) from it. Thus:

$$[4X_1 - 2(\tfrac{3}{6})X_1] + [2X_2 - 2(1)X_2] + [X_3 - 2(0)X_3] + [0X_4 - 2(\tfrac{1}{6})X_4]$$
$$= [32 - 2(6)]$$

or:

(1) $3X_1 + 0X_2 + X_3 - (\tfrac{1}{3})X_4 = 20$

and

(2) $\tfrac{3}{6}X_1 + X_2 + 0X_3 + \tfrac{1}{6}X_4 = 6$

Letting the scalar multiples for the nonunit vectors be zero, the resulting system is shown in Figure 16–4, and $X_3 = 20$ and $X_2 = 6$, which is consistent with the findings in Figure 16–2.

Figure 16–4

$$0\begin{pmatrix} 3 \\ \tfrac{3}{6} \end{pmatrix} + X_2\begin{pmatrix} 0 \\ 1 \end{pmatrix} + X_3\begin{pmatrix} 1 \\ 0 \end{pmatrix} + 0\begin{pmatrix} -\tfrac{1}{3} \\ \tfrac{1}{6} \end{pmatrix} = \begin{pmatrix} 20 \\ 6 \end{pmatrix}$$

The purpose of this discussion has been to point out that we may identify the values of the scalar multiples for the unit vectors by letting all other vectors be zero. Further, by manipulation, we may identify the values of the scalar multiples for all possible combinations of m positive and n zero scalar multiples.

For example, suppose that for the original problem (found in Figure 16–3) we wish to make P_2 the unit vector $\begin{pmatrix} 1 \\ 0 \end{pmatrix}$.[3] Then we proceed to divide equation (1) by 2, yielding:

---

[3] Note that we previously changed P_2 to the unit vector $\begin{pmatrix} 0 \\ 1 \end{pmatrix}$, which is different from the unit vector $\begin{pmatrix} 1 \\ 0 \end{pmatrix}$.

(1) $$2X_1 + X_2 + \tfrac{1}{2}X_3 + 0X_4 = 16$$

New equation (2) may be expressed as old equation (2) less six times new equation (1). That is:

$$[3X_1 - 6(2X_1)] + [6X_2 - 6(X_2)] + [0X_3 - 6(\tfrac{1}{2}X_3)] + [X_4 - 6(0X_4)]$$
$$= [36 - 6(16)]$$

which is $-9X_1 + 0 - 3X_3 + X_4 = -60$. The system is then:

$$2X_1 + X_2 + \tfrac{1}{2}X_3 + 0X_4 = 16$$
$$-9X_1 + 0 - 3X_3 + X_4 = -60$$

Letting $X_1 = 0$ and $X_3 = 0$, we have the result shown in Figure 16–5, and $X_2 = 16$ and $X_4 = -60$.

Figure 16–5

$$0 \begin{pmatrix} 2 \\ -9 \end{pmatrix} + X_2 \begin{pmatrix} 1 \\ 0 \end{pmatrix} + 0 \begin{pmatrix} \tfrac{1}{2} \\ -3 \end{pmatrix} + X_4 \begin{pmatrix} 0 \\ 1 \end{pmatrix} = \begin{pmatrix} 16 \\ -60 \end{pmatrix}$$

Assuring that nonnegativity constraint is not violated

However, the above solution violates the nonnegativity constraint. It can be seen that whenever a value in the P_0 vector (requirements vector) becomes negative, the nonnegativity constraint is violated, and we do not have a basic feasible solution.

When we made P_2 the unit vector $\begin{pmatrix} 0 \\ 1 \end{pmatrix}$ in Figure 16–4, P_4 was transformed from a unit vector (as in Figure 16–3) to a nonunit vector, and P_3 remained a unit vector. This can be understood if we see that it is the P_4 vector we are trying to replace. In equation 2, division of $0X_3$ by a number will result in a zero; and the X_3 in equation 1 is never disturbed by adding or subtracting another row, since the value at that row is zero. Thus the only unit vector disturbed is the one which is being changed to a nonunit vector. We can also see that when we made P_2 the unit vector $\begin{pmatrix} 1 \\ 0 \end{pmatrix}$ in Figure 16–5 P_3 was transformed from a unit vector to a nonunit vector. Which vector we replaced made quite a difference with respect to the presence of a basic feasible solution. Replacing P_4 resulted in a basic feasible solution, whereas replacing P_3 did not.

We can avoid the replacement which results in a violation of the nonnegativity constraint by dividing the value in the requirements (P_0) vector by the coefficient of the ith row. Any value except the smallest value (for the maximization case) will cause a violation of the nonnegativity constraint. This can be explained in a physical sense by recognizing that the maximum number of units of X_2 that can be processed in department 1 is 32/2, or 16. Further, the maximum number of units of X_2 that can be processed in department 2 is 36/6, or 6. This means that department 2 limits the production of good 2. Hence, if X_2 is greater than six, department 2 must obtain additional hours to accomodate that production, and this violates our constraints. Consequently, one rule to be used in order to assure a valid solution is that the unit vector which is to be replaced must have the 1 in the position where the ratio of the requirements vector to the coefficient in the new unit vector is the smallest.

A solution containing both real variables

The student may now ask how one progresses from $X_1 = 0$, $X_2 = 0$, $X_3 = 32$, and $X_4 = 36$ to positive values for X_1 and X_2 and zero values for X_3 and X_4. This requires a double replacement of unit vectors P_3 and P_4 to P_1 and P_2. Although double replacement is possible, an orderly progression in two steps is the most logical. Since we earlier transformed P_2 to the unit vector $\binom{0}{.}$, let us proceed, using the system from Figure 16–4:

(1) $\qquad (3)X_1 + 0X_2 + X_3 - (\frac{1}{3})X_4 = 20$

(2) $\qquad (\frac{3}{6})X_1 + X_2 + 0X_3 + (\frac{1}{6})X_4 = \ 6$

We now wish to exchange P_3 for P_1. First, we should check to see that no constraints will be violated by dividing the requirement vector (P_0) by the vector we wish to make the unit vector (P_1).

$$\frac{20}{3} = 6\frac{2}{3}$$

and

$$\frac{6}{\frac{3}{6}} = 12$$

Thus, since $6\frac{2}{3}$ is the smallest value, the one in the unit vector must be at the top. Thus, exchanging X_3 for X_1 will not violate the nonnegativity constraints. Dividing equation (1) by 3 gives:

(1) $\qquad X_1 + 0X_2 + (\frac{1}{3})X_3 - (\frac{1}{9})X_4 = 6\frac{2}{3}$

New equation (2) is old equation (2) less 3/6 of new equation (1):

$$\left[\frac{3}{6}X_1 - \left(\frac{3}{6}\right)X_1\right] + \left[X_2 - \frac{3}{6}(0X_2)\right] + \left[0X_3 - \frac{3}{6}\left(\frac{1}{3}X_3\right)\right]$$
$$+ \left[\frac{1}{6}X_4 - \left(\frac{3}{6}\right)\left(-\frac{1}{9}X_4\right)\right] = \left[6 - \frac{3}{6}\left(\frac{20}{3}\right)\right]$$

or:

$$0X_1 + X_2 - \frac{1}{6}X_3 + \frac{2}{9}X_4 = 2\frac{2}{3}$$

The system is shown below:

$$X_1 + 0X_2 + \left(\frac{1}{3}\right)X_3 - \left(\frac{1}{9}\right)X_4 = 6\frac{2}{3} = \frac{60}{9}$$

$$0X_1 + X_2 - \left(\frac{1}{6}\right)X_3 + \left(\frac{2}{9}\right)X_4 = 2\frac{2}{3} = \frac{24}{9}$$

When X_3 and X_4 equal zero, then $X_1 = 60/9$ and $X_2 = 24/9$, which (as we know from the previous chapter) is the profit-maximizing solution. The vector method merely gives us an orderly method for identifying all basic feasible solutions. The findings are summarized in Table 16–2. Ac-

Table 16–2

Positive values	Zero values	
$X_1 = 60/9$, $X_2 = 24/9$	X_3, X_4	
$X_1 = 8$, $X_4 = 12$	X_2, X_3	
$X_2 = 6$, $X_3 = 20$	X_1, X_4	
$X_1 = 12$, $X_3 = -16$	X_2, X_4	Violates nonnegativity constraint
$X_3 = 32$, $X_4 = 36$	X_1, X_2	
$X_2 = 16$, $X_4 = -60$	X_1, X_3	Violates nonnegativity constraint

cordingly, we have six candidates for the optimal solution, two of which must be eliminated because they violate the nonnegativity constraint.

Using the objective function to minimize the number of points considered

In any problem, we have $\dfrac{n!}{(n-m)!m!}$ possible candidates. It can readily be seen that as the number of equations increases, the number of candidates increases very rapidly. Therefore, we must find some solution method other than complete enumeration of all basic feasible solutions. The simplex algorithm provides a method for searching the basic feasible solutions by investigating only feasible solutions which offer a better fulfillment of the objective function than the present or starting solution. However, before formally structuring the simplex algorithm, let us look at the procedure in vector form.

In the first vector system shown (page 280), X_1 and X_2 were zero, and the scalar multiples for the initial unit vectors were equal to the corresponding value in the requirements vector. This must always be the starting structure because it assures a basic feasible solution. The next system should attempt to give us as large an improvement in the objective function as possible. In the case at hand, one can readily observe from the objective function that the next unit of X_2 contributes $5, whereas the next unit of X_1 contributes only $4. Let us then use as a criterion to decide which vector to bring into the solution (i.e., convert to a unit vector) the maximum *net* contribution of the next unit brought into the solution. Note that we are using the *net* contribution, which in this case is $5 because we are producing nothing. If we were already producing good 1, we might have to reduce the production of good 1 to produce good 2. Consequently, the net contribution depends upon the trade-off of good 1 for good 2. This concept is clearly brought out in the previous chapter under the section on exchange rates (pages 253–55).

A complete example

Thus, we have decided that we shall begin by bringing in good 2. The steps are reviewed below. For convenience, the variable is identified above the numbers found in the vector. The original system is shown in Table 16–3.

Table 16–3

X_1	X_2	X_3	X_4	*Requirements*
4	2	1	0	32
3	6	0	1	36

Step 1. Decide which vector will be a new unit vector, i.e., the vector brought into the solution. Since each unit of X_2 contributes $5 to the objective function and each unit of X_1 contributes $4, we shall bring X_2 into the solution.

Step 2. Decide which unit vector is to be replaced by dividing the requirements vector by the coefficient in the vector being introduced. Since 32/2 > 36/6, we replace X_4.

Step 3. Manipulate the system so that X_2 becomes the unit vector $\begin{pmatrix} 0 \\ 1 \end{pmatrix}$, as specified by steps 2 and 3, and shown in Table 16–4.

Table 16–4

	X_1	X_2	X_3	X_4	*Requirements*
(1)	3	0	1	$-\frac{1}{3}$	20
(2)	$\frac{1}{2}$	1	0	$\frac{1}{6}$	6

Step 4. If this solution is not optimal, decide which variable will be brought into the solution by finding the net contribution of those vectors not in the solution. Thus, assuming that we do not have an optimal solution, we must now discuss a method of expressing the net contribution of each variable not in the solution.

Identifying the net contribution

If we look at equation (2) (line 2 of Table 16–4), we can see that in order to attain one unit of X_1, we must give up one-half unit of X_2. This can be ascertained by recognizing that X_3 must remain 20 (having no impact on the outcome, since it has a coefficient of zero), and X_4 is 0; therefore, we let X_1 equal 1 and find X_2:

$$\tfrac{1}{2}(1) + X_2 + 0(20) + \tfrac{1}{6}(0) = 6$$
$$X_2 = 6 - \tfrac{1}{2} = 5\tfrac{1}{2}$$

which is one-half unit less than it was when we had no X_1 in the solution. This can be seen in a physical sense if we recognize that because it takes 6 hours per unit or 36 hours of productive capacity in department 2 to produce six units of good 2, all of the capacity of department 2 is used. Hence, good 1 can only be made in department 2 by displacing good 2. Since good 1 requires three hours of productive capacity and good 2 requires six hours of productive capacity in department 2, one-half unit of good 2 must be given up to produce one unit of good 1. Since each unit of X_1 contributes \$4 and each unit of X_2 contributes \$5, the net contribution (considering only department 2) is:

$$\$4 - (\tfrac{1}{2})(\$5) = \$1.50$$

If we look in the same fashion at equation 1 (line 1 of Table 16–4), we see that no units of X_2 must be given up to attain one unit of X_1. This can be seen in a physical sense by recognizing that because we have 20 hours of unused capacity and it takes 4 hours of capacity to produce one unit of good 1, unused capacity is reduced, but production of good 2 is not affected. It should be remembered that since department 2's capacity is exhausted, one unit of X_1 is attained by giving up one-half unit of X_2. Consequently, in department 1, one unit of capacity is generated by the half unit of X_2 given up. Since 4 hours of capacity are needed to produce one unit of X_1, 3 hours must come from the 20 hours of capacity not already used. Since utilizing the unused capacity in department 1 is costless, the next unit of X_1 brought into the solution makes a net contribution of \$1.50.

We may also evaluate the net contribution of bringing in one unit of X_4.

Looking at equation (2), where $X_1 = 0$, $X_3 = 20$, and $X_2 = 6$, then:

$$\tfrac{1}{2}(0) + X_2 + 0X_3 + \tfrac{1}{6}(1) = 6$$
$$X_2 = 6 - \tfrac{1}{6}$$
$$X_2 = 5\tfrac{5}{6}$$

In a physical sense, one unit of X_4 (unused capacity in department 2) can be attained only by reducing production of good 1 by one sixth of a unit.

Now, looking at equation 1, where $X_1 = 0$ and $X_2 = 6$, because they cannot be affected by bringing in X_4, then:

$$3(0) + 0(6) + 1(X_3) - \tfrac{1}{3}(1) = 20$$
$$X_3 = \tfrac{1}{3} + 20$$
$$X_3 = 20\tfrac{1}{3}$$

The physical interpretation is that the increase in X_4 reduced X_2 to $5\tfrac{5}{6}$, thus releasing one-third unit of productive capacity in department 1. Since this additional unused capacity has no accompanying profit, it does not affect contribution. Since an increase in X_3 contributes nothing, the effect of bringing in X_4 in equation 1 is not felt.

Since one unit of X_4 contributes nothing and the loss of one-sixth unit of X_2 costs 83 cents (i.e., $\$5(1/6) = \$0.83$), the net contribution of bringing X_4 into the solution is a loss of 83 cents.

Conclusion

These steps parallel the steps in the simplex algorithm, which are repeated until the objective function is maximized. The final step occurs when all net contributions are zero or negative.

III. THE SIMPLEX ALGORITHM

This is nothing more than an organized way of accomplishing the previously discussed steps. We shall now show the method of setting this up, using the previous example; that is:

$$\text{Maximize:} \quad P = 4X_1 + 5X_2 + 0X_3 + 0X_4$$
$$\text{Subject to:} \quad 4X_1 + 2X_2 + X_3 + 0X_4 = 32$$
$$3X_1 + 6X_2 + 0X_3 + X_4 = 36$$

The structure shown in Figure 16–6 is known as the simplex tableau. It should be noted that the initial simplex tableau incorporates all slack variables in the solution so as to assure a basic feasible solution at the outset. Given the initial simplex tableau, step 1 identifies the variable to be brought into the solution and the variable to be removed. The initial tableau with abbreviated titles is reproduced without accompanying comments (see Table 16–5).

Figure 16–6[4]

The objective row lists above each variable the respective objective coefficient. The variable row lists all the variables in the problem.

Objective row ──────────────────────────────────┐
Variable row ──────────────────────────────┐   │

Variables in the solution	Coefficients of the objective function	Magnitude of the requirement	4 X_1	5 X_2	0 X_3	0 X_4
X_3	0	32	4	2	1	0
X_4	0	36	3	6	0	1

This column shows the variables with unit vectors.	This column shows the unit value of the solution variable.	This column shows the magnitude of the linear structural constraint	Main body consists of the structural coefficients or trade-off ratios.	Identity matrix (i.e., unit vectors).

Net evaluation row*.............4   5   0   0

The numbers in the net evaluation row, under each column of the main body and the identity matrix, represent the opportunity cost of not having one unit of the respective column variables in the solution; in other words, the numbers represent the potential improvement in the objective function which will result by introducing one unit of the respective column variables.

* This refers to the net contribution discussed earlier. The terminology *net contribution* is applicable only to the maximizing case. Thus, *net evaluation* is used because it covers all cases.

As indicated in step 1 (page 286), the highest net value in the net evaluation row indicates the variable that should be brought into the solution. Thus, X_2 should be brought into the solution. Since we may bring in either X_1 or X_2 without giving up any variable which contributes to the objective function, the net evaluation of bringing in X_1 is its full contribution of $4, and the net evaluation of bringing in X_2 is its full contribution of $5. Accordingly, X_2 will be brought into the solution. For identification purposes, we shall call this the *key column*. The variable to be taken out, as indicated in step 2 (page 286), must be that one which assures no violation of the nonnegativity constraint. This is found by dividing the value in the

─────────
[4] Adapted by permission from N. P. Loomba, *Linear Programming: An Introductory Analysis* (New York: McGraw-Hill Book Co., Inc., 1964), p. 112.

Table 16–5

FIRST SIMPLEX TABLEAU

Solution	Value per unit	Require- ments	$4 X_1	$5 X_2	$0 X_3	$0 X_4
X_3	0	32	4	2	1	0
X_4	0	36	3	6	0	1
Net evaluation.........$4				$5	0	0

requirements vector by the corresponding value in the key column, and it is called the *critical ratio*. The reader will recall that the lowest critical ratio assures that the nonnegativity constraint is not violated. The solution variable with a 1 in that row is the one to be replaced. Since the critical

Table 16–6

SIMPLEX TABLEAU PRIOR TO MANIPULATION

Solution	Value per unit	Require- ments	$4 X_1	$5 X_2	$0 X_3	$0 X_4
X_3	0					
X_2	$5					
Net evaluation.........						

ratios are $32/2 = 16$ and $36/6 = 6$, X_4 will be removed. This row is known as the *key row*. So far, we have said that we wish to transform column 5 (X_2) to the unit vector shown in column 7 (X_4). This is the manipulation shown in step 3 on page 286. The setup of the simplex tableau prior to manipulation is shown in Table 16–6. Since we wish to have a 1 in the

Table 16–7

Solution	Value per unit	Require- ments	$4 X_1	$5 X_2	$0 X_3	$0 X_4
X_3	0					
X_2	$5	6	½	1	0	⅙
Net evaluation.........						

second element of X_2, we divide each element in old row 2 by 6 to get a new row 2 (see the simplex tableau in Table 16–7). Since we now wish a 0 in the first element of X_2, we subtract two times the new row 2 from the old row 1. We know that we subtract 2 because we have just placed a 1 in element 2 of column 2; thus a 0 is attained by subtracting the value in element 1 of old column 2. This gives the simplex tableau shown in Table

16–8. See Table 16–4 and the discussion surrounding it for the relationship to the vector approach.

Finally, we must calculate the net evaluation row. As we have pointed out in the discussion on identifying the net contribution, the values in the body (outlined in the tableau in Table 16–8) represent exchange rates. We

Table 16–8

Solution	Value per unit	Require- ments	$4 X_1	$5 X_2	$0 X_3	$0 X_4
X_3	0	20	3	0	1	$-\frac{1}{3}$
X_2	5	6	$\frac{1}{2}$	1	0	$\frac{1}{6}$
Net evaluation.........						

obtain one unit of the variable for the indicated number of units of the solution variable. Thus, to bring in one unit of X_1 in department 1, we exchange three units of X_3 for each unit of X_1 brought in. Since X_3 contributes nothing, the reduction in profit is zero. In department 2, we exchange one half of a unit of X_2 for each unit of X_1 brought in. This reduces profit by $5(\frac{1}{2}) = \$2.50$. Since each unit contributes $4, the net contribution is $4 − \$2.50 = \$1.50$. An alternate way of setting up the simplex tableau is

Table 16–9

Solution	Value per unit	Require- ments	$4 X_1	$5 X_2	$0 X_3	$0 X_4
X_3	0	20	3	0	1	$-\frac{1}{3}$
X_2	5	6	$\frac{1}{2}$	1	0	$\frac{1}{6}$
Unit reduction in objective function.....$2.50			$5.00	0	$0.83
Unit increase (in objective function).... 4.00			5.00	0	Zero
Net evaluation (increase minus reduction). 1.50			Zero	0	−$0.83

to recognize each stage in the calculation of the net evaluation (see Table 16–9). Hence the reduction row shows the reduction in the objective function for each unit of the respective column brought into the solution. This occurs because of the displacement of units presently in the solution. The increase row shows the increase in the objective function when one unit of the respective column is brought into the solution. It is simply a restatement of the objective row.

It should be noted that reduction is calculated by multiplying the ith element in the X_i column by the ith element in the "value per unit" column and summing these values for each column. Many texts include the reduction row (sometimes called the Z row) in all tableaux because it changes from tableau to tableau. Some also include calculations of total profit and place that figure under the requirements column. This is calculated recognizing that the requirement vector specifies the number of units in the solution and the value vector specifies their value. Thus, 20 units of X_3 contribute nothing and 6 units of X_2 each contribute \$5, for a total of $6(\$5) = \$30$.

Since the second tableau shows that each unit of X_1 brought in contributes \$1.50, we should continue to search for an optimal solution which includes X_1.

Before moving on to the next tableau, let us review the meaning of each value in the simplex tableau. The requirements vector represents the value of the variables in the solution. In this case, we have 20 hours of unused capacity in department 1 (X_3) and six units of good 2. The 3 under column X_1 reflects the fact that three units of X_3 must be given up for the next unit of X_1 brought into the solution. Similarly, the 1/2 under X_1 reflects the fact that one-half unit of X_2 must be given up to bring one unit of X_1 into the solution. The 0 under column X_2 reflects the fact that zero units of X_3 must be given up for the next unit of X_2 introduced. The 1 under column X_2 reflects the fact that one unit of X_2 must be given up for each unit of X_2 brought into the solution. This is, of course, a tautology, but it does reflect the fact that this figure represents a trade between like items. The remaining values are similarly identified.

It is the intent of the material covered in the previous chapter and thus far in this chapter that the reader have a clear understanding of each of the steps in the iteration process that makes up the simplex algorithm. This requires also a complete understanding of each value in the simplex tableau. Assuming this understanding now exists (at least for the maximization case discussed thus far), let us list all manipulation steps (for the maximization case) and then apply them to construct the third simplex tableau.

Step 1. Identify the key column as that with the highest positive value in the net evaluation row. (This is step 1 on page 286.)

Step 2. Identify the key row as that where the ratio of the ith element in the requirements vector to the ith value in the key column vector is the smallest, i.e., smallest critical ratio (step 2, page 286).

Step 3. Divide each value in the key row by the value found in the intersection of the key row and the key column (part of step 3, page 286).

Step 4. For each remaining row, the new row is the old row minus the ith value in the key column times the ith value in the new key row (part of step 3, page 286).

Step 5. The unit reduction is the sum of the ith value in the value vector times the ith value in the appropriate column (part of step 4, page 287).

Step 6. The net evaluation is the value in the objective coefficient (found at the very top of the tableau) less the gross reduction (part of step 4, page 287).

```
$••11.80→ CA
$••00.48Tx CA

S$••12.28• CA
$••12.35• AT

6 4 0 4 2 →$••00.07• YC
```

$**11.80
$**00.187X

$5*12.28
$**12.35

$**00.07

Step 7. The value of the objective function is the sum of the ith value in the requirements vector times the ith value in the value vector.

The values for each step are then:

Step 1. The X_1 column is the key column because the net evaluation of $1.50 is the largest.

Step 2. In row 1, the critical ratio is $\dfrac{20}{3} = 6\frac{2}{3}$. In row 2, the critical ratio is

$\dfrac{6}{\frac{1}{2}} = 12$. Thus the lowest critical ratio is $6\frac{2}{3}$, and row 1 is the key row.

Step 3. See Table 16–10(a) for the row 1 calculations. Hence the partial tableau is as shown in Table 16–10(b).

Table 16–10(a)

Requirements	X_1	X_2	X_3	X_4
$\dfrac{20}{3} = 6\dfrac{2}{3}$	$\dfrac{3}{3} = 1$	$\dfrac{0}{3} = 0$	$\dfrac{1}{3} = \dfrac{1}{3}$	$\dfrac{-\frac{1}{3}}{3} = -\dfrac{1}{9}$

Table 16–10(b)

Solution	Value per unit	Require-ments	$4 X_1	$5 X_2	$0 X_3	$0 X_4
X_1	$4	$6\frac{2}{3}$	1	0	$\frac{1}{3}$	$-\frac{1}{9}$
X_2	$5					

Step 4. Calculation of remaining rows is illustrated in the tableau in Table 16–11(a). The partial tableau is as given in Table 16–11(b).

Table 16–11(a)

Requirements	X_1	X_2	X_3	X_4
$6 - (\frac{1}{2})(6\frac{2}{3})$ $= 2\frac{2}{3}$	$\frac{1}{2} - (\frac{1}{2})(1)$ $= 0$	$1 - \frac{1}{2}(0) = 1$	$0 - \frac{1}{2}(\frac{1}{3})$ $= -\frac{1}{6}$	$\frac{1}{6} - (\frac{1}{2})$ $(-\frac{1}{9}) = \frac{2}{9}$

Table 16–11(b)

Solution	Value per unit	Require-ments	$4 X_1	$5 X_2	$0 X_3	$0 X_4
X_1	$4	$6\frac{2}{3}$	1	0	$\frac{1}{3}$	$-\frac{1}{9}$
X_2	$5	$2\frac{2}{3}$	0	1	$-\frac{1}{6}$	$\frac{2}{9}$

Step 5. The calculation of the reduction is shown in Table 16–12(a). Thus the tableau is as presented in Table 16–12(b).

Table 16–12(a)

X_1	X_2	X_3	X_4
$4(1) + 5(0) = 4$	$4(0) + 5(1) = 5$	$4(\frac{1}{3}) + 5(-\frac{1}{6}) = \frac{1}{2}$	$4(-\frac{1}{9}) + 5(\frac{2}{9}) = \frac{2}{3}$

Table 16–12(b)

Solution	Value per unit	Require-ments	$4 X_1	$5 X_2	$0 X_3	$0 X_4
X_1	4	$6\frac{2}{3}$	1	0	$\frac{1}{3}$	$-\frac{1}{9}$
X_2	5	$2\frac{2}{3}$	0	1	$-\frac{1}{6}$	$\frac{2}{9}$
Reduction............			4	5	$\frac{1}{2}$	$\frac{2}{3}$

Step 6. For the calculation of net evaluation, see Table 16–13(a). The tableau is as given in Table 16–13(b).

Table 16–13(a)

X_1	X_2	X_3	X_4
$4 - 4 = 0$	$5 - 5 = 0$	$0 - \frac{1}{2} = -\frac{1}{2}$	$0 - \frac{2}{3} = -\frac{2}{3}$

Table 16–13(b)

Solution	Value per unit	Require-ments	$4 X_1	$5 X_2	$0 X_3	$0 X_4
X_1	4	$6\frac{2}{3}$	1	0	$\frac{1}{3}$	$-\frac{1}{9}$
X_2	5	$2\frac{2}{3}$	0	1	$-\frac{1}{6}$	$\frac{2}{9}$
Reduction............			4	5	$\frac{1}{2}$	$\frac{2}{3}$
Net evaluation...........			0	0	$-\frac{1}{2}$	$-\frac{2}{3}$

Step 7. Calculation of objective function:

$$4 (6\tfrac{2}{3}) + 5 (2\tfrac{2}{3}) = 40$$

Thus the final tableau is given in Table 16–14.

Table 16–14

Solution	Value per unit	Require-ments	$4 X_1	$5 X_2	$0 X_3	$0 X_4
X_1	4	$6\frac{2}{3}$	1	0	$\frac{1}{3}$	$-\frac{1}{9}$
X_2	5	$2\frac{2}{3}$	0	1	$-\frac{1}{6}$	$\frac{2}{9}$
Reduction............			4	5	$\frac{1}{2}$	$\frac{2}{3}$
Net evaluation .40			0	0	$-\frac{1}{2}$	$-\frac{2}{3}$

Since no improvement can be made by introducing another variable, this is the optimal solution. In fact, the reader should be able to verify the fact that the $-\frac{1}{2}$ under X_3 means that introduction of one unit of slack in department 1 would result in a decline in profit of 50 cents. This is true because we trade off one third of a unit of X_1 but gain one sixth of a unit of X_2. The former is worth \$1.33 and the latter 83 cents, for a net reduction of 50 cents. An algebraic representation of this was shown in the previous chapter under the section on the value of added capacity (pages 253–55). However, it is worth repeating here. If we take out one unit of X_3, this is the same as reducing the available hours by one, yielding 31 hours of available capacity instead of 32. Since the solution will then involve only X_1 and X_2, the equation system can be represented as follows:

(1) $$4X_1 + 2X_2 = 31$$
(2) $$3X_1 + 6X_2 = 36$$

The solution of this equation system is $X_1 = 6\frac{1}{3}$, $X_2 = 2\frac{5}{6}$, which shows a decline of one third in X_1 and an increase of one sixth in X_2. This demonstrates the trade-off represented in the tableau as well as the net loss for each unit of X_3 brought into the solution.

These values are sometimes called *shadow prices* because they show the value of the next unit of reduced capacity.

It is well to remember that the trade-offs refer only to the next unit. One cannot trade off indefinitely, as illustrated by Figure 15–13 in Chapter 15.

IV. A FURTHER EXAMPLE

Let us add a third department to the example being used, as follows:

$$2X_1 + 3X_2 \leq 63$$

The linear system translates to:

Maximize: $\quad P = 4X_1 + 5X_2 + 0X_3 + 0X_4 + 0X_5$
Subject to: $\quad 4X_1 + 2X_2 + X_3 + 0X_4 + 0X_5 = 32$
$\qquad\qquad\quad 3X_1 + 6X_2 + 0X_3 + X_4 + 0X_5 = 36$
$\qquad\qquad\quad 2X_1 + 3X_2 + 0X_3 + 0X_4 + X_5 = 63$

The initial tableau is shown in Table 16–15.

Table 16–15

Solution	Value per unit	Require-ments	\$4 X_1	\$5 X_2	\$0 X_3	\$0 X_4	\$0 X_5
X_3	0	32	4	2	1	0	0
X_4	0	36	3	6	0	1	0
X_5	0	63	2	3	0	0	1
Reduction............0			0	0	0	0	
Net evaluation...........4			5	0	0	0	

Column X_2 is the key column and row X_4 is the key row. Table 16–16 shows a convenient way of calculating the values of the non-key rows for the second tableau (shown in Table 16–17).

Table 16–16

Row 1 (X_3)

Column identification	Values from old row	Minus	Value from key column	Times	Value from new key row	Equals	New row value
Requirements...........	32	—	2	×	6	=	20
X_1.....................	4	—	2	×	½	=	3
X_2.....................	2	—	2	×	1	=	0
X_3.....................	1	—	2	×	0	=	1
X_4.....................	0	—	2	×	⅙	=	−⅓
X_5.....................	0	—	2	×	0	=	0

Row 3 (X_5)

Column identification	Values from old row	Minus	Value from key column	Times	Value from new key row	Equals	New row value
Requirements...........	63	—	3	×	6	=	45
X_1.....................	2	—	3	×	½	=	½
X_2.....................	3	—	3	×	1	=	0
X_3.....................	0	—	3	×	0	=	0
X_4.....................	0	—	3	×	⅙	=	−½
X_5.....................	1	—	3	×	0	=	1

In the second tableau, column 1 is the key column because of the $1.50 net evaluation, and row 1 (X_3) is the key row because the critical ratios are: $\dfrac{20}{3} = 6\frac{2}{3}$, $\dfrac{6}{(\frac{1}{2})} = 12$, $\dfrac{45}{(\frac{1}{2})} = 90$. Sometimes, it aids computation to block out the key row and column, as shown in Table 16–17.

Table 16–17

Solution	Value per unit	Requirements	$4 X_1	$5 X_2	$0 X_3	$0 X_4	$0 X_5
X_3	0	20	3	0	1	−⅓	0
X_2.................	5	6	½	1	0	⅙	0
X_5.................	0	45	½	0	0	−½	1
Reduction......................			$2.50	5	0	$0.83	0
Net evaluation..................			1.50	0	0	−0.83	0

The third tableau is shown in Table 16–18. Row 2 (X_2) calculations in the form shown in Table 16–16 without column headings are given in Table 16–19. Row 3 (X_5) calculations are shown in Table 16–20. Thus the

Table 16–18

Solution	Value per unit	Requirements	$4 X_1	$5 X_2	$0 X_3	$0 X_4	$0 X_5
X_1..................	4	$6\frac{2}{3}$	1 0		$\frac{1}{3}$	$-\frac{1}{9}$	0
X_2..................	5	$2\frac{2}{3}$	0 1		$-\frac{1}{6}$	$\frac{2}{9}$	0
X_5..................	0	$41\frac{2}{3}$	0 0		$-\frac{1}{6}$	$-\frac{4}{9}$	1
Reduction..........................			4	5	$\frac{1}{2}$	$\frac{2}{3}$	0
Net evaluation....................			0	0	$-\frac{1}{2}$	$-\frac{2}{3}$	0

addition of the third constraint (department 3) does not affect the solution. However, we see that we have $41\frac{2}{3}$ units of unused capacity in de-

Table 16–19

Requirements......... 6	—	$\frac{1}{2}(6\frac{2}{3})$	=	$2\frac{2}{3}$
X_1.................$\frac{1}{2}$	—	$\frac{1}{2}(1)$	=	0
X_2................. 1	—	$\frac{1}{2}(0)$	=	1
X_3................. 0	—	$\frac{1}{2}(\frac{1}{3})$	=	$-\frac{1}{6}$
X_4.................$\frac{1}{6}$	—	$\frac{1}{2}(-\frac{1}{9})$	=	$\frac{2}{9}$
X_5................. 0	—	$\frac{1}{2}(0)$	=	0

Table 16–20

Requirements....... 45	—	$\frac{1}{2}(6\frac{2}{3})$	=	$41\frac{2}{3}$
X_1.................$\frac{1}{2}$	—	$\frac{1}{2}(1)$	=	0
X_2................. 0	—	$\frac{1}{2}(0)$	=	0
X_3................. 0	—	$\frac{1}{2}(\frac{1}{3})$	=	$-\frac{1}{6}$
X_4.................$-\frac{1}{2}$	—	$\frac{1}{2}(-\frac{1}{9})$	=	$-\frac{4}{9}$
X_5................. 1	—	$\frac{1}{2}(0)$	=	1

partment 3. In fact, since we must have three variables in the basic feasible solution, we must have one of the slack variables in the solution.

V. MINIMIZATION

In the last chapter, we examined a minimization case which is reproduced here:

$$\text{Minimize:} \qquad C = 32X_1 + 36X_2$$
$$\text{Subject to:} \quad (1) \quad 4X_1 + 3X_2 \geq 4$$
$$(2) \quad 2X_1 + 6X_2 \geq 5$$

It can be seen that the slack variable must assure that the sum on the left side of the inequality exceeds the sum on the right side. Consequently, it must be subtracted from the left side. For example, assume that $X_1 = 2$ and $X_2 = 4$ in equation 1. Then:

$$4(2) + 3(4) \geq 4$$
$$20 \geq 4$$

and the constraint is satisfied. In order to convert this to an equality, either X_3 (the slack variable) must be negative, or it must be positive and be subtracted from the left side of the equation. Since all X_i must be positive, the slack variable must be subtracted. Therefore, equation 1 is:

$$4X_1 + 3X_2 - X_3 + 0X_4 = 4$$

The system may then be expressed:

$$\text{Minimize:} \quad C = 32X_1 + 36X_2$$
$$\text{Subject to:} \quad 4X_1 + 3X_2 - X_3 + 0X_4 = 4$$
$$2X_1 + 6X_2 + 0X_3 - X_4 = 5$$

This presents a dilemma in using the simplex algorithm because we do not have the m unit vectors which make up the needed identity matrix. This is resolved by adding artificial variables. Artificial variables are added solely to provide an initial basic feasible solution. By assigning an infinitely high cost to each of these variables, we assure that they are not included in the optimal solution. The system then looks as follows:

$$\text{Minimize:} \quad C = 32X_1 + 36X_2 + 0X_3 + 0X_4 + mX_5 + mX_6$$
$$\text{Subject to:} \quad 4X_1 + 3X_2 - X_3 + 0X_4 + X_5 + 0X_6 = 4$$
$$2X_1 + 6X_2 + 0X_3 - X_4 + 0X_5 + X_6 = 5$$

It is not our intent to make the student proficient in the use of the simplex algorithm. Accordingly, this book will not discuss the use of the simplex in the minimization case.

VI. PROBLEMS WITH MIXED CONSTRAINTS

The mixed constraint case occurs when the nature of the original constraints includes inequalities which are both "less than" and "greater than." In the maximization example used thus far, assume that the company has a contract with a purchaser which says that he will purchase a total of four units of either good. This yields the following additional equation:

$$X_1 + X_2 \geq 4$$

and the system becomes:

$$\text{Maximize:} \quad P = 4X_1 + 5X_2$$
$$\text{Subject to:} \quad 4X_1 + 2X_2 \leq 32$$
$$3X_1 + 6X_2 \leq 36$$
$$X_1 + X_2 \geq 4$$

The third inequality is transformed into an equation by the addition of a slack variable and an artificial variable with an infinite negative contribution to overhead and profit, thus yielding:

Maximize: $P = 4X_1 + 5X_2 + 0X_3 + 0X_4 + 0X_5 - mX_6$
Subject to: $4X_1 + 2X_2 + X_3 + 0X_4 + 0X_5 + 0X_6 = 32$
              $3X_1 + 6X_2 + 0X_3 + X_4 + 0X_5 + 0X_6 = 36$
              $X_1 + X_2 + 0X_3 + 0X_4 - X_5 + X_6 = 4$

On some occasions, an equality will be included in the original constraint. In this case, only an artificial variable need be added.

VII. DEGENERACY AND OTHER BREAKDOWNS IN THE SIMPLEX ALGORITHM

Thus far, we have assumed that the system could be solved (i.e., the optimum found) with m positive variables and by satisfaction of the constraints (i.e., an optimum solution which is a basic feasible solution). Such may not always be the case. One of the following three cases may occur.

Case 1

The constraints may be inconsistent, in which case a feasible solution is not possible. As long as the constraints are not mixed, this condition will not exist. However, assume that the company in the example used thus far has a contract to deliver 20 units of some combination of good 1 and good 2, thus yielding the following system of inequalities:

Maximize: $P = 4X_1 + 5X_2$
Subject to: $4X_1 + 2X_2 \leq 32$
              $3X_1 + 6X_2 \leq 36$
              $X_1 + X_2 \geq 20$

The graph in Figure 16–7 shows that the constraints can never be met.

Case 2

The structure of the system is such that in the calculation of the critical ratios a tie is produced. In this case, some way must be found to resolve the tie and assure a solution. This is true degeneracy. General methods of resolving degeneracy have been devised. One such method was developed by A. Charnes and W. Cooper.[5] This procedure is:

---

[5] A. Charnes and W. Cooper, *An Introduction to Linear Programming* (New York: John Wiley & Sons, Inc., 1953), pp. 20–24 and 62–69.

Figure 16-7

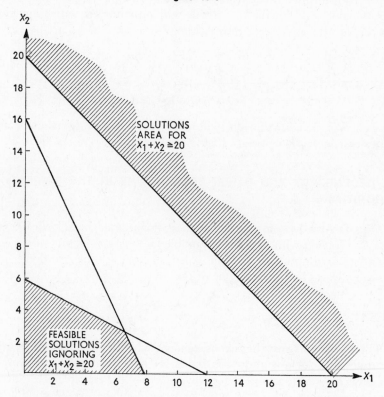

1. Identify the tied variables or rows.
2. For each of the columns in the identity (starting with the extreme left-hand column of the identity and proceeding one at a time to the right), compute a ratio by dividing the entry in each tied row by the key column number in that row.
3. Compare these ratios column by column, proceeding to the right. The first time the ratios are unequal, the tie is broken.
4. Of the tied rows, the one in which the smaller algebraic ratio falls is the key row.
5. If the ratios in the identity do not break the tie, form similar ratios for the columns of the main body, and select the key row as described in steps 3 and 4.

An example of this condition is:

$$\begin{aligned}
\text{Maximize:} \quad & P = 12X_1 + 15X_2 + 13X_3 \\
\text{Subject to:} \quad & 2X_1 + 2X_2 + 0X_3 \le 100 \\
& 2X_1 + X_2 + X_3 \le 100 \\
& X_1 + 2X_2 + 2X_3 \ge 100
\end{aligned}$$

It is left as an exercise for the reader to verify that the method of resolving this tie works.

Case 3

We can also have a tie in the net evaluation row. Normally, this does not cause a real problem if we make an arbitrary choice, although there are more efficient methods.

DISCUSSION TOPICS AND PROBLEMS

1. Products A and B are made in departments 1 and 2. To make A requires two hours in department 1 and four hours in department 2. To make B requires three hours in department 1 and five hours in department 2. There are 64 hours available in department 1 and 75 hours in department 2. Use the vector method to solve when profit on product A is $4 and $6 on product B.

2. A diet is to contain at least 10 ounces of nutrient P, 12 ounces of nutrient R, and 20 ounces of nutrient S. These nutrients are acquired from foods A and B. Each pound of A costs 4 cents and has 4 ounces of P, 3 ounces of R, and no S. Each pound of B costs 7 cents and has 1 ounce of P, 2 ounces of R, and 4 ounces of S. Desiring minimum cost, how many pounds of each food should be purchased if the stated dietary requirements are to be met?

3. To sell a unit of A requires one hour; B, two hours; and C, three hours. For delivery, A takes two hours; B, three hours; and C, two hours. For installation, A requires two hours; B, three hours; and C, five hours. There are 220 man-hours available, of which 50 are available for selling, 60 for delivery, and 110 for installation. With profit on A of $20, B of $40, and C of $60, find the maximum profit combination of A, B, and C.

4. Explain the theory behind the simplex by explaining the reasoning behind the following (if necessary, use Problem 1 from Chapter 15 for a specific reference):
a) Choice of key column
b) Choice of key row
c) Transformation of the body of a tableau from one iteration to the next
d) Meaning of the net evaluation row

5. Discuss conditions necessary for a linear programming problem.

6. The following linear programming case and simplex solution are:

$$\begin{aligned}
\text{Maximize:} \quad & \pi = 6X_1 + 8X_2 + 6X_3 \\
\text{Subject to:} \quad & (1) \quad 3X_1 + 4X_2 + 2X_3 \leq 36 \\
& (2) \quad 4X_1 + 3X_2 + 2X_3 \leq 36 \\
& (3) \quad 2X_1 + 2X_2 + 4X_3 \leq 36
\end{aligned}$$

where equations 1, 2, and 3 represent time in departments 1, 2, and 3, respectively (i.e., the standard case).

Then the first simplex tableau gives:

FIRST TABLEAU

Solution	Unit π	Require-ments	6 X_1	8 X_2	6 X_3	0 X_4	0 X_5	0 X_6
X_4.............0		36	3	4	2	1	0	0
X_5.............0		36	4	3	2	0	1	0
X_6.............0		36	2	2	4	0	0	1
Net evaluation...........		0	6	8	6	0	0	0

SECOND TABLEAU

Solution	Unit π	Require-ments	6 X_1	8 X_2	6 X_3	0 X_4	0 X_5	0 X_6
X_2...........8		9	3/4	1	1/2	1/4	0	0
X_5...........0		9	7/4	0	1/2	-3/4	1	0
X_6...........0		18	1/2	0	3	-1/2	0	1
Net evaluation.........		72	0	0	2	-2	0	0

THIRD TABLEAU

Solution	Unit π	Require-ments	6 X_1	8 X_2	6 X_3	0 X_4	0 X_5	0 X_6
X_2...........8		6	2/3	1	0	1/3	0	-1/6
X_5...........0		6	5/3	0	0	-2/3	1	-1/6
X_3...........6		6	1/6	0	1	-1/6	0	1/3
Net evaluation.......		84	-1/3	0	0	-5/3	0	-2/3

a) Explain and verify the meaning of the circled numbers in the second tableau.

b) What is the optimal solution to this linear programming problem? Be sure to explain any slack variables in the solution vector.

c) The X_2 was brought into the solution vector because the net evaluation value was eight. Can you define another criterion for bringing a variable into the solution vector?

d) If you contemplated adding capacity, where would you add that capacity? Why?

e) This company has conducted additional demand studies and has found that the contribution to overhead and profit on good 2 drops by \$1 on all goods produced above 4. Explain verbally how you would handle this problem.

f) The company must produce two units of good 1. How would you handle this? Note that the condition described in part (*e*) does not hold here.

7. A company is producing two products for the military. These products include component parts which are kept in inventory. The company has received a rush order and must use its existing inventory of components. One of the products contains more expensive components than the other. However, the cheaper equipment may be made with one, two, or all of the more expensive components. The following table shows cost, present inventory, and interchange ability (i.e., when component $A1$ is called for, $A2$ may be used).

Component	Interchangeable with:	Cost	Inventory
$A1$........................Nothing		$2	1,100
$A2$........................ $A1$		3	1,000
$B1$........................Nothing		3	1,000
$B2$........................ $B1$		4	1,000
$C1$........................Nothing		4	900
$C2$........................ $C1$		5	1,000

Good 1 is made from $A1$, $B1$, and $C1$, and sells for $20. Good 2 is made from $A2$, $B2$, and $C2$, and sells for $25. This good must pass through two production departments, and each good requires the following amounts of productive capacity:

	Department		
Good		A	B
1....................		3	2
2....................		4	5
Available capacity....		6,500	6,000

The amount of productive capacity used to process good 1 is independent of what components are used. The government must have 1,200 units of good 1 and 600 units of good 2 (i.e., demand is an equality).

a) Can the company fulfill this obligation? Show why or why not.
b) Set up the linear programming system for this problem. (*Hint:* Maximize contribution to overhead and profit, and assume that demand is an equality.)
c) Discuss the impact of the productive capacity on part (*b*) above.
d) Make an approximation to the answer to part (*b*) above. (*Hint:* You should be able to arrive at the exact answer by a logical deduction process.)
e) Assume that the company anticipates an order for 1,214 units of good 1 and 814 units of good 2. Further, assume that available production capacity is fixed at 6,500 units for department A and 6,000 units for department B.

Should the company produce to inventory; i.e., should it use the extra capacity now?

8. The Schell Oil Company produces and distributes two different types of gasoline: regular and premium. These gasolines must meet the following specifications:[6]

REGULAR GASOLINE SPECIFICATIONS

Vapor pressure index.........................≤ 26
Performance number..........................≥ 61.4
Fraction distilling off at 150° F.................$\leq 32\%$

PREMIUM GASOLINE SPECIFICATIONS

Vapor pressure index.........................≤ 20
Fraction distilling off at 150° F.................$\leq 40\%$

On a particular day the company has four different gasoline components (C_1, C_2, C_3, and C_4) available for blending into regular and premium gasolines. These components have the following technical characteristics:

Characteristics	C_1	C_2	C_3	C_4
Contribution to vapor pressure index...............12		24	0	140*
Performance number (analogous to octane number)........56		58	57	74
Fraction distilling off off at 150 F. (percent)............. 8		20	0	115

Note: Percentages greater than 100 percent are due to the "carry" effect—distilling vapors carry along other, less volatile components.

The maximum availabilities of the four gasoline components (in barrels per day) are tabulated below:

Component	Availability
C_1...................	11,500 barrels
C_2...................	5,000 barrels
C_3...................	1,500 barrels
C_4...................	Unlimited

The contributions to profit and overhead (per barrel of gasoline component utilized) are shown below:

Component	Contribution
C_1.......................	\$0.448
C_2.......................	0.464
C_3.......................	0.456
C_4.......................	0.592

---

[6] Adapted by permission from Thomas H. Naylor and Eugene T. Byrne, *Linear Programming* (Belmont, Calif., Wadsworth Publishing Co., Inc., 1963), pp. 157–59.

a) The firm is presently realizing profits of $15,000 per day by blending its gasolines by trial-and-error and intuitive means. Should the company consider using linear programming to blend its gasolines if the cost of processing the required data and solving the problem on a computer amounts to $250 per day?

b) State the linear programming problem as a system of linear inequalities.

c) Set up the initial simplex tableau.

d) Choose the key row and key column, using the most effective means of making that choice.

9. What is the condition which signals a degenerate solution?

10. Can the requirements (quantity) vector ever assume a negative value? If not, why?

11. In the maximization case with *no* mixed inequalities (as in Problem 6 of this chapter), suppose you wished to start out with three real variables in the solution vector. How would you identify a correct first tableau? (*Hint:* Use matrix inversion to solve a set of simultaneous linear equations.)

SELECTED REFERENCES

Gass, S. I. *Linear Programming: Methods and Applications.* 2d ed. New York: McGraw-Hill Book Co., Inc., 1966.

Levin, Richard I., and Lamone, Rudolph P. *Linear Programming for Management Decisions.* Homewood, Ill.: Richard D. Irwin, Inc., 1969.

Llewellyn, Robert W. *Linear Programming.* New York: Holt, Rinehart & Winston, Inc., 1964.

Loomba, N. P. *Linear Programming: An Introductory Analysis.* New York: McGraw-Hill Book Co., Inc., 1964.

Naylor, Thomas H., and Byrne, Eugene T. *Linear Programming.* Belmont, Calif.: Wadsworth Publishing Co., Inc., 1963.

Spivey, W. Allen. *Linear Programming: An Introduction.* New York: Macmillan Co., 1963.

17

Network models

I. QUANTITATIVE TOOLS AND MANAGERIAL ACTIVITIES

The manager's job is to allocate valuable resources to fulfill the objectives of the organization. His job may also include expansion, contraction, or modification in resource holdings. The allocation of resources may be explicit, as in the linear programming model, or implicit, as in the classical economic model. In the classical economic model the optimum price is found, which in turn dictates the quantity of goods to produce. In the linear programming model, we have seen that at least some data (the shadow prices) were available to assist in the decision to increase (or decrease) the investment in productive facilities. Thus the model has multiple uses. The models presented in this chapter may be concerned with the proper level and the kind of activities which optimize organizational objectives as well as with increasing or decreasing resource holdings. Along the same line the inventory model identifies the level of resources devoted to inventory as well as the size of the production run, which itself allocates productive resources. Some tools can be used for either changing resource holdings or allocating resources.

In this chapter, we shall look at techniques which may be used either to combine resources (implicitly or explicitly) or to control the activities to see that they are in fact carried out according to plan. The techniques are PERT (program evaluation and review technique) and CPM (critical path method). They are especially suited to projects which are not routine or repetitive and which will be conducted only once or a few times.

II. INTRODUCTION TO NETWORK ANALYSIS

A network is a series of identifiably related activities which immediately or ultimately result in a service or product which in turn contributes to the objectives of the organization. The specific nature of the activities can be described by the use of a flow model. A flow model merely identifies the order or progression of events. An example of a network is the assembly of some structure.[1] A product is composed of three subassemblies, 1, 2 and 3. Subassemblies 1 and 2 are combined to form a new subassembly 12. After subassembly 3 is completed, it must be extensively tested before being added to the final product, which is identified as 123. This network is shown in Figure 17–1.

Figure 17–1

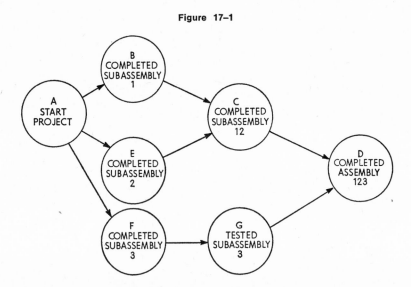

Many kinds of networks exist. The distinguishing feature between network models is the acceptable order and conditions imposed on that order. In the subassembly model in Figure 17–1, some steps may be taken in parallel, but each must be completed before moving on. Included in network models are routing and sequencing models.

III. CRITICAL PATH METHOD (CPM)

Given the network shown in Figure 17–1, let us add above the arrows the time in workdays which it takes to complete each task. This is shown in Figure 17–2. Each circle is called an event and represents the start or completion of some activity. An event consumes *no* time and is identified by the first letter in the circle. Activities are defined by arrows connecting two events. The activity represents action and thus represents time. Each

---

[1] The pictorial detail does not necessarily indicate mathematical or computational complexities.

activity is identified by its preceding and ending event. For example, activity *AB* represents the activity of producing subassembly 1. Events must occur in the order presented. Thus, subassemblies 1 and 2 must be completed before assembly 12 can be completed. Activity *AB* takes eight days and leads to completion of subassembly 1. Consequently, one set of activities which must be completed in order to complete the project is *AB, BC,* and *CD.* Another set is *AE, EC,* and *CD.*

Figure 17–2

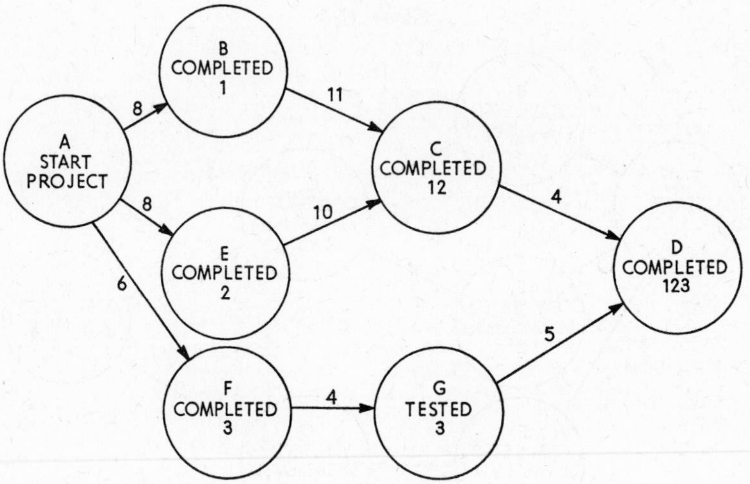

The critical path

Since the time required to complete each activity is known, we may ascertain how long it takes to complete each set of activities and thus find the activity path which will take the longest. The following paths and times for this assembly process are shown:

Path 1: *AB, BC, CD* = 8 + 11 + 4 = 23 days
Path 2: *AE, EC, CD* = 8 + 10 + 4 = 22 days
Path 3: *AF, FG, GD* = 6 + 4 + 5 = 15 days

It can be seen that path 1 is critical because it controls the completion date of the project. On the other hand, path 3 has little influence on the completion date. If some of the resources used to complete path 3 could be diverted to path 1, the completion time might be reduced. If so, path 2 might become critical.

Usually, the total cost of the project is quite important, and some method of incorporating costs would be desirable. Also, the analysis so far has assumed that the completion time for each activity is known with certainty. This assumption may be true in some cases, but not all. At one extreme are activities which have never been performed before, e.g., research leading to the development of a new product. These activities will have a large variance in their performance time because they contain many chance elements. On the other hand, there are activities which have only a slight variance in performance time. Production activities which have been performed frequently are of this nature.

Slack

The difference in time between the required completion date for the entire project and the length of any path is termed *slack*. Slack may be either positive or negative. Often the completion date is determined from the total time estimates for the critical path activities. When this is the case, all the slack is positive except along the critical path, where it is zero. The time required to accomplish activities in any noncritical path may then increase in magnitude up to the amount of slack before it will affect the time required to achieve the project objective. Thus, slack in path 2 is one day; and in path 3, it is eight days.

When the completion date is determined in other ways (e.g., contractual agreement), it is possible for a path to require more time than allowed for the project. In this case the slack would be negative. For example, if the contract for the assembly of *ABCD* specified a finish date 20 working days after the beginning of the project, path 1 would have 3 days of negative slack because it requires 23 days to achieve the project objective.

Slack is generally not desirable. Positive slack represents idle time and resources, with corresponding implicit costs. Negative slack occurs when the project requires more resources than are normally available. One can choose either not to meet the completion date and assume any penalties that may be imposed, or to use more resources and absorb the corresponding increase in costs in order to finish the project on time.

Adjusting the system

Determination of the critical path and the recognition of where slack occurs in the system are the two most important revelations of CPM. When this information is known, adjustments can be made for the better utilization of resources and time. Some of the possible adjustments that can be made are:[2]

1. Reduction of time estimates for critical path activities
2. Elimination of some project activities

---

[2] Harry F. Evarts, *Introduction to PERT* (Boston: Allyn and Bacon, Inc., 1964), p. 89.

3. Transfer of resources from slack paths to activities on the critical path
4. Addition of resources to the project
5. Restructuring of the network in order to reduce project duration

When the network has been developed, evaluated, and revised, the analysis has produced an improved plan, based on estimated time and cost information, for the achievement of the project objective.

As the project progresses, actual information becomes available, and the network can be revised to reflect this information. Each time information is entered, the plan can be reevaluated. Often the location of the critical path and/or of the slack in the system changes. When used in this manner, the network ceases to be static in nature and becomes a dynamic controlling device.

Cost considerations

It costs money to conduct each of the activities. The cost is dependent upon the length of time required plus a fixed element. Thus, cost for each step may be expressed:

$$C_i = A_i + B_i T_i$$

where C_i is the cost of the ith step, A_i and B_i are constants, and T_i is the time required to complete the step. Consequently, step A (completion of subassembly 1) is expressed:

$$C_{AB} = A_{AB} + B_{AB}(8)$$

Table 17–1 expresses these cost equations, in hundreds of dollars, for each step.

Table 17–1

$$
\begin{aligned}
C_{AB} &= 200 + 5T \\
C_{AE} &= 160 + 4T \\
C_{AF} &= 150 + 3T \\
C_{FG} &= 60 + 2T \\
C_{EC} &= 100 + 4T \\
C_{BC} &= 100 + 6T \\
C_{CD} &= 50 + 2T \\
C_{GD} &= 40 + 2T
\end{aligned}
$$

Given this information, we can determine the cost of completing the project or any portion of the project. The cost equations shown here represent the costs of producing 123 via the present network. If the network or times are changed, the cost equations may have to be changed. If the project must be completed in 20 days, not only may it be necessary to divert resources from other activities, but it may also be necessary to go to overtime and other speedup methods.

The fixed term (A_i) in the cost equation represents the total costs of performing the activity under normal circumstances independent of the time required. The variable term (B_iT_i) represents costs that vary with the time required to complete the project. Thus the variable costs of the space used for the construction of subassembly 1 is one ingredient that makes $B_{AB} = 5$. In order completely to recognize costs of this project, a total cost equation which recognizes the aggregate unallocated costs of the total project must be developed. An example of this cost is the cost of capital provided for some period of time. Let that cost be represented by:

$$C_v = 300 + 10T_v$$

where T_v is overall time.

Suppose we conclude that no resources can be diverted from path 3 to reduce paths 1 and 2 to the 20 days allotted for completion. Then we must undertake a crash program of overtime and other means of reducing completion time. Obviously, time can be reduced only so far. Let us recognize this by identifying the following two times, T_n (normal time) and T_c (crash time).

Figure 17–2 contains normal time. Crash time is the fastest possible time. In most instances, these costs increase at an increasing rate. For example, the added costs of a crash program for production of subassembly B can be expressed by the term: $5\,(T_{a,\ AB} - T_{n,\ AB})^2$, where $T_{a,\ AB}$ is actual time taken to complete step AB and $T_{n,\ AB}$ is the normal time required to complete step AB. Thus the equation which expresses the complete situation for production of subassembly 1 is:

$$C_{AB} = 200 + 5T_{a,\ AB} + 5(T_{a,\ AB} - T_{n,\ AB})^2$$

For ease of discussion, assume that the coefficient for the third term in each equation is the same as the coefficient for the second term. Also, assume that the overall equation is linear with respect to time; therefore:

$$C_v = 300 + 10T_v$$

still holds. Now the cost system is as shown in Table 17–2.

Table 17–2

Cost equations	Shortest possible time
$C_{AB} = 200 + 5T_{a,\ AB} + 5(T_{a,\ AB} - T_{n,\ AB})^2$	$T_{c,\ AB} = 4$
$C_{AE} = 160 + 4T_{a,\ AE} + 4(T_{a,\ AE} - T_{n,\ AE})^2$	$T_{c,\ AE} = 4$
$C_{AF} = 150 + 3T_{a,\ AF} + 3(T_{a,\ AF} - T_{n,\ AF})^2$	$T_{c,\ AF} = 4$
$C_{FG} = 60 + 2T_{a,\ FG} + 2(T_{a,\ FG} - T_{n,\ FG})^2$	$T_{c,\ FG} = 2$
$C_{EC} = 100 + 4T_{a,\ EC} + 4(T_{a,\ EC} - T_{n,\ EC})^2$	$T_{c,\ EC} = 5$
$C_{BC} = 100 + 6T_{a,\ BC} + 6(T_{a,\ BC} - T_{n,\ BC})^2$	$T_{c,\ BC} = 5$
$C_{CD} = 50 + 2T_{a,\ CD} + 2(T_{a,\ CD} - T_{n,\ CD})^2$	$T_{c,\ CD} = 2$
$C_{GD} = 40 + 2T_{a,\ GD} + 2(T_{a,\ GD} - T_{n,\ GD})^2$	$T_{c,\ GD} = 3$
$C_v = 300 + 10T_v$	

Remember that $T_{a,\,i} \geqq T_{c,\,i}$ where:

$T_{a,i} =$ Actual time for the ith step
$T_{n,i} =$ Normal time for the ith step
$T_{c,i} =$ Crash or shortest possible time for the ith step

Referring to Table 17–1 for the equation and Figure 17–2 for the times, the normal costs, in hundreds of dollars, are as shown in Table 17–3.

Table 17–3

$$
\begin{aligned}
C_{AB} &= 200 + 5(8) &=& 240 \\
C_{AE} &= 160 + 4(8) &=& 192 \\
C_{AF} &= 150 + 3(6) &=& 168 \\
C_{FG} &= 60 + 2(4) &=& 68 \\
C_{EC} &= 100 + 4(10) &=& 140 \\
C_{BC} &= 100 + 6(11) &=& 166 \\
C_{CD} &= 50 + 2(4) &=& 58 \\
C_{GD} &= 40 + 2(5) &=& 50 \\
C_v &= 300 + 10(23) &=& \underline{530}
\end{aligned}
$$

1,612, which is $161,200

One way of reducing path 1 to 20 days while at the same time reducing path 2 to 20 days is to undertake a crash program to reduce step BC from 11 to 10 days and CD to two days. Thus:

$$C_{BC} = 100 + 6(10) + 6(-1)^2 = 166$$

and

$$C_{CD} = 50 + 2(2) + 2(2)^2 = 62 \text{ which is}$$

an increase of $400. However:

$$C_V = 300 + 10(20) = 500$$

a decrease of $3,000 and an overall decrease of $2,600. Hence, both the time and the cost are reduced. This example demonstrates that the best performance time for an activity is not necessarily normal time. This analysis has recognized fixed costs, time-variable costs, normal costs, and crash costs. Clearly, there is an interaction among the above costs that should be considered. In determining how much time a project should take, the time-cost trade-off should also be considered. Further discussion of the interaction between the various kinds of costs and the interaction between time and cost is beyond the scope of this book. It should be noted that the example shown above is an unusual occurrence.

The foregoing discussion is a description of CPM in PERT terminology. This approach is used because the concepts seem readily understandable under conditions of data certainty and the somewhat novel approach taken here enhances the analytical ingredient in CPM. Finally, the time-cost trade-off takes on meaning with this presentation. The following pages will describe the background of CPM and PERT, and will explain PERT in more detail.

The critical path method (CPM) was developed in 1956 at the E. I. du Pont de Nemours & Co., to aid in the scheduling of routine plant overhaul, maintenance, and construction work. Because this type of project is comprised of activities which have a relatively small variance in their performance time, CPM does not incorporate any statistical analysis in determining time estimates. Two time and two cost estimates are obtained for each activity. The first time-cost estimate is for the normal situation. The second time-cost estimate is for the crash situation, when it is assumed that no cost will be spared to reduce the time required to perform the activity.

Although CPM was unique because of its use of the time-cost trade-off concept, it has been incorporated into other network analysis programs. Nevertheless, one of the primary assumptions of CPM is still the direct relationship between time and costs.

CPM differs from other methods of network analysis in that it differentiates between planning and scheduling. Planning is the determination of the activities that must be accomplished to achieve a project objective, and the order in which they should be performed. Scheduling is the introduction of time into the plan, thus creating a timetable. It is more difficult to use CPM as a controlling device than it is to use PERT. Because CPM was initially developed as a static planning model, one must repeat the entire evaluation and manipulation phase each time changes are introduced into the network.

IV. PROGRAM EVALUATION AND REVIEW TECHNIQUE

The program evaluation and review technique (PERT) originated in 1958 through the work of William Fazar, C. R. Clark, and Navy personnel working on the Polaris fleet ballistic missile program.[3] PERT is most applicable to long-range research and development projects. These projects are usually unique and subject to a considerable degree of uncertainty. They are comprised of activities which demonstrate a large variance performance time and often are pursued in many different geographic locations.

Variation in time estimates

PERT deals explicitly with this problem of uncertainty by the application of statistical analysis to the determination of job duration estimates. Three estimates are obtained for each activity, usually from the group

---

[3] William Fazar, "The Origin of 'PERT.'" *The Controller* Vol. XXX (December 1962), pp. 34–36.

which will actually perform the task. The three figures represent optimistic (a), most likely (m), and pessimistic (b) estimates of the time required to accomplish the activity. An expected time (t_e) and its standard deviation (σ) are determined for each activity in the following manner:[4]

$$t_e = \frac{a + 4m + b}{6}$$

$$\sigma = \frac{b - a}{6}$$

In addition to the statistical approach to time estimation, PERT is unique in its emphasis on the control phase of project management. Because of this emphasis, it is easier to revise the plan each time changes are introduced into the network than with other network analysis techniques.

When it was initially developed, PERT did not consider the direct relationship between cost and time. However, the latest versions offer highly sophisticated cost analysis procedures.

Some examples

In order to explore further the methodology for dealing with uncertainty, let us examine three examples:

Example 1. Let us use as an example the testing of subassembly 3 in the example (see Figure 17–2). We indicated that testing took four days. However, a further look tells us that the four days are the most likely length of time. If things go very well, the testing might be completed in one day. However, this is likely to happen at least 1 time in 10; thus the optimistic time (a) is 1. At least once in 10 times, things can go wrong so that it takes five days; accordingly, the pessimistic time (b) is 5. The probability that a job will be completed in a given amount of time can be shown graphically. There is, for our example, a greater probability that our job will take four days than any other time. This is the highest point on the curve shown in Figure 17–3. To compute the expected time, t_e, from the three time estimates given, we must find the time that will divide the area under the curve in half. This would mean that there is a 50–50 chance of completing the job at that time.

---

[4] The formula to show variation in time estimates is frequently shown as:

$$\sigma^2 = \left(\frac{b - a}{b}\right)^2$$

This is due to the fact that σ^2 is used in the formula to calculate the variation in the expected completion time of the entire project. The formula to calculate variation in the expected completion time of the entire project is:

$$\sigma_s = \frac{T_S - T_E}{\sqrt{\Sigma \sigma^2}}$$

Figure 17–3

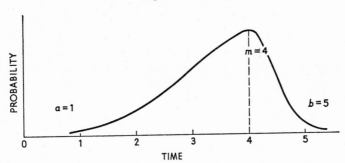

The expected time and variation can be estimated satisfactorily by using the previously shown formulas:

$$t_e = \frac{a + 4m + b}{6}$$

$$\sigma = \frac{b - a}{6}$$

For our example:

$$t_e = \frac{1 + (4)(4) + 5}{6} = 3\frac{2}{3}$$

$$\sigma = \frac{5 - 1}{6} = \frac{2}{3}$$

The 50–50 dividing line is shown in Figure 17–4.

Figure 17–4

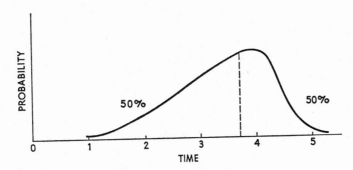

Example 2. To illustrate further the range of distributions, suppose that we have an activity for which little time variation is expected even under the most unusual circumstances.

The time estimates might be:

$$a = 3 \text{ (Optimistic time)}$$
$$m = 4 \text{ (Most likely time)}$$
$$b = 5 \text{ (Pessimistic time)}$$

Hence, using the formula, we find:

$$t_e = 4$$

and

$$\sigma = 1/3$$

The expected time is close to that computed for the first example, but we can see that there is less uncertainty for this job and less chance of saving time by extra supervision, effort, or attention to detail.

This distribution is shown in Figure 17–5.

Figure 17–5

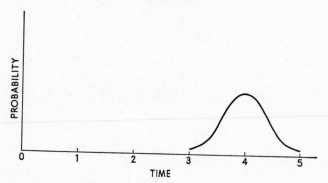

Example 3. As a further illustration, assume that our three time estimates are as folows:

$$a = 3 \text{ (Optimistic time)}$$
$$m = 4 \text{ (Most likely time)}$$
$$b = 7 \text{ (Pessimistic time)}$$

We would find that:

$$t_e = 4\tfrac{1}{3}$$

and

$$\sigma = \tfrac{2}{3}$$

In this case, although little time can be saved on the job, there is a much greater possibility that carelessness or chance can cause great difficulty in our schedule.

Calculation of slack

In the PERT approach, slack is calculated using the earliest and latest time.

The *earliest time* an event can occur is the earliest time we can expect all activities preceding the event to be completed. This will be identified as T_E.

Figure 17–6

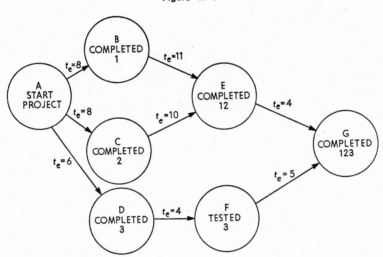

The *latest time* an event can occur is the latest allowable time it can occur without affecting the final completion date. This will be known as T_L.

Let us use the network shown earlier and assume that the times shown are the expected times. This network, slightly changed, is reproduced in Figure 17–6.

The earliest time, T_E, for each event can be calculated by starting with the first event at time 0 and adding the activity times along the paths to the event in question.

The earliest times for each event are shown in Table 17–4. Event E can be reached by two paths. Along the path consisting of activities AC and CE, T_E appears to be 18 weeks. However, event E cannot occur until the activities along all paths leading to it are completed. Since the longest path leading to event E totals 19 weeks, the earliest time we can expect event E to occur is at the end of 19 weeks. By the same token, event G must take 23 weeks rather than the 15 weeks to run AD, DF, and FG.

Finding T_L. The latest time, T_L, that an event can occur without affecting the final completion date of the project can be found by starting with the time for the end event of the project and subtracting the time required for activities back to the event in question. The T_L for the events has been arrived at by subtracting activity time from the 23-week total.

The latest times for each event are shown in Table 17–5.

Table 17–4

Event	Time (in weeks)
A	0
B	8
C	8
D	6
E	19
F	10
G	23

Table 17–5

Event	Time (in weeks)
G	23
F	18
E	19
D	14
C	9
B	8
A	0

Thus, event *F* must be completed by week 18, since it takes five weeks for activity *FG*. Likewise, event *D* must be completed by week 14, since it takes four weeks for activity *DF*.

Let us now review the possible paths:

1. *ABEG*
2. *ACEG*
3. *ADFG*

We shall see that the critical path occurs when all $T_E = T_L$ (see Table 17–6). As indicated in the discussion of CPM, path 3 contains eight days of slack. Thus, activities along that path have eight weeks of spare time and can consequently be diverted to other uses with little or no penalty.

If a scheduled completion time of 20 days had been imposed, each T_L would have been smaller by 3 days. If the difference between T_L and T_E ($T_L - T_E$) is negative, this indicates negative slack, as discussed earlier.

With the information from PERT, the manager is in a better position to know where trouble may occur, where supervision may be needed, and where resources may be shifted to keep the project on schedule. With a PERT network before him, he can easily grasp the interrelationships that exist in the project; and with the network, he can explain clearly to man-

Table 17-6

PATH 1

Event	T_E	T_L	$T_L - T_E$
A...........	0	0	0
B...........	8	8	0
E...........	19	19	0
G...........	23	23	0

PATH 2

Event	T_E	T_L	$T_L - T_E$
A...........	0	0	0
C...........	8	9	1
E...........	19	19	0
G...........	23	23	0

PATH 3

Event	T_E	T_L	$T_L - T_E$
A...........	0	0	0
D...........	6	14	8
F...........	10	18	8
G...........	23	23	0

agement above and below him just what his objectives are, how the project is progressing, and where difficulty is predicted.

V. ROUTING MODELS

Another class of network models deals with networks for which many paths or routes may be taken to complete the objective. An example of such a network is the case of a salesman who must cover all of his allotted territory. In order to do so, he must find an efficient route or sacrifice either valuable calling time or his own leisure time. Figure 17-7 shows the placement of his home (H) and four customers ($A, B, C,$ and D). You will note that he lives in a city with main connecting streets running north and south, which form a neat grid. His house is located at point 2, 3 (i.e., two miles east and three miles north of the southwest corner. In order to reach customer A, he drives two miles south and one mile east, or a total of three miles. If he is at A, he drives five miles directly north to get to customer D. The conditional mileage matrix in Figure 17-8 shows miles to get to a point, given that he is at another point.

We shall assume that minimizing mileage will most effectively maxi-

Figure 17-7

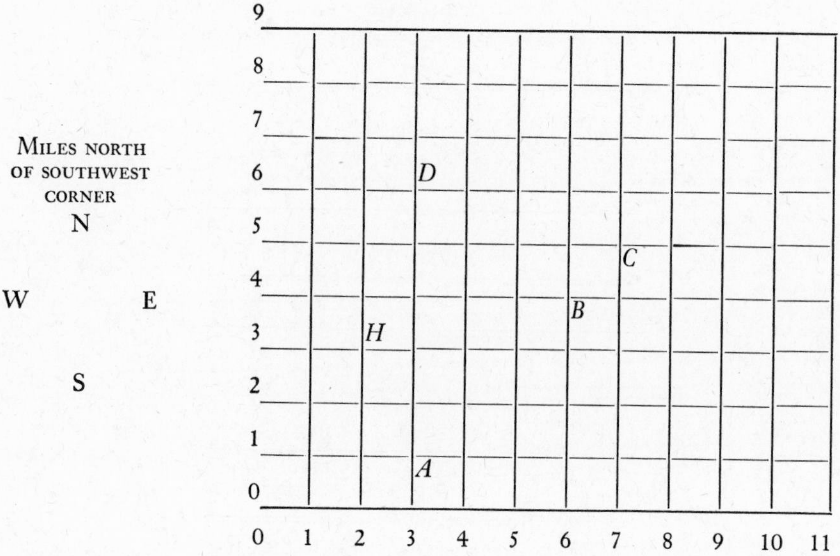

MILES NORTH
OF SOUTHWEST
CORNER

N

W   E

S

mize the salesman's overall objective. In Chapter 1, we pointed out that by placing a dollar value on time, we could identify costs and thus minimize total costs instead of miles. One obvious method to identify the shortest round trip is to enumerate all possible paths and the total distance required to cover each. Then we could choose that route which minimizes distance. In the case at hand, there are 24 possible routes, which are listed in Table 17-7. Fortunately, we do not need to investigate all of these alternative routes because they are symmetrical. Thus the distance required to cover the route *HABCDH* is the same as that to cover the route *HDCBAH*, which is the first route in reverse. In fact, a look at the conditional mileage matrix will show that elements $a_{ij} = a_{ji}$. When this con-

Figure 17-8

MILES TO:

MILES FROM:		Home	A	B	C	D
	Home	0	3	5	7	4
	A	3	0	6	8	5
	B	5	6	0	2	5
	C	7	8	2	0	5
	D	4	5	5	5	0

Table 17–7

Route possibility	Route order	Short notation
1	H to A to B to C to D to H	ABCD
2	H to A to B to D to C to H	ABDC
3	H to A to C to B to D to H	ACBD
4	H to A to C to D to B to H	ACDB
5	H to A to D to C to B to H	ADCB
6	H to A to D to B to C to H	ADBC
7	H to B to A to C to D to H	BACD
8	H to B to A to D to C to H	BADC
9	H to B to C to D to A to H	BCDA
10	H to B to C to A to D to H	BCAD
11	H to B to D to A to C to H	BDAC
12	H to B to D to C to A to H	BDCA
13	H to C to A to B to D to H	CABD
14	H to C to A to D to B to H	CADB
15	H to C to B to A to D to H	CBAD
16	H to C to B to D to A to H	CBDA
17	H to C to D to B to A to H	CDBA
18	H to C to D to A to B to H	CDAB
19	H to D to A to B to C to H	DABC
20	H to D to A to C to B to H	DACB
21	H to D to B to A to C to H	DBAC
22	H to D to B to C to A to H	DBCA
23	H to D to C to A to B to H	DCAB
24	H to D to C to B to A to H	DCBA

dition holds, we have a symmetrical matrix. However, the symmetrical condition need not exist. It is possible that traffic or other factors might make the time required to cover the distance differ, depending upon whether the salesman is traveling to or from one point to another.

Table 17–8, showing routes and distances, then must be investigated.

Table 17–8

Route	Short notation	Distance	Same as:
1	ABCD	$3 + 6 + 2 + 5 + 4 = 20$	24
2	ABDC	$3 + 6 + 5 + 5 + 7 = 26$	17
3	ACBD	$3 + 8 + 2 + 5 + 4 = 22$	22
4	ACDB	$3 + 8 + 5 + 5 + 5 = 26$	12
5	ADCB	$3 + 5 + 5 + 2 + 5 = 20$	9
6	ADBC	$3 + 5 + 5 + 2 + 7 = 22$	16
7	BACD	$5 + 6 + 8 + 5 + 4 = 28$	23
8	BADC	$5 + 6 + 5 + 5 + 7 = 28$	18
10	BCAD	$5 + 2 + 8 + 5 + 4 = 24$	20
11	BDAC	$5 + 5 + 5 + 8 + 7 = 30$	14
13	CABD	$7 + 8 + 6 + 5 + 4 = 30$	21
15	CBAD	$7 + 2 + 6 + 5 + 4 = 24$	19

Thus, the salesman concludes that route 1, 5, 24, or 9 will minimize the distance traveled. Although certain search methods which reduce the work exist, they are beyond the scope of this book.[5]

DISCUSSION TOPICS AND PROBLEMS

1. Place the following jobs in the form of a PERT network:
Tune engine
Test car
Move car to service station
Assemble carburetor
Remove car to owner's garage
Finish entire tune-up
Clean carburetor
Rotate tires
Remove carburetor

2. On the arrows in the network shown below the first number is the optimistic time, the second is the most likely time, and the third is the pessimistic time.

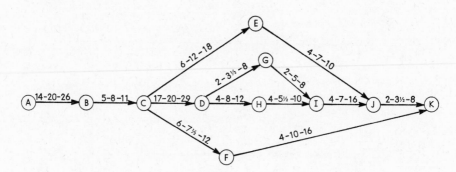

a) Find the critical path, considering only the most likely time. What is the slack in the remaining paths?
b) Under the conditions of part (a) above, what is the slack in all paths if the project has to be completed in 65 days? What general recommendations would you give the manager in this situation?
c) Find the critical path using PERT methods. What is the slack in the remaining paths?

---

[5] See, for example, Frederick S. Hilliard and Gerald J. Lieberman, *Introduction to Operations Research* (San Francisco: Holden-Day, Inc., 1967), pp. 208–38; and Maurice W. Sasieni, A. Yaspan, and L. Friedman, *Operations Research* (New York: John Wiley & Sons, Inc., 1959), pp. 250–69.

d) Given the following cost equations for the conditions of part (*a*) above, reduce the critical path to 65 days or less:

$$C_{AB} = 150 + 6t$$
$$C_{BC} = 100 + 4t$$
$$C_{CD} = 120 + 5t$$
$$C_{DH} = 80 + 4t$$
$$C_{DG} = 100 + 6t$$
$$C_{HI} = 80 + 5t$$
$$C_{GI} = 90 + 6t$$
$$C_{IJ} = 80 + 4t$$
$$C_{JK} = 100 + 6t$$
$$C_V = 200 + 8t$$

3. On the arrows shown below, the first number is the optimistic time, the second is the most likely time, and the third is the pessimistic time.

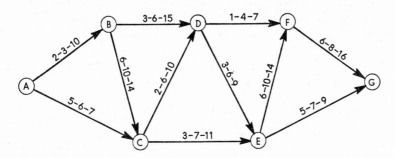

a) Find the critical path, considering only the most likely time.
b) Find the critical path using PERT methods.

4. On the arrows shown below, the first number is the optimistic time, the second is the most likely, and the third is the pessimistic time.

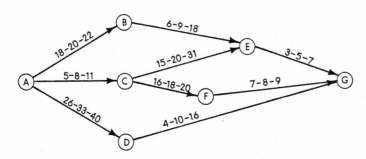

a) Find the critical path, considering only the most likely time.
b) Find the critical path using PERT methods.

5. Find the shortest route for a traveling salesman to follow if he must make all of the following stops. Roads do not go where the lines are not joined.

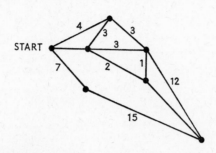

SELECTED REFERENCES

Baker, B. N., and Eris, R. L. *An Introduction to PERT–CPM*. Homewood, Ill.: Richard D. Irwin, Inc., 1964.

Bock, R. H., and Holstein, W. K. *Production Planning and Control*. Columbus, Ohio: C. E. Merrill, 1963.

Busacker, Robert G., and Saaty, Thomas L. *Finite Graphs and Networks*. New York: McGraw-Hill Book Co., Inc., 1965.

Evarts, Harry F. *Introduction to PERT*. Boston: Allyn and Bacon, Inc., 1964.

Martino, R. L. *Finding the Critical Path*. New York: American Management Association, 1964.

Miller, R. W. *Schedule, Cost, and Profit Control with PERT*. New York: McGraw-Hill Book Co., Inc., 1963.

Olsen, Robert A. *Manufacturing Management: A Quantitative Approach*. Scranton: International Textbook Co., 1968.

18

Decision theory:
Payoff matrix models

I. THE BASIC STRUCTURE OF DECISIONS

It is useful to focus upon certain elements in the decision situation which are basic to all decisions but which, when structured as a payoff matrix, form the body of decision theory via payoff matrix models. These elements are:

1. Alternative courses of action (strategies)
2. Various states of nature
3. Knowledge about the likelihood of occurrence of each state of nature
4. Net value (payoff) to decision maker for each outcome
5. Decision maker's objectives

The first element recognizes the alternative courses of action (strategies) which may be taken by the decision maker. These are actions the decision maker may take at his option and are thus controllable variables. Alternative courses of action must be identified so that they are mutually exclusive.

The second element recognizes the condition or states of nature which may occur. These conditions are not under the control of the decision maker. The classical economic order quantity formula assumes a single state of nature because demand (the state of nature) is assumed to be one single figure. States of nature must be identified so that they are mutually exclusive and collectively exhaustive.

The third element recognizes that it is not enough simply to know what the states of nature are, but that decision making becomes effective and indeed possible only when the analyst has knowledge about the likelihood of occurrence of each state of nature. The student will later see that in some cases a great deal of this information exists; and in other cases, almost none exists. Information on the likelihood of occurrence of any state of nature may be objective or subjective, or a combination of subjective and objective information. There are some decision theorists who believe that decision theory can make a contribution when objective information is used and that decision theory is better left out of decisions when objective information is lacking. Other theorists believe that subjective information is representative of managerial experience and judgment and that to ignore such information is to waste a valuable asset.

The fourth element recognizes the payoff or payout which results for each combination of strategy and state of nature. Although the payoff is frequently measured in dollar terms, some other basis may also be used.

Table 18–1

	N_1	N_2	....	N_n
S_1	P_{11}	P_{12}	....	P_{1n}
S_2	P_{21}	P_{22}	....	P_{2n}
..	...	...		...
..	...	...	....	...
..	...	...		...
S_m	P_{m1}	P_{m2}	....	P_{mn}

The fifth element recognizes the role of the decision maker's objective in choosing the course of action to be taken. Two decision makers facing similar situations may take different actions because they have different objectives. Some decision makers prefer the small, sure gain to the large, but improbable gain. The decision maker's objectives influence both the appropriate method of identifying the payoff and the appropriate method of choosing the best course of action.

We have shown payoff matrixes earlier in the text without naming them as such. In abstract form the payoff matrix looks like Table 18–1.

The S_i refers to the ith alternative course of action, and the N_j refers to the jth state of nature. Thus, P_{ij} refers to the payoff for the jth state of nature when the ith course of action is taken. If any basis exists for predicting the occurrence of the states of nature as a probability distribution, this information is recorded above the state of nature as a probability, as shown in Table 18–2.

In Chapter 12, we showed a payoff matrix for Ira Optimist, who wishes to decide how to invest $1,000. He is concerned with his return at the end of one year. He is considering whether to purchase blue-chip stocks, speculative stocks, or government bonds. These represent the alternative courses of action. The return per dollar on each of these investments is dependent upon general economic conditions, which fall into three categories: good, average, or bad. These are the states of nature. The return

Table 18–2

	$P(N_1)$ N_1	$P(N_2)$ N_2	. . . .	$P(N_n)$ N_n
S_1	P_{11}	P_{12}	. . . .	P_{1n}
S_2	P_{21}	P_{22}	. . . .	P_{2n}
. . . .	. . . .	. . . .	. . . .	. . . .
S_m	P_{m1}	P_{m2}	. . . .	P_{mn}

for each investment, given the state of nature, is shown in Table 18–3.[1] This return is the payoff. Accordingly, the payoff (per dollar invested) when blue-chip stocks are purchased and good economic conditions prevail is 8 cents. If speculative stocks are purchased and bad economic conditions prevail, the payoff (per dollar invested) is a loss of 10 cents.

Table 18–3

		ECONOMIC CONDITIONS		
		Good	Average	Bad
ACTIONS	Buy government bonds	0.04	0.04	0.04
	Buy blue-chip stocks	0.08	0.04	0.0
	Buy speculative stocks	0.15	0.05	−0.10

Thus far, we have not discussed the knowledge about the likelihood of occurrence of each state of nature. In Chapter 12, we said that good economic conditions prevailed 30 percent of the time, average conditions 50 percent of the time, and bad conditions 20 percent of the time. Given this information, we have discussed four of the five elements.

---

[1] This discussion will assume no variance in the returns; consequently, this table is not identical to Table 12–1.

The decision maker's objectives are only vaguely stated when we say that he is concerned with his return at the end of one year. If for some reason his objectives preclude him from incurring a loss, but he does not *have* to show a positive return, his best action is to buy blue-chip stocks. Obviously, if he *has* to show a positive return, he will buy government bonds because he takes a 20 percent risk of bad conditions occurring, in which case any other action violates the necessity of showing a positive return. This paragraph has demonstrated that the objectives play a major role in the choice of the best course of action. We shall now go on to classify payoff matrix models.

II. CLASSIFYING PAYOFF MATRIX MODELS: CLASSICAL BASIS

The classical basis for classifying payoff matrix models centers on knowledge about the occurrence of the state of nature. Four different classifications are recognized: (1) certainty, (2) risk, (3) uncertainty, and (4) conflict.

The condition of certainty occurs when the decision maker is certain which state of nature will occur and he must choose the best course of action. In the EOQ model, demand (the state of nature) is known, and the course of action has to be found using the mathematical tools of calculus. Being certain which state of nature will occur does not necessarily mean that the decision problem is simple. Since the previous chapters have dealt with this condition, this chapter will not cover the condition of certainty. The condition of risk occurs when the decision maker has faced the same situation repeatedly and can reasonably construct a relative frequency distribution for the occurrence of the states of nature.

The condition of uncertainty occurs at the opposite end of the spectrum from certainty. Uncertainty occurs when the decision maker has no knowledge or expectation about the probability of the occurrence of the state of nature. It is important to remember that both a lack of reasonable knowledge about the probability of the state of nature (objective information) and a lack of expectation about the outcomes (subjective information) exist.

The condition of conflict exists when the only information about the occurrence of the state of nature is that an opponent is present who will act to harm the decision maker. In gambling, your opponent's gain comes at your expense. Thus, if the state of nature is the action to be taken by a gambling opponent, your only knowledge is that its occurrence will be dependent upon its ability to harm you. In this case the occurrence of any state of nature is dependent upon the opponent's action. Under conflict, it is normally assumed that the action of the decision maker or his opponent is taken without knowledge of the action taken by the other.

It should be noted that conflict models are different in kind from the previous three models. Conflict models are centrally concerned with conflict and are treated in a different fashion than the other models. Conflict models often use terminology built around the conditions of conflict.

Let us now discuss the classical models for risk and uncertainty. As mentioned earlier, the condition of certainty has been covered in earlier chapters. Following this material, we shall look critically at the models of uncertainty. Then we shall present some of the problems in developing valid payoffs. Following this, we shall look at the models of conflict. Then this text will reevaluate the classical categories and suggest an improved structure. Finally, we shall cover some special topics.

III. THE PAYOFF MATRIX UNDER CONDITIONS OF RISK

The condition of risk is a condition where the decision maker has faced the same situation repeatedly and can reasonably construct a relative fre-

Table 18-4

Number demanded	Number of times demanded	Relative frequency
0–12	0	Zero
13	5	0.05
14	10	0.10
15	20	0.20
16	30	0.30
17	25	0.25
18	10	0.10
Over 18	0	Zero
Total	100	1.00

quency distribution for the occurrence of the state of nature. Thus the owner of a retail store predicting daily sales of a perishable item may have a historical record of the number of items demanded.[2] Such a record may be the one presented in Table 18–4.

We call the demand in any given day a random variable. A random variable is a value or magnitude that changes occurrence after occurrence or event after event, in no predictable sequence. The values of a random variable correspond to the number demanded, i.e., 13, 14, 15, 16, 17, or 18. Given the information above, the retail store can determine the expected or average sales by multiplying the values of the random variables by the relative frequency of each. Hence:

$$\text{Expected average sale} = EAS = 13(0.05) + 14(0.1) + 15(0.2) + 16(0.3)$$
$$+ 17(0.25) + 18(0.1) = 15.9$$

---

[2] It should be noted that in order to assure that this is an accurate reflection of demand, the amount on hand at the beginning of the day must have exceeded the amount sold.

Assume that each of these items sells for $8 and is purchased for $5. Therefore, each item sold results in a profit of $3. However, if it is not sold at the end of the day, it must be discarded, resulting in a loss of $5. The situation facing the decision maker can be structured in a payout matrix which shows conditional profits. Thus, if 16 cases are ordered and 14 are sold, this results in a profit of $3 each on 14 items and a loss of $5 each on the 2 items not sold; that is:

$$14(3) - 2(5) = \$42 - \$10 = \$32$$

The conditional profit table is shown in Table 18–5.

Table 18–5

DEMAND (STATE OF NATURE)

		13	14	15	16	17	18
	13	39	39	39	39	39	39
	14	34	42	42	42	42	42
STOCK POLICY	15	29	37	45	45	45	45
	16	24	32	40	48	48	48
	17	19	27	35	43	51	51
	18	14	22	30	38	46	54

The best action to be taken is found by calculating the expected profit for each stock action and then choosing the highest. Recalling the relative frequency of occurrence of each demand condition, the expected profits are:

$$EP_{13} = 0.05(39) + 0.1(39) + 0.2(39) + 0.3(39) + 0.25(39) + 0.1(39)$$
$$= \$39.0$$
$$EP_{14} = 0.05(34) + 0.1(42) + 0.2(42) + 0.3(42) + 0.25(42) + 0.1(42)$$
$$= 41.6$$
$$EP_{15} = 0.05(29) + 0.1(37) + 0.2(45) + 0.3(45) + 0.25(45) + 0.1(45)$$
$$= 43.4$$
$$EP_{16} = 0.05(24) + 0.1(32) + 0.2(40) + 0.3(48) + 0.25(48) + 0.1(48)$$
$$= 43.6$$
$$EP_{17} = 0.05(19) + 0.1(27) + 0.2(35) + 0.3(43) + 0.25(51) + 0.1(51)$$
$$= 41.4$$
$$EP_{18} = 0.05(14) + 0.1(22) + 0.2(30) + 0.3(38) + 0.25(46) + 0.1(54)$$
$$= 37.2$$

where EP_i is the expected profit from the *i*th stock action. Thus the optimal course of action under this condition of risk is to stock 16 items.

Finding the best course of action under risk appears elementary. However, we must look at further complications. These include the effect of salvage value. We shall also present another form of payoff as an alternative way of expressing the decision maker's goals. This leads to a method of identifying the value of added information on the state of nature which will actually occur. The reader can see that improved information may provide a better fix on the expected outcome. Finally, we shall deal with marginal analysis as a way of avoiding heavy computation, especially when the alternatives are large. The technique for marginal analysis is, however, limited to certain conditions.

The effect of salvage value

The previous discussions assumed that the product being sold was completely worthless if not sold on the day of delivery. It may of course be more realistic to assume that the product does have some salvage value. Such salvage value reduces the loss from overstocking. Suppose that the salvage value of the perishable product discussed earlier is $1. Thus the overstock loss is $5 minus $1, or $4 per unit. Consequently, when the retailer stocks 14 units and sells 13, he salvages the remaining unit for $1. We may now construct a new conditional profit payout matrix, as shown in Table 18–6. The expected profits are:

$$EP_{13} = 0.05(39) + 0.1(39) + 0.2(39) + 0.3(39) + 0.25(39) + 0.1(39)$$
$$= \$39.00$$

$$EP_{14} = 0.05(35) + 0.1(42) + 0.2(42) + 0.3(42) + 0.25(42) + 0.1(42)$$
$$= 41.65$$

$$EP_{15} = 0.05(31) + 0.1(38) + 0.2(45) + 0.3(45) + 0.25(45) + 0.1(45)$$
$$= 43.60$$

$$EP_{16} = 0.05(27) + 0.1(34) + 0.2(41) + 0.3(48) + 0.25(48) + 0.1(48)$$
$$= 44.15$$

$$EP_{17} = 0.05(23) + 0.1(30) + 0.2(37) + 0.3(44) + 0.25(51) + 0.1(51)$$
$$= 42.60$$

$$EP_{18} = 0.05(19) + 0.1(26) + 0.2(33) + 0.3(40) + 0.25(47) + 0.1(54)$$
$$= 39.30$$

Hence the optimal stock action is still 16 units. However, the optimal stock action might have been different if the payout values were changed sufficiently. The presence of salvage value does not alter the application of the principles discussed earlier. It simply means that the decision maker must recognize the effect that salvage value has on the conditional profit table.

Table 18-6

DEMAND (STATE OF NATURE)

		13	14	15	16	17	18
	13	39	39	39	39	39	39
	14	35	42	42	42	42	42
ACTION	15	31	38	45	45	45	45
	16	27	34	41	48	48	48
	17	23	30	37	44	51	51
	18	19	26	33	40	47	54

Different payoffs: Regret considerations

This decision maker may say that he is concerned about minimizing the cost of overstocking (if that condition occurs) or the lost opportunity to make a sale. In this case, we could say that he is minimizing regret. Therefore, referring to the original problem (Table 18–5), if the decision maker stocks 13 and 14 are demanded, he loses the opportunity to sell an additional unit at a \$3 profit, and his regret is thus \$3. Conversely, if the decision maker stocks 14 and 13 are demanded, he loses the \$5 cost, and his regret is \$5. However, if he stocks 14 and sells 14, he has no regret because, in retrospect, he has taken the best possible action. Accordingly, the conditional regret matrix is as shown in Table 18–7.

The decision maker may now calculate the expected regret and choose the course of action which minimizes regret:

$$ER_{13} = 0.05(0) + 0.1(3) + 0.2(6) + 0.3(9) + 0.25(12) + 0.1(15)$$
$$= 8.7$$
$$ER_{14} = 0.05(5) + 0.1(0) + 0.2(3) + 0.3(6) + 0.25(9) + 0.1(12)$$
$$= 6.1$$
$$ER_{15} = 0.05(10) + 0.1(5) + 0.2(0) + 0.3(3) + 0.25(6) + 0.1(9)$$
$$= 4.3$$
$$ER_{16} = 0.05(15) + 0.1(10) + 0.2(5) + 0.3(0) + 0.25(3) + 0.1(6)$$
$$= 4.1$$
$$ER_{17} = 0.05(20) + 0.1(15) + 0.2(10) + 0.3(5) + 0.25(0) + 0.1(3)$$
$$= 6.3$$
$$ER_{18} = 0.05(25) + 0.1(20) + 0.2(15) + 0.3(10) + 0.25(5) + 0.1(0)$$
$$= 10.5$$

where ER_i is the expected regret from the ith stock action. Again, the least regret is experienced when 16 units are stocked. It should be noted that the increase in loss when not at 16 is the same as the decrease in profits when not at 16. Thus, when 13 units are stocked, expected profit is $39, which is $4.60 less than the optimal profit of $43.60. Likewise, regret at 13 units is $8.70, which is $4.60 more than the minimum regret of $4.10 at 16 units. Table 18–8 demonstrates this relationship.

Table 18–7

STATE OF NATURE

		13	14	15	16	17	18
	13	0	3	6	9	12	15
	14	5	0	3	6	9	12
ACTION	15	10	5	0	3	6	9
	16	15	10	5	0	3	6
	17	20	15	10	5	0	3
	18	25	20	15	10	5	0

Table 18–8 illustrates that under conditions of risk the regret matrix and profit matrix yield the same optimum. The reader may also note that the addition of a constant (the same constant) to each payoff under either the risk or the profit condition will not affect the course of action nor the

Table 18–8

Stock action	13	14	15	16	17	18
1. Expected profit.......	$39.00	$41.60	$43.40	$43.60	$41.40	$37.20
Divergence from optimum..........	4.60	2.00	0.20	Zero	2.20	6.40
2. Expected regret........	8.70	6.10	4.30	4.10	6.30	10.50
Divergence from optimum..........	4.60	2.00	0.20	Zero	2.20	6.40

divergence from the optimum. For example, the effect of adding $1 to each payoff is shown in Table 18–9.

The concept of regret can be utilized further by recognizing that regret is costly and avoidance of that cost is worth money. The decision maker stocking 16 (because that is the best policy) could make an additional $6 of profit if he knew that demand would be 18 when it was 18.

Table 18–9

Stock action	13	14	15	16	17	18
1. Expected profit........	$45.00	$47.60	$49.40	$49.60	$47.40	$43.20
Divergence from optimum..........	4.60	2.00	0.20	Zero	2.20	6.40
2. Regret:						
Expected regret.....	14.70	12.10	10.30	10.10	12.30	10.40
Divergence from optimum.........	4.60	2.00	0.2	Zero	2.20	6.40

Expected value of perfect information

The following discussion will demonstrate that the decision maker should be willing to pay any cost up to $4.10 which will provide him with a means for predicting demand with certainty. This means that the decision maker knows demand when he orders the goods. In this case only, the diagonal of the payout matrix is relevant, and each demand condition occurs in the relative frequency cited earlier. This matrix is shown in Table 18–10. The expected profits are:

$$EP = 0.05(39) + 0.1(42) + 0.2(45) + 0.3(48) + 0.25(51) + 0.1(54)$$
$$= \$47.70$$

Table 18–10

STATE OF NATURE

		13	14	15	16	17	18
	13	39	..	..	..	..	..
	14	..	42	..	..	..	..
ACTION	15	..	..	45	..	..	..
	16	..	..	..	48	..	..
	17	..	..	..	..	51	..
	18	..	..	..	..	..	54

Thus, 5 percent of the time, profit is $39; 10 percent of the time, $42, etc., giving expected daily profits of $47.70. This represents the profit when the condition of risk has been transformed into a condition of certainty. The difference between profits under risk and certainty is

$$47.7 - 43.6 = \$4.10$$

which is the regret or loss calculated above. Since perfect information transforms risk into certainty, this transformation is worth $4.10 and is a way of expressing the value of perfect information.

Use of marginal analysis for risk problems

In most problems, completely enumerating the expected value of each course of action would be difficult because of the number of computations required. We shall use the original example shown in Table 18–4, with 6 possible stock actions and 6 possible sales levels, resulting in 36 conditional profit situations. Suppose there had been 200 possible values for sales volume and an equal number of possible stock actions. There would have been a tremendous number of calculations in determining the conditional and expected profits for each possible combination. The marginal approach avoids this problem of excessive computational work. The marginal approach is only applicable when the gains increase linearly and losses decrease linearly. In the example, each additional unit sold yields a gain of $3, and each unit not sold yields a loss of $5.

When an additional unit of an item is bought, either the unit will be sold, or it will not be sold. The sum of the probabilities of these two events must be one. For example, if the probability of selling the additional unit is 0.4, the probability of not selling it must be 0.6. The sum is one. If we let p represent the probability of selling one additional unit, then $1 - p$ must be the probability of not selling it. If the additional unit is sold, we shall realize an increase in our conditional profits as a result of the profit from the additional unit. This is referred to as *marginal profit* and is designated *MP*.

We must also consider the effect on profits of stocking an additional unit and not selling it. This reduces our conditional profit. The amount of the reduction is referred to as the marginal loss (*ML*) resulting from the stocking of an item which is not sold.

Additional units should be stocked as long as the expected marginal profit from stocking each of them is greater than the expected marginal loss from stocking each. The size of each order should be increased up to that point where the expected marginal profit from stocking one more unit if it sells is just equal to the expected marginal loss from stocking that unit if it remains unsold.

In our illustration, the probability of demand is as shown in Table 18–11.

If we wish to test the desirability of stocking 14 units rather than 13 units, we need to know the probability of selling the 14th unit. Since the 14th unit is sold when we sell 14 or more units, the probabilities of interest are cumulative probabilities which tell the probability of selling that number or more. The probability of selling 18 units is 0.10. The probability of

Table 18–11

Demand	Probability of demand
13	0.05
14	0.10
15	0.20
16	0.30
17	0.25
18	0.10

selling 17 or more units is 0.25 (the probability of selling exactly 17) plus 0.10 (the probability of selling 18 units) which is 0.35. The cumulative probability of selling 16, 15, 14, and 13 units is figured in a like manner. See the cumulative probability table (Table 18–12).

We may now test the desirability of stocking 14 units by recognizing that the expected profit on the marginal unit is the probability of selling the marginal unit times the profit on that unit. Likewise, the loss on the

Table 18–12

Sales of this number or more	Cumulative probability
13	1.00
14	0.95
15	0.85
16	0.65
17	0.35
18	0.10

marginal unit is the probability of not selling the marginal unit times the loss on that unit. Thus, when we move from 13 to 14 units:

$$EP = 0.95(3) = \$2.85$$

and

$$EL = 0.05(5) = \$.25$$

where EP is expected profit and EL is expected loss. Marginal gain or loss is $EP - EL$ or:

$$\$2.85 - .25 = \$2.60$$

When we move from 14 to 15 units, we must remember that 85 percent of the time the 15th unit will be sold, but 15 percent of the time the 15th unit will not be sold. Consequently, marginal gain or loss is:

$$0.85(3) - 0.15(5) = 2.55 - 0.75 = \$1.80$$

We may express the computation of marginal gain or loss as:

$$p(MP) - (1 - p)(ML)$$

where p is the probability of selling this many or more. In the section on marginal analysis in Chapter 12, we said that we should move to the point where the marginal benefit is greater than or equal to the marginal cost. Since MP is benefit and ML is cost, we move up to the point where expected marginal profit is greater than or equal to expected marginal loss. Hence:

$$p(MP) \geq (1 - p)(ML)$$
$$\geq ML - pML$$

Add pML to both sides:

$$pMP + pML = ML$$

Divide by $ML + MP$:

$$p \geq \frac{ML}{ML + MP}$$

Accordingly, we should stock up to this point. In our example:

$$p \geq \frac{5}{5 + 3}$$
$$\geq 0.60$$

Since the cumulative probability of selling 14 is 0.95, we should clearly stock 14 units. Since the cumulative probability of selling 15 units is 0.85, we should clearly stock 15 units. In a similar manner, one decides to sell 16 units but not 17 units. Therefore the optimal stock action is 16 units, as verified earlier.

Let us apply this rule to the example with salvage value. In this example, $MP = 3$ and $ML = 4$. Thus:

$$p \geq \frac{4}{4 + 3}$$
$$\geq 0.57$$

Consequently, the optimal stock action is still to stock 16 units. If salvage value were $3.50, then $ML = 1.50$, and:

$$p \geq \frac{1.5}{1.5 + 3.0}$$
$$\geq 0.333$$

In this case, we stock 17 units. It can be seen that when marginal loss is small relative to marginal profit, the stock action will be relatively high; and when marginal loss is large relative to marginal profit, the stock action will be relatively low.

IV. UNCERTAINTY

As indicated earlier, the condition of uncertainty occurs when the decision maker has no information on the probability of the occurrence of the state of nature. In this case, we have no probabilities on the states of nature. Suppose we face the payoff table (Table 18–13). We shall discuss four widely recognized rules for deciding upon the best course of action.

The minimax rule

The minimax rule, sometimes referred to as the rule of pessimism, stems from the work of John von Neumann and Oskar Morgenstern.[3] This rule states that the decision maker should minimize the maximum harm. This means that the decision maker looks for the most harmful payoff for

Table 18–13

STATE OF NATURE

		N_1	N_2	N_3
	A_1	3	−2	1
ACTION	A_2	−6	5	4
	A_3	6	−3	2

Table 18–14

STATE OF NATURE

		N_1	N_2	N_3
	A_1	13	8	11
ACTION	A_2	4	15	14
	A_3	16	7	12

each course of action. He then chooses that course of action which gives the least harmful of these most harmful payoffs. Expressed another way, he chooses that course of action which minimizes the maximum harm— thus the term *minimax*. The worst outcome for action 1 is a payoff of −2, the worst outcome for action 2 is a payoff of − 6, and the worst outcome

---

[3] See John von Neumann and Oskar Morgenstern, *Theory of Games and Economic Behavior* (2d ed.; Princeton: Princeton University Press, 1947).

for action 3 is a payoff of — 3. It can readily be seen that taking action 1 minimizes these most harmful payoffs.

If the payoffs are all positive, the most harmful is the lowest payoff because it is the least desirable. For example, given the payoff matrix in Table 18–14, verify for yourself that the minimax rule says: Take action 1.

In these circumstances, the minimax rule is an implied assumption about the occurrence of any state of nature. It says: Assume that the worst will happen, and guard against it. Minimizing the damage of an unfavorable state of nature causes one to bypass an action that in retrospect would have been much more profitable. This line of thinking leads to L. J. Savage's regret rule.[4]

Savage's minimax regret rule

Savage maintains that the decision maker experiences regret if a state of nature occurs which does not give him the highest yield on his strategy. Therefore, he proposes that the payoff matrix be constructed as a regret matrix and that the minimax principle then be applied.

The regret matrix could equally be called an opportunity loss matrix. The regret is found by stating: If I knew what the state of nature would be, I would take that action and have no regrets. Hence, if I take an action, regret is the difference between the payoff I have received and that which I could have received if I had known what the state of nature would be. Accordingly, in Table 18–14, when state of nature (N_1) occurs, the best action to take is A_3 because the payoff is the largest (16 versus 4 and 13). One will have no regrets if he takes A_3 when N_1 occurs. However, if he takes action 2 (A_2), he gains only 4 instead of 16 and misses the opportunity to gain an additional 12. Thus, he has a regret of 12. The regret matrix is constructed using this line of reasoning. In a more formal manner this is accomplished by finding the highest column value and assigning it zero, and subtracting the other values in the same column from it to get their value.

Given:

A_{ij} = Payoff value for the cell in the ith row of the jth column (i.e., the original matrix)

R_{ij} = Regret value in the cell for the ith row of the jth column (i.e., the regret matrix)

Max A_j = Maximum value in the jth column[5]

---

[4] L. J. Savage, "The Theory of Statistical Decision," *Journal of the American Statistical Association*, Vol. XLVI (March, 1951), p. 55.

[5] When the payoffs represent undesirable or harmful outcomes (as when costs are being minimized), these outcomes must be recorded as negative payoffs.

Table 18–15

ORIGINAL MATRIX

	N_1	N_2	N_3
A_1	3	−2	1
A_2	−6	5	4
A_3	6	−3	2

Table 18–16

COMPLETE REGRET MATRIX

	N_1	N_2	N_3
A_1	3	7	3
A_2	12	0	0
A_3	0	8	2

The cell values in the regret matrix are:

$$R_{ij} = \text{Max } A_j - A_{ij}$$

We shall illustrate with Table 18–15. Hence, for example:

$$R_{11} = \text{Max } A_1 - A_{11} = 6 - 3 = 3$$

The complete regret matrix is given in table 18–16. Minimizing the maximum regret leads to choice A_1.

However, this criterion of decision making is open to much the same criticism as the pure mimimax principle and has led others to propose the equiprobable rule which assumes equally probable occurrence of events. This is sometimes called the principle of insufficient reason.

The equiprobable rule

This rule asserts that if one has no reason to believe any state of nature will occur more frequently than another it is rational to assume all occur with equal probability. For example, in the absence of information to the contrary, the most rational assumption about the occurrence of any one of the six sides of a randomly thrown die is that each side has an equally probable chance of occurring. David W. Miller and Martin K. Starr term this the "criterion of rationality."[6] The value of each alternative outcome is computed through the use of expected value. Thus:

$$EV_i = \frac{A_{i1}}{n} + \frac{A_{i2}}{n} + \cdots + \frac{A_{in}}{n}$$

$$= \frac{1}{n}(A_{i1} + A_{i2} + \cdots + A_{in})$$

where:

EV_i = Expected value of the ith row
A_{i1} = Cell value of the first cell in the ith row
n = Number of cells in the row (and correspondingly, number of states of nature)

Again using the above example, we find:

$$EV_1 = \frac{1}{3}(3 - 2 + 1) = \frac{2}{3}$$
$$EV_2 = \frac{1}{3}(-6 + 5 + 4) = 1$$
$$EV_3 = \frac{1}{3}(6 - 3 + 2) = \frac{5}{3}$$

Therefore, using the equiprobable or rationality rule, we would choose A_3 as our best alternative course of action, assuming that the cell values are of positive utility.

Others have criticized the above criterion (in addition to the minimax criterion) on the ground that a person's belief in nature may actually be one of optimism rather than merely one of equally probable favorable and unfavorable outcomes.

Hurwicz rule of optimism

This has led to the criterion of optimism, which was formulated by Hurwicz.[7]

In its purest form, the player may assume a completely benevolent nature and choose the alternative course of action which will yield him the highest possible income (payoff). For example, in the original payoff matrix (Table 18–15) used in our regret discussion, the player would choose A_3 because, with the occurrence of N_1, he receives the highest income. But it is not realistic to assume a completely benevolent nature, so the decision maker (player) will choose a coefficient of optimism which indicates his degree of optimism. Such coefficient may have a value from zero to one, inclusive. Hence, in the example cited above, the coefficient would equal

---

[6] David W. Miller and Martin K. Starr, *Executive Decisions and Operations Research* (Englewood Cliffs, N.J.: Prentice-Hall, Inc., 1960), p. 90.

[7] Cited by J. W. Milnor, "Games against Nature," in R. M. Thrall, J. Coombs, and R. Davis (eds.), *Decision Processes* (New York: John Wiley & Sons, Inc., 1954), pp. 49–60.

one. One of the methods presented to arrive at this coefficient is for the player to assign to the maximum payoff a probability which he would be willing to accept in a lottery between that maximum payoff and the minimum payoff. Once this is chosen, an expected-value approach may be used to compute the values of each alternative course of action and thus make the choice. Again using the above examples:

$$EV_i = (W)(\text{Max } A_i) + (1 - W)(\text{Min } A_i)$$

where:

$$W = \text{Coefficient of optimism}$$
$$\text{Max } A_i = \text{Maximum value of the } i\text{th row}$$
$$\text{Min } A_i = \text{Minimum value of the } i\text{th row}$$

$$EV_1 = 0.6(3) + 0.4(-2) = 1.0$$
$$EV_2 = 0.6(5) + 0.4(-6) = 0.6$$
$$EV_3 = 0.6(6) + 0.4(-3) = 2.4$$

Consequently, using the criterion of optimism with $W = 0.6$, we would choose A_3 as our best course of action.

R. D. Luce and Howard Raiffa present further analysis which leads to some methods for selection of W.[8] Though the selection of W is a vital part of this decision method, we shall not present any further analysis leading to its selection.

Validity in all uncertainty rules

Each of the decision rules proposed implies a subjective judgment about the probability of nature. The minimax rule implies that the expected state of nature is dependent upon the worst outcome. The minimax rule ignores

Table 18–17

	N_1	N_2	N_3
A_1	100	-3	50
A_2	-2	-2	-2
A_3	200	-4	100

all values in the payoff matrix except the worst outcome for each course of action. The decision for the payoff matrix in Table 18–17, using the minimax rule, ignores any gain possibility. A decision maker following the

---

[8] R. D. Luce and Howard Raiffa, *Games and Decisions* (New York: John Wiley & Sons, Inc., 1957), pp. 275–308.

minimax rule is assuming that the expected state of nature is a function of the values in the payoff matrix. This conclusion cannot be logically supported.

The rule of optimism implies the same thing when it says that the probability of the occurrence of any state of nature is dependent upon the best (or at most, the best and worst) outcomes. If you switch signs in the matrix in Table 18–17 and let $W = 1.0$, you take A_3 with the tremendous loss possibility. The matrix when signs are switched is shown in Table 18–18.

Table 18–18

	N_1	N_2	N_3
A_1	− 100	3	− 50
A_2	2	2	2
A_3	− 200	4	− 100

It is interesting to compare the decision for the matrix in Tables 18–17 and 18–18, using the reader's intuitive choice of action and that dictated by either Savage's or the equiprobable rule.

The equiprobable calculations for Table 18–17 are:

$$E(A_1) = \tfrac{1}{3}(100 - 3 + 50) = 49$$
$$E(A_2) = \tfrac{1}{3}(-2 - 2 - 2) = -2$$
$$E(A_3) = \tfrac{1}{3}(200 - 4 + 100) = 98\tfrac{2}{3}$$

The equiprobable calculations for Table 18–18 are:

$$E(A_1) = \tfrac{1}{3}(-100 + 3 - 50) = -49$$
$$E(A_2) = \tfrac{1}{3}(2 + 2 + 2) = 2$$
$$E(A_3) = \tfrac{1}{3}(-200 + 4 - 100) = -98\tfrac{2}{3}$$

Calculating the decision for Savage's minimax regret rule, we must first develop the regret matrix. The calculations for this follow.

Table 18–19

REGRET MATRIX FOR TABLE 18–17

	N_1	N_2	N_3	Maximum regret	Minimax regret
A_1	100	1	50	100	
A_2	202	0	102	202	
A_3	0	2	0	2	*

Table 18–20

Regret matrix of Table 18–18

	N_1	N_2	N_3	Maximum regret	Minimax regret
A_1	102	1	52	102	
A_2	0	2	0	2	*
A_3	202	0	102	202	

Most people agree that A_3 is the rational choice in the first case and that A_2 is the rational choice in the second case. This is meant to demonstrate that Savage's rule is based more upon considerations of the decision maker's values and is thus more tenable. However, as with the other rules, the chance of any given outcome is assumed to be related to the regret values in the matrix.

As will later be seen, the minimax rule was developed for conflict situations, in which it is completely tenable. Its application to uncertainty, as presented here, is supported by the contention that the decision maker's objective may be to minimize harm when faced with true uncertainty. This indicates that some of the problems with these rules arise because the decision maker's objectives and information on the likelihood of occurrence are not clearly identified.

It seems highly probable that a decision maker cannot estimate the likelihood of any given outcome (state of nature). It appears as though he normally makes a decision based upon a subjective guess that one event is more likely to occur than another. If he truly has no reason to believe that one event is more likely to occur than another, the equiprobable rule seems most rational. If, on the other hand, he really does have a feeling, no matter how subjective, it should be recognized by a probability distribution, which means that we are not uncertain about the outcomes. Thus, this author believes that the equiprobable rule is the only reasonable one under true uncertainty.

Utility

The payoffs illustrated thus far might have been represented in dollars for each combination of state of nature and course of action. This assumes that dollars and utility or disutility are equivalent. Utility is a measure of the value of the payoff to the decision maker.

A foreign company that ships six months' worth of production on one boat cannot measure the value of its loss, if the ship goes down, by the dollar value of its goods. Assume that the value of the shipment is $10,000 and the probability of the ship sinking is 0.08 and the probability of the ship arriving safely is 0.92 (no intermediate state of nature occurs). Assume that insurance covering the loss costs $1,000. The payoff matrix is given in Table 18–21. If the company decides to purchase insurance, the net value of its shipment is $9,000, i.e., $10,000 less the $1,000 insurance premium. The expected value of each action is:

$$0.92(10,000) + 0.08(0) \quad = \$9,200$$
$$0.92(9,000) \quad + 0.08(9,000) = \$9,000$$

Thus, using expected values, we would not insure the shipment. This conclusion is drawn because over many repeated trials it is less costly not to insure than to insure.

Table 18–21

STATE OF NATURE

		Safe arrival	Sink
ACTION	Do not insure	10,000	0
	Insure	9,000	9,000

Does the $10,000 loss, if the ship sinks, measure the loss to the company? This depends upon the effect of the loss on further operations of the company. General Motors is faced with this decision every time it sends out a tractor-trailer loaded with cars. Since it sends large numbers of tractor-trailers per day, it does not risk a large loss relative to its overall value. On the other hand, the small foreign shipper is risking a very large portion of his assets.

Let us assume that the value of the shipper's assets is $18,000. A single $10,000 loss would be so harmful as to place him on the verge of ruin. Daniel Bernoulli in 1730 hypothesized that the utility of money to an individual is inversely proportional to the amount of money he possesses. In other words, the more dollars he has, the less the utility of an additional dollar. Although a number of mathematical relationships could be used to represent this one, Bernoulli assumed that the logarithm of the number of dollars could be used as a reasonable approximation to utility.

Since further discussion of Bernoulli's contribution is based upon the final wealth position, let us first identify the expected value of the final wealth position. The payoff matrix is shown in Table 18–22. Using expected value to identify the best course of action, we would choose not to insure; that is:

$$0.92(18,000) + 0.08(8,000) \quad = \$16,560 + \$640 = \$17,200$$
$$0.92(17,000) + 0.08(17,000) = \$17,000$$

It can be seen that this is the same decision as that made when the shipment alone was considered. This is so because we have merely added the $8,000 not being risked to each course of action. This method is preferable to the net gain method shown by the matrix in Table 18–21 because it may then be compared with the payoff matrix in Bernoulli utility terms.

Table 18–22

PAYOFF MATRIX, SHOWING WEALTH POSITION

STATE OF NATURE

		Safe arrival	Sink
ACTION	Do not insure	18,000	8,000
	Insure	17,000	17,000

This situation expressed in Bernoulli utility terms (i.e., logarithms) is presented in Table 18–23. Since the log of 18,000 is 4.25527, the utility of 18,000 is 4.25527. Calculating the expected value of each course of action gives:

$$0.92(4.25527) + 0.08(3.9031) = 3.9148484 + 0.312248 = 4.2270964$$
$$0.92(4.23045) + 0.08(4.23045) = 4.2304500$$

Table 18–23

STATE OF NATURE

		Safe arrival	Sink
ACTION	Do not insure	4.25527	3.9031
	Insure	4.23045	4.23045

The course of action to be chosen here is to insure the shipment. One can further observe that as the safety margin of wealth minus amount risked decreases, the utility of insuring increases. If everything is being risked, the payoff matrix looks like Table 18–24. You will note that this is Table 18–21 converted to logarithms because the entire wealth position is at stake. The expected values are:

$$0.92(4.0) + 0.08(0) = 3.74 + 0$$
$$0.92(3.95424) + 0.08(3.95424) = 3.95424$$

Thus the decision is to insure.

In this situation, it seems that the logarithmic measure of utility is not adequate. In this example, we would expect a greater utility for the decision to insure. The purpose of this discussion is to emphasize that the payoffs must be expressed in terms of utility, not merely dollars.

Table 18–24

STATE OF NATURE

		Safe arrival	Sink
ACTION	Do not insure	4.0	0
	Insure	3.95424	3.95424

V. CONFLICT

The condition of conflict is often included as a part of the subject area known as game theory. The simplest example of game theory and conflict is the two-person zero-sum game.

For example, assume that two grocery stores are competing for the same business. They are considering certain promotional actions, such as (1) doubling the number of trading stamps, (2) using loss-leader pricing on good A, and (3) giving away prizes. The effect on customers in each case is dependent upon the action taken by the competitor.

Table 18–25

ACTION OF STORE 2

		A	B	C
ACTION OF STORE 1	A	0	20	−60
	B	30	−10	−20
	C	70	−80	−30

The payoff matrix in Table 18–25 shows the gain or loss in customers for store 1.

Let us assume that store 1 gains or loses at the expense of store 2. Thus, when store 1 takes action B and store 2 takes action A, 30 customers are gained by store 1. A moment's reflection will show that we have ignored the alternative of not engaging in any of these promotional activities. Consequently, a fourth row and column must be added, yielding Table 18–26. If store 1 knew what store 2 was going to do, it would plan accordingly.

Table 18–26

ACTION OF STORE 2

		A	B	C	No change
	A	0	20	−60	80
ACTION OF STORE 1	B	30	−10	−20	30
	C	70	−80	−30	120
	No change	20	−120	−100	0

However, such strategies are kept confidential until they are simultaneously released to the public. Under these circumstances, we cannot see an obviously desirable action for either store to take.

Given these assumptions, we have no way of meaningfully predicting what the other store will do. John von Neumann and Oskar Morgenstern proposed the use of the minimax rule to find the best strategy for each player.[9] The minimax rule states that the store (called a player) should minimize its maximum loss (which correspondingly means maximizing its minimum gain if no losses are present).

Table 18–27

Action of store 1	Worst outcome	Decision	Action of store 2	Worst outcome	Decision
A.............	−60		A.............	−70	
B.............	−20	*	B.............	−20	
C.............	−80		C.............	+20	*
No change.....	−120		No change......	−120	

Accordingly, in the case at hand, the worst condition that can befall store 1 if it takes action *A* is a loss of 60 customers. If the store takes action *B*, the worst condition is a loss of 20 customers. Table 18–27 summarizes these conditions.

Store 1 will take action *B*, and store 2 will take action *C*, which will result in a loss of 20 customers for store 1 and a gain of 20 customers for store 2.

It is worthwhile to note that there is no need for each store to have an equal number of actions available. Suppose, for example, that the payoff matrix in Table 18–28 reflects a different situation. In this case, store 1

---

[9] See von Neumann and Morgenstern, *op. cit.*

finds that strategy B is in all cases better than A. Here, we have a condition of dominance; i.e., strategy B dominates strategy A because in all cases it is preferable to strategy A. Thus, action A for store 1 may be eliminated; the effective payoff matrix is shown as Table 18–29. Table 18–30 shows

Table 18–28

ACTION OF STORE 2

		A	B	C	No change
	A	0	−20	−60	30
ACTION OF STORE 1	B	30	−10	−20	80
	C	70	−80	−30	120
	No change	20	−120	−100	0

Table 18–29

ACTION OF STORE 2

		A	B	C	No change
ACTION OF STORE 1	B	30	−10	−20	80
	C	70	−80	−30	120
	No change	20	−120	−100	0

Table 18–30

Action of store 1	Worst outcome	Decision	Action of store 2	Worst outcome	Decision
B............	−20	*	A............	−70	
C............	−80		B............	+10	
No change......	−120		C............	+20	*
			No change......	−120	

the minimax results. Thus, store 1 takes action B, and store 2 takes action C, with a loss of 20 customers from store 1 to store 2.

Note that the minimax rule is based upon the assumption that no way exists to predict the competitor's behavior, i.e., complete uncertainty. This example has dealt with two competitors where one competitor's gain is another's loss and is thus called a two-person zero-sum game.

VI. THE PAYOFF MATRIX ASSUMPTIONS

The payoff matrix assumes that the states of nature are mutually exclusive and exhaustive. Hence the states of nature, which in the inventory case are actual units demanded, should cover all possible quantities demanded. However, states of nature may be combined if the payoff for all actions is the same. Table 18–31 shows a case where the payoffs are the

Table 18–31

	$P(N_1) = 0.3$ N_1	$P(N_2) = 0.4$ N_2	$P(N_3) = 0.2$ N_3	$P(N_4) = 0.1$ N_4
A_1	7	-8	3	3
A_2	2	7	-5	-5
A_3	-3	2	2	2

same and thus the states of nature can be collapsed. The payoff for N_3 and N_4 is the same; consequently, the combined states of nature N_3 and N_4 may be recognized as one. Note that the requirement that the states of nature be mutually exclusive and exhaustive has not been violated.

The recognition of mutually exclusive states of nature can be illustrated by the example of a grocer who must decide upon his weekend promotion actions. The states of nature are influenced by such things as the promotion activities of his immediate competitors, the weather, and local economic conditions. Assume that each of these factors may exist in three forms (i.e., three weather conditions may be identified, three conditions for other competitors, etc.). This results in 27 states of nature. However, we may take the economic condition as given; i.e., we are making a decision for next weekend, and economic conditions do not change that fast. Consequently, we may assume present economic conditions. If we let C_i be the ith competitive condition and W_i be the ith weather condition, the states of nature can be labeled as follows:

$$C_1W_1 = N_1$$
$$C_1W_2 = N_2$$
$$C_1W_3 = N_3$$
$$C_2W_1 = N_4$$
$$C_2W_2 = N_5$$
$$C_2W_3 = N_6$$
$$C_3W_1 = N_7$$
$$C_3W_2 = N_8$$
$$C_3W_3 = N_9$$

Thus the process of identifying states of nature should proceed by identifying the variables which affect outcomes, so that they may be separately recognized in the states of nature. It should be obvious that the number of possible states of nature can be very large. Accordingly, some way may have to be found to reduce the number of states of nature. In some instances, one or two catchall states of nature may be identified for those states of nature which exist so rarely as to be of no consequence. For example, the payoff matrix for the retailer discussed earlier did not recognize the possibility of less than 13 units being sold nor more than 18. This omission occurs as a practical matter because the probability of either condition is nil. The records for 200 days are shown in Table 18–32.

Table 18–32

Daily sales	Number of days this amount was sold	Probability of each number being sold
11....................	1	0.005
12....................	0	Zero
13....................	9	0.045
14....................	20	0.100
15....................	40	0.200
16....................	60	0.300
17....................	50	0.250
18....................	19	0.095
19....................	0	Zero
20....................	1	0.005
	200	1.000

On the basis of this information, it would seem irrational to assume that daily sales could not be 10, or even 8. If a condition of 10 or less units is recognized, the calculation of the expected values becomes impossible, since the number of sales is multiplied by the probability of a sale. Therefore, 10 or less cases cannot be used. This may be resolved by using an expected value in the cell; e.g., assuming that each number from 1 to 10 is equally likely, we use 5.5 to represent 10 or less. Since it appears as likely that the retailer will sell above 18 as below 13, he may as a practical matter ignore either condition because it is unlikely to influence the decision.

The grocer trying to decide upon his promotional strategy will find it difficult to identify all possible states of nature. He may wish to identify some states of nature which could be further subdivided but for which such subdivision may be cumbersome or impossible. For example, the promotion practices of other area grocers will have an impact upon his sales. However, the possible combinations of those practices for all the area stores would make the payoff matrix almost infinite. Thus the figures used in the cells of the payoff matrix will themselves represent expected values.

Another assumption of the analysis thus far in the chapter is that the action taken by the decision maker will not influence the probability of the occurrence of any state of nature. In most instances, this assumption seems reasonable. However, the retail grocer deciding upon his promotion strategy would certainly influence the strategy of his competitor if that competitor knew his strategy. Consequently, this assumption could be very important to the validity of the analysis.

VII. PARTIAL UNCERTAINTY: AN EXTENSION OF THE CLASSICAL CLASSIFICATIONS

The classical classifications of payoff matrix models contain gaps which are not adequately covered. Between the two extremes of certainty and uncertainty, we recognize only risk. The reader will recall that under the condition of risk the decision maker has faced the same situation repeatedly and can reasonably construct a relative frequency distribution for the occurrence of the states of nature.

What about those instances in which the decision maker has not faced the same situation repeatedly? Some decision theorists resolve this dilemma by saying that the decision maker can act on the basis of probabilities he assigns to the states of nature, choosing that alternative which yields the highest expected value. They bypass the question of how the decision maker assigns probabilities by leaving that problem to executive judgment.

The models of uncertainty were criticized earlier. In all but the equi-probable rule, the relationship between the state of nature and the action is foggy. The classical assumption of decision theory (excluding conflict) is that the course of action is independent of (does not influence) the state of nature. The decision dictated by the various rules of uncertainty ignores information on the occurrence of the various states of nature and makes a decision on the structure of the payoffs and the decision maker's objectives. However, the implied assumption of the minimax rule is: If I take this course of action, I expect the state of nature to be the one which yields the greatest harm. Is this evidence of an interrelationship between the course of action and the state of nature? The answer can be yes or no, depending upon the outlook of the decision maker. If he truly has the goal of minimizing harm, no interrelationship exists. If he truly believes there is a relationship, he is applying a rule which has not been theoretically validated.

This author advocates the use of a category called partial uncertainty to deal with the cases in which (1) executive judgment is present and/or (2) the relationship between the state of nature and courses of action are not independent. This would mean that the rules for dealing with uncertainty are valid only when there is a clear assumption of independence between the course of action and the state of nature.

It should also be clear that the category of conflict (including game theory) falls into the category of partial uncertainty. The area of game theory has an extensive body of literature. This text will cover only the two-person zero-sum game.

Game theory does offer a partial approach to some situations in which the courses of action and the states of nature are interrelated. The models for dealing with interrelationships between courses of action and states of nature are generally highly complex and beyond the scope of this book.

Let us now discuss more fully both the range of decisions involving executive judgment and the means of aiding the executive to derive probabilities of the occurrence of the states of nature. Between certainty and partial uncertainty, the accuracy and method of computing assigned probabilities vary widely. At one end of the continuum, we have an executive subjectively assigning probabilities to the success, partial success, or failure of a completely new product. At the other end of the continuum, we have a relative frequency for the purchase of size 8 through size 12 of men's shoes.

The probability of the occurrence of events may be based upon a priori, relative frequency (historical), or judgmental considerations. Further, these may be combined to establish the probabilities. A priori probabilities are those which exist by logic or assumption. The expected frequency of dots on a die is 1/6 each for one, two, three, four, five, and six dots because there are six sides and we assume a perfect die and rolling device. Thus, no factor intervenes to change these probabilities. Analogously, a ball park with six entrances each placed one sixth of the distance around might a priori expect one sixth of its customers to enter each gate. One can see that the distribution of roads and population surrounding the ball park will have a substantial impact upon actual entrance patterns. This alone should indicate that the practical use of a priori probabilities is as a starting point so that other factors may be brought into consideration.

Relative frequency is a historical record of events which is only useful if it allows us to make the best prediction of the future. Consequently, relative frequencies must often be modified subjectively on the basis of either subjective judgment or objective information. The model of revised probabilities in the previous chapter is an example of modification based upon objective information. The store buyer trying to predict the sale of women's dresses may have a raft of past purchase figures. For example, he may know that the distribution of purchases by basic colors changes very little from season to season despite drastic changes in style. Such information may be used to assist in assigning a likelihood of wide acceptance, limited acceptance, or nonacceptance of any particular dress, thus combining objective information with judgment to assign these probabilities.

In situations where subjective probabilities must be assigned, the analyst assists the manager to recognize all of the factors which affect the possibility of any outcome. Such a procedure should either strengthen the conviction or change the probabilities. The method of establishing odds on a football team is a process of gathering a vast array of information which may affect the outcome of a game. It should therefore follow that the odds maker with the most information (other things being equal) should be in the best position to predict the outcome. The same holds true for assignment of subjective probabilities by the manager.

The line of demarcation between risk and partial uncertainty is difficult to draw. However, risk is the condition in which the probability of occur-

Table 18–33

Proposition	Answer
$A > B$	Yes
$A > C$	Yes
$A > D$	Yes
$B > A$	No
$B > C$	Yes
$B > D$	Yes
$C > A$	No
$C > B$	No
$C > D$	Yes
$D > A$	No
$D > B$	No
$D > C$	No

rence of the states of nature is readily predictable, either a priori or on the basis of relative frequency. The method of dealing with the condition of risk or partial uncertainty is the same, but the faith the decision maker places in the recommended course of action is not the same. This is not to say that the course of action should not be taken, but that the actual outcome and the expected outcome may be quite different.

Another method of assisting the decision maker is by using a logic table. For example, assume that there are four states of nature, identified as A, B, C, and D, respectively. The decision maker is asked to compare the probability of occurrence of one or a combination to each event. If the proposition holds, he answers yes. If the proposition does not hold, he answers no. Given these answers, the execution can first be checked for internal consistency. If the decision maker's answers are internally consistent, he provides a first subjective approximation to the probability of each outcome. This approximation is either accepted because it is consistent with all the propositions or rejected because it is inconsistent. Let us look at all possible propositions, comparing each state of nature to each other state of nature. Table 18–33, with answers to the proposition, shows a 1-to-1 comparison.

The condition of equality is handled by answering "indifferent." In this instance, none of the states of nature exist with equal frequency. The reader can further see that $A > B$ implies $B < A$ and is thus not recognized as a separate proposition. If $A > B$ is yes, it follows that $B > A$ should be no. If we had answered $A > C$ yes and answered $C > A$ yes, this would be an example of a lack of internal consistency. Asking for a response to $A > C$ and $C > A$ is one form of duplication. We could also ask for a response to $A < C$ and $C < A$. This would amount to asking the same question four times, which seems highly redundant. However, some duplication may be necessary in order to check for internal consistency. In fact, the following propositions from Table 18–33 are included only to check for internal consistency: $B > A$, $C > A$, $C > B$, $D > A$, $D > B$,

Table 18–34

1-to-1 proposition	Answer	2-to-1 proposition	Answer	3-to-1 proposition	Answer
$A > B$	..... Yes	$A + B > C$	...... Yes	$A + B + C > D$	..... Yes
$A > C$	..... Yes	$A + B > D$	..... Yes	$A + C + D > B$	..... Yes
$A > D$	..... Yes	$A + C > B$	...... Yes	$A + B + D > C$	..... Yes
$B > C$	..... Yes	$A + C > D$	...... Yes	$B + C + D > A$	..... Yes
$B > D$	..... Yes	$A + D > B$	..... Yes		
$C > D$	..... Yes	$A + D > C$	..... Yes		
		$B + C > A$	...... Yes		
		$B + C > D$	...... Yes		
		$B + D > A$	..... Indifferent		
		$C + D > A$	..... No		
		$C + D > B$	...... Indifferent		

and $D > C$. Assume that we are given the responses shown in Table 18–34 after checking for internal consistency *via duplication* and then eliminating duplications.

What information is contained in Table 18–34? We may check further for internal consistency by comparing the 1-to-1 answers with the 2-to-1 answers. Thus, if $A > B$, then $A + C > B$ and $A + D > B$ must hold. In fact, all of the 2-to-1 propositions containing A can be inferred from the 1-to-1 answers. Also, the $B + C > D$ can be inferred from the 1-to-1 proposition answers. Consequently, for the case at hand, only four new pieces of information have been provided over Table 18–33. A look at the 3-to-1 proposition answers yields no new data when we have four states of nature. The relationships to be investigated may also include 2-to-2 propositions. Since there are only three unduplicated 2-to-2 propositions, they are included in the table of summary data (Table 18–35).

Let us investigate this information. Since $A > B$ and $A > C$ and $A > D$, we know that the probability of A occurring is greater than the probability of any other event occurring. Further, since $B > C$ and $B > D$, the probability of B occurring is second highest. Finally, we know that

Table 18–35

Proposition	Answer
$A > B$	Yes
$A > C$	Yes
$A > D$	Yes
$B > C$	Yes
$B > D$	Yes
$C > D$	Yes
$B + C > A$	Yes
$B + D > A$	Indifferent
$C + D > A$	No
$C + D > B$	Indifferent
$A + B > C + D$	Yes
$A + C > B + D$	Yes
$A + D > B + C$	Indifferent

$C > D;$ thus, we have a strict ordering of $A, B, C,$ and D. In other words:

$$A > B > C > D$$

Since $B + C > A$, we know that the probability of A is less than 0.5. Earlier, we said that indifference is an indication of equality. Hence:

$$B + D = A$$

and

$$C + D = B$$

Also:

$$A + D = B + C$$

If we work with the equality conditions, that is:

(1) $$C + D = B$$

and

(2) $$B + D = A$$

(3) $$A + D = B + C$$

and the logic condition that:

(4) $$A + B + C + D = 1.0$$

we may identify four different equations and four unknowns. We may reexpress equation (1) by subtracting B from both sides and adding A with a coefficient of zero:

$$0A - B + C + D = 0$$

Equation (2) and (3) may be similarly modified.

In summary, the equation system is:

(3)
$$A - B - C + D = 0.0$$
(4)
$$A + B + C + D = 1.0$$
(1)
$$0A - B + C + D = 0.0$$
(2)
$$-A + B + 0C + D = 0.0$$

The reader will recall that matrix algebra can be used to solve a system of linear equations.

This system may be expressed in the form $Ax = b$; then, multiplying by A^{-1}:

$$A^{-1}Ax = A^{-1}b$$
$$Ix = A^{-1}b$$
$$x = A^{-1}b$$

Thus, if we can find the inverse of the A matrix, we can uniquely identify the probability of the occurrence of each state of nature. The A matrix is shown in case the student wishes to invert it:

$$A = \begin{pmatrix} 1 & -1 & -1 & 1 \\ 1 & 1 & 1 & 1 \\ 0 & -1 & 1 & 1 \\ -1 & 1 & 0 & 1 \end{pmatrix}$$

The student may verify that $P(A) = 0.4$, $P(B) = 0.3$, $P(C) = 0.2$, and $P(D) = 0.1$.

Although the student may be justifiably proud that he has found a unique answer using the simple mathematical tools presented in this text, a unique answer is unfortunately very rare. In fact, the final system may contain only inequalities, and the number of answers may be infinite. This is why the usual procedure involves a suggested probability distribution by the decision maker which is checked for consistency against all of the propositions. If it is consistent, it is probably a very good estimate and can be used to calculate expected values. If it is not consistent, the decision maker is told where it fails, and he then adjusts either his response to the relevant propositions or his probability distribution until the distribution and propositions are consistent.

In summary, the approaches suggested to aid the decision maker in estimating the probability of occurrence of the states of nature are: (1) Provide the decision maker with information on the factors which influence the states of nature which occur, (2) obtain probability distributions on the states of nature for similar problems, and (3) use the logic table.

VIII. MULTIPLE OBJECTIVES

The reader may recall the discussion in Chapter 5 about one method of handling multiple objectives. In that chapter the company had the following two objectives: (1) a $500,000 profit and (2) a 25 percent market share. Table 18–36 summarizes the situation.

Assume that the actual profit condition is dependent upon a possible increase in raw material prices which will reduce profits. However, the in-

Table 18–36

	Profit (objective 1)	Market share (objective 2)
A_1...............	$375,000	25.0%
A_2...............	450,000	22.5
A_3...............	500,000	20.0

crease in raw material prices is different for each alternative. Table 18–37 summarizes this possible situation.

Management believes that there is a 50 percent chance of an increase in raw material prices. Remember that objective 1 is three times as important as objective 2, and that objective 1 is $500,000 in profit and objective 2 is

Table 18–37

	Profit (objective 1)	Market share (objective 2)
A_1...............	$350,000	25.0%
A_2...............	400,000	22.5
A_3...............	425,000	20.0

Table 18–38

	N_1		N_2	
	Objective 1	Objective 2	Objective 1	Objective 2
A_1.........	0.75	1.0	0.70	1.0
A_2.........	0.90	0.9	0.80	0.9
A_3.........	1.00	0.8	0.85	0.8

a 25 percent market share; Table 18–38 shows the probability of fulfillment for each objective under each state of nature. Remembering that objective 1 carries a weight of 0.75 and objective 2 a weight of 0.25, we may now calculate the percent fulfillment of combined objectives for each action and each state of nature; that is:

$$A_1N_1 = 0.75(0.75) + 0.25(1.0) = 0.8125$$
$$A_2N_1 = 0.75(0.9) + 0.25(0.9) = 0.9$$

Table 18-39

	$P(N_1) = 0.5$ N_1	$P(N_2) = 0.5$ N_2
A_1	0.8125	0.775
A_2	0.90	0.825
A_3	0.95	0.8375

and so on. Given this information, the resulting payoff matrix and expected fulfillment are as shown in Table 18–39. Thus, action 3 is still the best action to take.

$$EV_1 = 0.5(0.8125) + 0.5(0.775) = 0.79375$$
$$EV_2 = 0.5(0.9) + 0.5(0.825) = 0.8625$$
$$EV_3 = 0.5(0.95) + 0.5(0.8375) = 0.89375$$

IX. THE VALUE OF DECISION THEORY

In a hard practical sense, decision theory is of limited usefulness. However, it does provide a meaningful conceptual framework for improved decision making. This is so because, in using the decision theory framework, the decision maker is forced to consider and at least attempt to structure the information pertinent to the decision.

DISCUSSION TOPICS AND PROBLEMS

1. Discuss the elements of decision making represented in the payoff matrix.

2. Discuss the classification of information about the states of nature.

3. Explain the conditions of dependence and independence between the states of nature and courses of action.

4. Explain the difference between subjective and objective probability and its implemention for the businessman.

5. Why is the payoff matrix an effective way of communicating the basic elements of a decision-making situation? What vital elements are not directly shown by the payoff matrix?

6. A utility company repeatedly purchases generators which have a component part that costs $500 if ordered with the generator. If the part is needed and is ordered without the generator, the cost of having it made plus the cost of

the time the generator is out of operation is $2,000. Each generator is unique. The probability distribution for failures of the part is:

Number of spare parts needed	Probability
0	0.40
1	0.30
2	0.20
3	0.10

a) Which of the following payoff matrixes is the correct payoff matrix to use? Why?

STATES OF NATURE
(parts needed)

		0	1	2	3
	0	0	2,000	4,000	6,000
STRATEGIES (parts or- dered for inventory)	1	500	0	2,000	4,000
	2	1,000	500	0	200
	3	1,500	1,000	500	0

STATES OF NATURE

		0	1	2	3
	0	0	2,000	4,000	6,000
	1	500	500	2,500	4,500
STRATEGIES	2	1,000	1,000	1,000	3,000
	3	1,500	1,500	1,500	1,500

b) Choose the optimal course of action.
c) Assume that the company is purchasing two identical generators.
   1) Present the payoff matrix.
   2) Choose the optimal course of action.

7. Suppose that you are a beer distributor for the Terrapin Beer Company. You are presently faced with the problem of how many kegs you should keep in stock on an average day (assume that all the kegs left at the end of the day are worthless). Each keg costs $8.00 and is sold for $12.00. Over the last 100 days, you have kept close tab on your daily sales, and you have arrived at the following distribution of sales during this period:

Kegs sold	Number of days
20	5
21	20
22	30
23	35
24	10
	100

You are asked to find:

a) The expected profits under each possible stocking decision. What is the optimal decision? Why?

b) Assuming that you have perfect knowledge, what would be your expected profits?

c) Taking into account your obsolescence losses and opportunity losses, what is the minimum expected loss you can expect? What else does this figure show you?

8. You are given the following game against nature:

	N_1	N_2	N_3
S_1	3	-2	1
S_2	-6	5	4
S_3	6	-3	2

a) Choose the strategy for:

1) The minimax criterion
2) The Hurwicz criterion ($w = 1$) and ($w = 0.6$)
3) The equiprobable criterion
4) The Savage criterion
5) The criterion of pessimism
6) The criterion of optimism (state assumptions made)
7) The criterion of regret
8) The criterion of rationality

b) Given the following probabilities for the various events, what strategy should you select to maximize your average payoff over a long period of time?

$$P\,(N_1) = 0.30$$
$$P\,(N_2) = 0.20$$
$$P\,(N_3) = 0.50$$

c) Each of these rules claims to offer a method of decision making under uncertainty. Do you agree? (Discuss why or why not.)

d) Discuss the validity of these rules.

9. Explain the difference between minimax and maximin.

10. Suppose you have a total capital of $4,000. You have an opportunity to make a speculative investment of $3,000, which will either be totally lost or will be worth $5,000.

a) Set up the payoff matrix for this investment.

b) What is the point of indifference between the probability (x) of a gain and not making the investment, using dollar value directly?

c) How would you alter this to compute this point using the logarithmic measure of utility?

11. Assume that you are given a choice of the following paired alternatives. Select one of the *A* choices and one of the *B* choices. Discuss briefly your choices in light of your knowledge concerning expected monetary value and expected utility.

$A_1 =$ The certainty of a $100,000 gift tax-free

$A_2 =$ On the flip of a fair coin, nothing if it comes up heads, or a tax-exempt gift of $200,002 if the coin turns up tails

$B_1 =$ A certain loss of $10

$B_2 =$ One chance out of 2,500 of incurring a $20,000 debt, but 2,499/2,500 chance of losing nothing

12. Discuss the importance of the concept *utility* in managerial analysis.

13. Criticize the criteria for decision making under conditions of uncertainty.

14. Assume that candidate X and candidate Y have received their respective party nominations. Develop a two-person zero-sum game out of this situation. Discuss the desirability of applying the minimax criterion in this case.

15. A decision maker has four measures of effectiveness: $A, B, C,$ and D. He has ranked them as follows:

Measure	Rank
A	3
B	1
C	2
D	4

After the measures have been ranked, a managerial analyst tells the decision maker to answer yes or no to the combinations of weighting, as follows:

	Yes	No
$B > C$	X	
$B > A$	X	
$B > D$	X	
$C > A$	X	
$C > D$	X	
$A > D$	X	
$B > A + C + D$		X
$B > A + C$		X
$B > C + D$	X	
$C > A + D$		X
$B > A + D$	X	

From this, the decision maker concludes that the weighting he devised after the above considerations is correct. This weighting follows:

Measure	Weights
A	0.5
B	1.0
C	0.7
D	0.4

a) Are the decision maker's conclusions correct?
b) Comment briefly on the procedure he used.

16. A decision maker has two objectives: (1) $1 million profit this year and (2) a market share of 25 percent. He has two possible strategies and two possible states of nature. For each combination of objectives, strategies, and states of nature $(O_i S_j N_k)$, a probability distribution of the relative frequency of fulfilling each objective is known and is shown in the following table:

	Percent fulfillment				
	0%	25%	60%	100%	120%
$O_1 S_1 N_1$ . . . . Zero	0.2	0.2	0.5	0.1
$O_1 S_1 N_2$ . . . . Zero	0.4	0.5	0.1	Zero
$O_1 S_2 N_1$ . . . . Zero	0.4	0.3	0.3	Zero
$O_1 S_2 N_2$ 0.1	0.1	0.2	0.4	0.2
$O_2 S_1 N_1$ . . . . Zero	Zero	0.1	0.4	0.5
$O_2 S_1 N_2$ . . . . Zero	Zero	0.5	0.3	0.2
$O_2 S_2 N_1$ . . . . Zero	Zero	0.7	0.2	0.1
$O_2 S_2 N_2$ . . . . Zero	Zero	0.2	0.6	0.2

Line 1 then means that 20 percent of the time a profit of $250,000 is made, 50 percent of the time a profit of $600,000 is made, 20 percent of the time a profit of $1 million is made, and 10 percent of the time a profit of $1.2 million is made.

Line 5 then means that 10 percent of the time, market share is 15 percent; 40 percent of the time, market share is 25 percent; and 50 percent of the time, market share is 30 percent.

a) Given the information that objective 1 is three times as important as objective 2 and that the probability of nature N_1 is 0.8 and N_2 is 0.2, calculate the weighted expected percentage of goal fulfillment for strategy 1.
b) Assume that the decision maker will only accept a strategy which will yield $250,000 profit under any circumstances. What strategy would he take?

17. Suppose a company has two goals: to make $100,000 profit and to gain 40 percent of the market. It estimates its level of profit and percentage of market share to be gained by using each of four different materials, under three different possible states of nature:

Material	Profit (objective 1)	Market share (objective 2)	Profit (objective 1)	Market share (objective 2)	Profit (objective 1)	Market share (objective 2)
A	$ 80,000	40.0%	$50,000	40.0%	$40,000	40.0%
B	85,000	37.5	65,000	37.5	55,000	37.5
C	92,500	35.0	80,000	35.0	72,500	35.0
D	100,000	32.5	92,500	32.5	87,500	32.5

Which is the best material to use if the company considers profit to be four times as important as market share?

18. There are two players, A and B. A has four possible strategies, and B has five. The results of any two are as follows:

E_1V........B pays \$9		G_1X......B pays \$3	
F_1V........B pays \$6		H_1X......B pays \$2	
G_1V........A pays \$2		E_1Y......B pays \$8	
H_1V........B pays \$5		F_1Y......B pays \$6	
E_1W......B pays \$3		G_1Y......B pays \$3	
F_1W......B pays \$5		H_1Y......B pays \$2	
G_1W......B pays \$4		E_1Z......Even	
H_1W......B pays \$6		F_1Z........B pays \$7	
E_1X........B pays \$1		G_1Z......B pays \$8	
F_1X........B pays \$4		H_1Z......A pays \$1	

Find the best strategy for each player.

SELECTED REFERENCES

Blackwell, David, and Girshick, M. A. *Theory of Games and Statistical Decisions.* New York: John Wiley & Sons, Inc., 1954.

Chernoff, Herman, and Moses, Lincoln E. *Elementary Decision Theory.* New York: John Wiley & Sons, Inc., 1959.

Levin, Richard I., and Kirkpatrick, C. A. *Quantitative Approaches to Management.* New York: McGraw-Hill Book Co., Inc., 1965.

Luce, R. D., and Raiffa, Howard. *Games and Decisions.* New York: John Wiley & Sons, Inc., 1957.

Miller, David W., and Starr, Martin K. *Executive Decisions and Operations Research.* Englewood Cliffs, N.J.: Prentice-Hall, Inc., 1960.

Savage, L. J. *The Foundations of Statistics.* New York: John Wiley & Sons, Inc., 1954.

Schlaifer, R. *Introduction to Statistics for Business Decisions.* New York: McGraw-Hill Book Co., Inc., 1961.

Schlaifer, R. *Probability and Statistics for Business Decisions.* New York: McGraw-Hill Book Co., Inc., 1959.

Thrall, R. M.; Coombs, C.; and Davis, R. (eds.). *Decision Processes.* New York: John Wiley & Sons, Inc., 1954.

Von Neumann, John, and Morgenstern, Oskar. *Theory of Games and Economic Behavior.* 2d ed. Princeton: Princeton University Press, 1947.

19

Systems analysis

I. INTRODUCTION

It would appear that this book is primarily concerned with quantitative analysis as opposed to systems analysis. The order of presentation is not meant to minimize the importance of systems analysis. However, systems analysis contains a much smaller collection of well-defined tools and techniques which lead to an identifiable solution. Systems analysis usually deals with problems much less well structured than those presented earlier. As indicated in Chapters 1 and 2, its essence is an approach which:

1. Identifies the system or environments about which the decision must be made (including relationships between all relevant variables)
2. Identifies the courses of action or alternatives which may be taken to fulfill the objectives of the decision maker
3. Identifies the costs of each action
4. Identifies the benefits of each action (relative to the measurable objective of the decision maker)

If this truly describes systems analysis, one might ask: How is this different from the approach suggested when using a payoff matrix? In truth, as long as these conditions are met, systems analysis has been conducted. However, it is a very elementary form of systems analysis and fails to consider explicitly certain features which provide systems analysis with its strength. These additional desirable features of systems analysis will now be discussed.

One feature required of better systems analysis is recognition of costs and benefits over the life cycle of the alternatives. Thus, expansion of productive facilities cannot be justified on the basis of a spurt in demand. A meaningful analysis must be made about the permanency of the need for the facility as well as the costs and alternative uses of the resources to be devoted to the facility over its entire life. It is, of course, true that an

367

estimate of use in the near future is better than an estimate of use in the distant future. However, the total time horizon should be considered. This will require the use of present-value concepts, which will be discussed later in this chapter.

Another feature of better systems analysis deals with the identification of alternatives as well as the scope and opportunity to modify alternatives. In systems analysis, one usually proceeds by defining the objectives of the study and then identifying all possible alternatives, being careful not to restrict or discourage the alternatives so identified. The process may be somewhat analogous to brainstorming and requires that a variety of backgrounds be represented among the group proposing alternatives. After a period of incubation, the proposed alternatives are examined critically and discarded if they are obviously unmeritorious or further investigated if they are of questionable merit. During this same process, new but apparently meritorious alternatives may be proposed. By a process of cycling, which reduces the number of alternatives to manageable proportions, the analysis begins in earnest. Whether this process of identifying alternatives is real or fictional, the point is that better systems analysis makes provision for alternatives which are of diverse scope and are based upon pooled judgment. Elimination of an alternative should be based upon something more than a vague feeling that it will not work. Also, the process of choosing alternatives must be flexible enough that at some point new ones may be added.

Another feature of better systems analysis is its willingness to wrestle with problems for which it can provide only a partial answer. Widest use has been made of this process in the military forces, where uncertainties abound. It may not provide the Secretary of Defense with the answer to his question about what kinds of weapons should be developed, but it can provide him with some deeper insights. Like the ball-bearing manufacturer in Chapter 14, systems analysis attempts to provide information in order that the decision maker can revise his probabilities and thus improve his decisions.

In summary, it can be seen that systems analysis is particularly suited to analysis for decisions involving the future. Thus, it is especially useful to assist in research and development decisions, capital acquisition decisions, and expansion decisions.

II. COST-BENEFIT ANALYSIS AND THE "BLACK BOX"

The term *cost-benefit analysis* has found wide usage in the government and increasing usage in industry. In the structure of this book the definition of cost-benefit analysis is identical with the definition of systems analysis. The reason for the existence of the two terms is primarily because of lack of agreement on the definition of systems analysis.

The term *cost-benefit analysis* may mislead the analyst into thinking of the system as a "black box." Overconcern with costs and benefits may yield a blind acceptance of the cost of resource inputs and resulting benefits. If one is considering the purchase of a machine and he ignores its placement, maintenance, etc., his knowledge about the purchase of a machine can be depicted as shown in Figure 19–1. The analyst does not know what causes the benefit to be *YYY*.

Figure 19–1

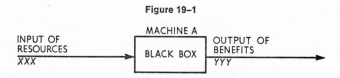

A thorough knowledge of the system may yield multiple alternatives about how machine *A* can be used and may drastically modify the conclusion. The lesson is not that the term *cost-benefit analysis* should be discarded in favor of *systems analysis*, but that an understanding of the system is as essential as an understanding of the costs and benefits.

III. SYSTEMS DESCRIPTION

Earlier, we defined a system as an interconnected complex of functionally related components. A great deal of insight can be gained by trying to abstract and describe the system of concern to the decision maker. If the system is described in flow diagrammatic fashion, it may not be used directly for analysis, but may be used to help the decision maker to create some order out of the confusing environment he faces. With this pictorial representation, he may be better able to cope with identification of problems and interrelationships. Thus, Figure 19–2 was used by Elwood S. Buffa in his book on production and inventory systems to assist the student to understand the inventory system.[1]

IV. LEASE-OR-BUY ANALYSIS

In much of the work in systems analysis, the incidence of costs and benefits does not occur at a single point in time. Frequently, the costs are immediate, and the benefits accrue later. For example, when a company acquires new equipment, the purchase cost is usually incurred immediately, but it benefits the company over its entire life. This poses a problem, because we cannot compare today's expenditure dollar with the

[1] Elwood S. Buffa, *Production-Inventory Systems: Planning and Control* (Homewood, Ill.: Richard D. Irwin, Inc., 1968), p. 7.

Figure 19–2

<small>Schematic diagram of multistage inventory system material and information flow, typical system time delays, and major problems of inventory management at each stage</small>

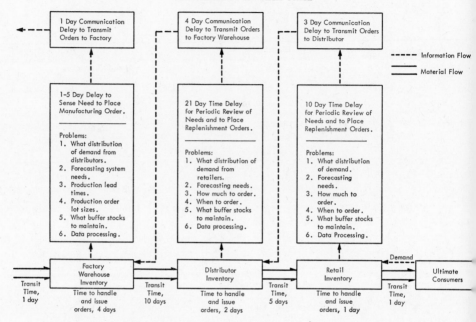

* By permission from Elwood S. Buffa, *Production-Inventory Systems: Planning and Control* (Homewood, Ill:. Richard D. Irwin, Inc., 1968), p. 7.

dollar of benefit received 10 years from now. This section will deal with a method for making those dollars comparable.

An elementary problem can be used to show a methodology for making these dollars comparable. Suppose that a company has been leasing a car for use by its executives. Based upon projections of future usage and future costs, the outlay pattern for the next four years for leasing versus buying is shown in Table 19–1 (note that the expenditures are assumed to

Table 19–1

Year	Buy	Lease
0	$4,000	....
1	1,000	$ 2,520
2	1,000	2,646
3	1,600	2,777
4	2,300	2,916
Total	$9,900	$10,859

take place at the end of the year; thus the $4,000 in year 0 represents the initial purchase cost). Ignoring time considerations, it would cost less to buy than lease. However, the incidence or timing of the expenditures differs widely. For example, the $4,000 spent in year 0 might have been invested for a 10 percent return. The remainder of this discussion will assume that we can always make an alternative investment which yields a 10 percent rate of return. Let us bring all of the future dollars up to today's dollars, i.e., the end of year 0. Accordingly, the $4,000 spent now is worth $4,000. We now need to know the value of $1 one year from now, considering the 10 percent rate of return, i.e., what we would receive today for a promise to pay $1 a year from now. In order to calculate this value, we need to know how much we would need to invest now to have $1 one year from now at a 10 percent rate of interest. This can be expressed as follows:

(1) $$A + iA = 1.0$$

where A is the unknown amount and i is the rate of interest. Modifying this, we get:

$$A(1 + i) = 1.0$$
$$A = \frac{1.0}{1.0 + i}$$

This is the standard formula for calculating the present value of $1 one interest period hence. Therefore, when $i = 0.1$:

$$A = \frac{1}{1 + 0.1} = \frac{1}{1.1} = 0.90909$$

The present value of the $1,000 expenditure at the end of year 1 is $909.09. The value of the amount to invest now to obtain $1 two years from now can be expressed:

(2) $$A + iA + i(A + iA) = 1.0$$

A is the original amount, iA is the interest earned the first year, and $i(A + iA)$ is the interest earned the second year. This can be reduced as follows:

$$A + iA + iA + Ai^2 = 1.0$$
$$A + 2iA + Ai^2 = 1.0$$
$$A(1 + 2i + i^2) = 1.0$$
$$A = \frac{1.0}{1 + 2i + i^2}$$

Factoring, we get:

$$A = \frac{1.0}{(1 + i)(1 + i)} = \frac{1.0}{(1 + i)^2}$$

Table 19–2

Present Value of $1*

Years Hence	1%	2%	4%	6%	8%	10%	12%	14%	15%	16%	18%	20%	22%	24%	25%	26%	28%	30%	35%	40%	45%	50%
1	0.990	0.980	0.962	0.943	0.926	0.909	0.893	0.877	0.870	0.862	0.847	0.833	0.820	0.806	0.800	0.794	0.781	0.769	0.741	0.714	0.690	0.667
2	0.980	0.961	0.925	0.890	0.857	0.826	0.797	0.769	0.756	0.743	0.718	0.694	0.672	0.650	0.640	0.630	0.610	0.592	0.549	0.510	0.476	0.444
3	0.971	0.942	0.889	0.840	0.794	0.751	0.712	0.675	0.658	0.641	0.609	0.579	0.551	0.524	0.512	0.500	0.477	0.455	0.406	0.364	0.328	0.296
4	0.961	0.924	0.855	0.792	0.735	0.683	0.636	0.592	0.572	0.552	0.516	0.482	0.451	0.423	0.410	0.397	0.373	0.350	0.301	0.260	0.226	0.198
5	0.951	0.906	0.822	0.747	0.681	0.621	0.567	0.519	0.497	0.476	0.437	0.402	0.370	0.341	0.328	0.315	0.291	0.269	0.223	0.186	0.156	0.132
6	0.942	0.888	0.790	0.705	0.630	0.564	0.507	0.456	0.432	0.410	0.370	0.335	0.303	0.275	0.262	0.250	0.227	0.207	0.165	0.133	0.108	0.088
7	0.933	0.871	0.760	0.665	0.583	0.513	0.452	0.400	0.376	0.354	0.314	0.279	0.249	0.222	0.210	0.198	0.178	0.159	0.122	0.095	0.074	0.059
8	0.923	0.853	0.731	0.627	0.540	0.467	0.404	0.351	0.327	0.305	0.266	0.233	0.204	0.179	0.168	0.157	0.139	0.123	0.091	0.068	0.051	0.039
9	0.914	0.837	0.703	0.592	0.500	0.424	0.361	0.308	0.284	0.263	0.225	0.194	0.167	0.144	0.134	0.125	0.108	0.094	0.067	0.048	0.035	0.026
10	0.905	0.820	0.676	0.558	0.463	0.386	0.322	0.270	0.247	0.227	0.191	0.162	0.137	0.116	0.107	0.099	0.085	0.073	0.050	0.035	0.024	0.017
11	0.896	0.804	0.650	0.527	0.429	0.350	0.287	0.237	0.215	0.195	0.162	0.135	0.112	0.094	0.086	0.079	0.066	0.056	0.037	0.025	0.017	0.012
12	0.887	0.788	0.625	0.497	0.397	0.319	0.257	0.208	0.187	0.168	0.137	0.112	0.092	0.076	0.069	0.062	0.052	0.043	0.027	0.018	0.012	0.008
13	0.879	0.773	0.601	0.469	0.368	0.290	0.229	0.182	0.163	0.145	0.116	0.093	0.075	0.061	0.055	0.050	0.040	0.033	0.020	0.013	0.008	0.005
14	0.870	0.758	0.577	0.442	0.340	0.263	0.205	0.160	0.141	0.125	0.099	0.078	0.062	0.049	0.044	0.039	0.032	0.025	0.015	0.009	0.006	0.003
15	0.861	0.743	0.555	0.417	0.315	0.239	0.183	0.140	0.123	0.108	0.084	0.065	0.051	0.040	0.035	0.031	0.025	0.020	0.011	0.006	0.004	0.002
16	0.853	0.728	0.534	0.394	0.292	0.218	0.163	0.123	0.107	0.093	0.071	0.054	0.042	0.032	0.028	0.025	0.019	0.015	0.008	0.005	0.003	0.002
17	0.844	0.714	0.513	0.371	0.270	0.198	0.146	0.108	0.093	0.080	0.060	0.045	0.034	0.026	0.023	0.020	0.015	0.012	0.006	0.003	0.002	0.001
18	0.836	0.700	0.494	0.350	0.250	0.180	0.130	0.095	0.081	0.069	0.051	0.038	0.028	0.021	0.018	0.016	0.012	0.009	0.005	0.002	0.001	0.001
19	0.828	0.686	0.475	0.331	0.232	0.164	0.116	0.083	0.070	0.060	0.043	0.031	0.023	0.017	0.014	0.012	0.009	0.007	0.003	0.002	0.001	
20	0.820	0.673	0.456	0.312	0.215	0.149	0.104	0.073	0.061	0.051	0.037	0.026	0.019	0.014	0.012	0.010	0.007	0.005	0.002	0.001		
21	0.811	0.660	0.439	0.294	0.199	0.135	0.093	0.064	0.053	0.044	0.031	0.022	0.015	0.011	0.009	0.008	0.006	0.004	0.002	0.001		
22	0.803	0.647	0.422	0.278	0.184	0.123	0.083	0.056	0.046	0.038	0.026	0.018	0.013	0.009	0.007	0.006	0.004	0.003	0.001	0.001		
23	0.795	0.634	0.406	0.262	0.170	0.112	0.074	0.049	0.040	0.033	0.022	0.015	0.010	0.007	0.006	0.005	0.003	0.002	0.001			
24	0.788	0.622	0.390	0.247	0.158	0.102	0.066	0.043	0.035	0.028	0.019	0.013	0.008	0.006	0.005	0.004	0.003	0.002	0.001			
25	0.780	0.610	0.375	0.233	0.146	0.092	0.059	0.038	0.030	0.024	0.016	0.010	0.007	0.005	0.004	0.003	0.002	0.001				
26	0.772	0.598	0.361	0.220	0.135	0.084	0.053	0.033	0.026	0.021	0.014	0.009	0.006	0.004	0.003	0.002	0.002	0.001				
27	0.764	0.586	0.347	0.207	0.125	0.076	0.047	0.029	0.023	0.018	0.011	0.007	0.004	0.003	0.002	0.002	0.001	0.001				
28	0.757	0.574	0.333	0.196	0.116	0.069	0.042	0.026	0.020	0.016	0.010	0.006	0.004	0.002	0.002	0.002	0.001	0.001				
29	0.749	0.563	0.321	0.185	0.107	0.063	0.037	0.022	0.017	0.014	0.008	0.005	0.003	0.002	0.002	0.001	0.001					
30	0.742	0.552	0.308	0.174	0.099	0.057	0.033	0.020	0.015	0.012	0.007	0.004	0.003	0.002	0.001	0.001	0.001					
40	0.672	0.453	0.208	0.097	0.046	0.022	0.011	0.005	0.004	0.003	0.001	0.001										
50	0.608	0.372	0.141	0.054	0.021	0.009	0.003	0.001	0.001	0.001												

* By permission from Robert N. Anthony, *Management Accounting* (Homewood, Ill.: Richard D. Irwin, Inc. 1956), p. 495.

At $i = 0.1$:

$$A = \frac{1}{(1.1)^2} = \frac{1}{1.21} = 0.826$$

Fortunately, we need not compute A every time; Table 19–2 gives us the present value of \$1. Thus the present value of \$1 three years hence at the 10 percent rate of interest is 0.751.

Table 19–3 brings the lease-or-buy costs to present dollars. Based upon

Table 19–3

	Original data		Present-value factor	Present value	
Year	Buy	Lease		Buy	Lease
0........	\$4,000	......	1.000	\$4,000.00	....
1........	1,000	\$2,520	0.909	909.00	\$2,290.68
2........	1,000	2,646	0.826	826.00	2,185.60
3........	1,600	2,777	0.751	1,201.60	2,085.52
4........	2,300	2,916	0.683	1,570.90	1,991.62
				\$8,507.50	\$8,553.42

this analysis, we would still choose to buy because the present value of this alternative is less than the lease alternative. However, the differential between these two alternatives is very slight. We may now wish to investigate the possible effects of uncertainty.

Projected average expenditures in year 1 for maintenance and upkeep when buying are \$1,000; however, the range of expenditures is from \$800 to \$1,200. Let us assume that this means that working capital requirements must be more flexible when buying than when leasing. This is because there is no expected variation in lease expenditures. Assume that all expenditures under the "buy" alternative may vary 20 percent. Assuming that total expenditures do not vary, we must add as a cost the cost of the capital committed for this contingency. The contingent capital and its

Table 19–4

Year	Contingent commitment	Ten percent cost of capital	Present value
0........	......	0	......
1........	\$200	\$20	\$18.18
2........	200	20	16.52
3........	320	32	24.03
4........	460	46	31.42
			\$90.15

cost are shown in Table 19–4. Adding this cost of uncertainty to the "buy" alternative yields a cost of $8,597.65, which is higher than the lease alternative.

V. THE DOCK FACILITIES PLANNING MODEL

Thus far, the systems shown have been elementary and indeed have been presented to illustrate points or concepts essential to systems analysis. We shall now show a more complex (although still highly elementary) example of systems analysis.

The existing facility

Assume that you are responsible for a receiving warehouse which has one unloading dock. Trucks arrive randomly at the dock during the 8⅓ hours the dock is open. The trucks all contain a standard cargo and may all be serviced in the same length of time, which is 400 man-minutes or 6⅔ man-hours. The day is broken into 25 20-minute intervals, and a log has been kept of the actual arrivals during each interval. Any trucks not unloaded remain in the dock (or in line if they cannot get into the dock) until the next morning when work resumes.

As a starting point, the decision maker wishes to have sufficient information to know the cost of the present system. Then he will investigate other alternatives to see the cost of alternative systems. Table 19–5 shows the result of four days of operations, using the logbook of arrivals.

It was assumed that trucks arrived midway in the period. Hence, in period 9 the truck moved directly into the dock, and each member of the crew worked 10 minutes, or a total of 20 minutes, which resulted in 5 percent of the truck being unloaded. In period 10, both men worked the entire period, thus spending 40 minutes unloading, which is one 10th of the total unloading time. Consequently, the amount left to unload at the end of the period is 10 percent less than the amount left to unload at the beginning of the period. Other periods are figured in the same fashion. It should be noted that during the 100 periods, 9 trucks arrived and 7.95 trucks were unloaded. If this is a representative sample, the probability of arrival in any period is 0.09. However, let us assume that the actual probability of an arrival over the last 2,500 periods (100 days) is 0.1.

The total number of trucks remaining in the queue at the end of all periods plus those in the queue part of a period divided by 100 periods will provide the waiting time as a percentage of total time. This will be in error if trucks do not in fact arrive, on the average, midway in the period. The total of the last column is 62. Since in seven periods the queue was overstated and in six it was understated, the total periods when a truck was waiting is 62.5. Assuming that the variable cost of the truck and driver is $5 per hour, the variable cost of each dock laborer is

Table 19–5

Data from logbook			Calculated data		
Day	Period	Did a truck arrive?	Truck in dock at end of period	Percent left to unload at end of period	Size of queue at end of period
1...............	1	No	No	None	None
	2	No	No	None	None
	3	No	No	None	None
	4	No	No	None	None
	5	No	No	None	None
	6	No	No	None	None
	7	No	No	None	None
	8	No	No	None	None
	9	Yes	Yes	0.95	None
	10	No	Yes	0.85	None
	11	No	Yes	0.75	None
	12	No	Yes	0.65	None
	13	No	Yes	0.55	None
	14	No	Yes	0.45	None
	15	No	Yes	0.35	None
	16	No	Yes	0.25	None
	17	Yes	Yes	0.15	1†
	18	No	Yes	0.05	1
	19	No	Yes	0.95	None*
	20	No	Yes	0.85	None
	21	No	Yes	0.75	None
	22	No	Yes	0.65	None
	23	No	Yes	0.55	None
	24	No	Yes	0.45	None
	25	Yes	Yes	0.35	1†
2...............26		No	Yes	0.25	1
	27	Yes	Yes	0.15	2†
	28	Yes	Yes	0.05	3†
	29	No	Yes	0.95	2*
	30	No	Yes	0.85	2
	31	No	Yes	0.75	2
	32	No	Yes	0.65	2
	33	No	Yes	0.55	2
	34	No	Yes	0.45	2
	35	No	Yes	0.35	2
	36	No	Yes	0.25	2
	37	No	Yes	0.15	2
	38	No	Yes	0.05	2
	39	No	Yes	0.95	1*
	40	No	Yes	0.85	1
	41	No	Yes	0.75	1
	42	No	Yes	0.65	1
	43	No	Yes	0.55	1
	44	No	Yes	0.45	1
	45	No	Yes	0.35	1
	46	No	Yes	0.25	1
	47	No	Yes	0.15	1
	48	No	Yes	0.05	1
	49	No	Yes	0.95	None*
	50	No	Yes	0.85	None

* Indicates movement from queue to dock. During this period average queue size is ½ truck larger.

† Movement into queue. Average queue size is ½ truck less.

Table 19–5 (continued)

		Data from logbook		Calculated data	
Day	Period	Did a truck arrive?	Truck in dock at end of period	Percent left to unload at end of period	Size of queue at end of period
3...............51		Yes	Yes	0.75	1†
	52	No	Yes	0.65	1
	53	No	Yes	0.55	1
	54	No	Yes	0.45	1
	55	No	Yes	0.35	1
	56	No	Yes	0.25	1
	57	No	Yes	0.15	1
	58	No	Yes	0.05	1
	59	No	Yes	0.95	None*
	60	No	Yes	0.85	None
	61	No	Yes	0.75	None
	62	No	Yes	0.65	None
	63	No	Yes	0.55	None
	64	No	Yes	0.45	None
	65	No	Yes	0.35	None
	66	No	Yes	0.25	None
	67	No	Yes	0.15	None
	68	No	Yes	0.05	None
	69	No	No	None	None
	70	No	No	None	None
	71	No	No	None	None
	72	No	No	None	None
	73	No	No	None	None
	74	No	No	None	None
	75	No	No	None	None
4...............76		No	No	None	None
	77	No	No	None	None
	78	No	No	None	None
	79	No	No	None	None
	80	No	No	None	None
	81	Yes	Yes	0.95	None
	82	No	Yes	0.85	None
	83	No	Yes	0.75	None
	84	No	Yes	0.65	None
	85	No	Yes	0.55	None
	86	No	Yes	0.45	None
	87	Yes	Yes	0.35	1†
	88	No	Yes	0.25	1
	89	No	Yes	0.15	1
	90	Yes	Yes	0.05	2†
	91	No	Yes	0.95	1*
	92	No	Yes	0.85	1
	93	No	Yes	0.75	1
	94	No	Yes	0.65	1
	95	No	Yes	0.55	1
	96	No	Yes	0.45	1
	97	No	Yes	0.35	1
	98	No	Yes	0.25	1
	99	No	Yes	0.15	1
	100	No	Yes	0.05	1

* Indicates movement from queue to dock. During this period average queue size is ½ truck larger.
† Movement into queue. Average queue size is ½ truck less.

$2.50 per hour, and overtime costs are 150 percent of normal costs, total costs for the 100 periods are:

$$C_t = C_v + C_d + C_c$$

where:

C_t = Total variable costs
C_v = Variable cost of vehicle and driver
C_d = Variable cost of dock facilities
C_c = Cost of closing dock at end of analysis

It should be noted that the last term is necessary so that the alternatives are comparable. At the end of this analysis, we empty the dock by going into overtime. The supporting model is:

(2) $$C_d = (R_d)(H_d)(F)$$

where:

R_d = Hourly rate for dock workers
F = Number of dock workers
H_d = Total hours dock is in normal service

and

$$H_d = (P)(D)(L) = (25)(1/3)(4) = 33\ 1/3$$

where:

P = Total periods per day
L = Length of period (in hours)
D = Number of days

Then:

$$C_d = (2.50)(33\ 1/3)(2) = 166.67$$

(3) $$C_v = C_r + C_w$$

where:

C_r = Cost of trucks while in dock
C_w = Cost of trucks while waiting in queue

(4) $$C_r = (R_t)(H_t)$$

where:

R_t = Hourly rate for truck and driver
H_t = Total time a truck is being unloaded during regular operations

and

$$H_t = [A - (Q + D)](U/F)$$

where:

A = Total truck arrivals
U = Unloading time per truck (in hours)
Q = Queue size at end
D = Percentage left to unload at end of analysis

$$H_t = [9 - (1+.05)] \frac{6\frac{2}{3}}{2} = 26.5$$

Then:

$$C_r = (5.00)(26.5) = 132.50$$

(5) $$C_w = (R_t)(H_d)(P_w)$$

where:

R_t = Hourly rate for truck drivers
P_w = Average number of trucks in queue

Then:

$$C_w = (5.00)(33 \ 1/3)(0.625) = 104.17$$

Thus:

$$C_v = 132.50 + 104.17 = 236.67$$

(6) $$C_c = (R_d)(H_c)(F)(R_o)$$

where:

R_o = Overtime costs as a multiple of regular labor costs
H_c = Amount of time required to unload remaining trucks

and

$$H_c = (Q + D)(U/F) = (1 + 0.05) \left(\frac{6\frac{2}{3}}{2} \right) = 3.5$$

Then:

$$C_c = (2.50)(3.5)(2)(1.5) = 26.25$$

Therefore:

$$C_t = 166.67 + 236.67 + 26.25 = \$429.59$$

The alternatives

The manager of the terminal has a number of alternatives open to him which may be investigated. Presently, he has two workers working 25 20-minute periods, which is 1,000 productive minutes available during the day. Since he expects 2.5 arrivals during the average day, and it takes 400 minutes to unload each truck, thus requiring

$$400(2.5) = 1,000 \text{ minutes to unload}$$

these workers should be busy all the time. Obviously, an increase in arrival rate will cause a line to build up. Thus, he may consider at least five pure alternatives:

1. Increase the work force
2. Use overtime to unload some or all of the trucks remaining at the end of the day
3. Use driver to help unload
4. Improve unloading methods
5. Expand to two docks, using one worker per dock

Note that expansion to two docks is a pure alternative only by assuming that such expansion would not require additional employees. A tacit assumption is that unloading time is directly proportionate to the number of dock workers. Accordingly, it was assumed that if two employees took 200 minutes, one employee would take 400 minutes, and three employees would take 133⅓ minutes. If this is not true, it must be recognized in the analysis.

Calculations for an additional employee

Let us add one employee and observe the effect on the system. This results in an unloading time of 133⅓ minutes. Table 19–6 summarizes this situation.

Thus the total of the last column is 19. Again, we shall assume that trucks arrive midway in the period. Since the queue was overstated in three periods and understated in three periods we will ignore this impact. Thus average queue length is 19/100 or 0.19 trucks. Calculating total costs as before, we get:

$$C_t = [R_d \, PDLF] + [R_t(A - [Q + D])(U/F) + R_t \, PDLP_w] \\ + [R_d(Q + D)(U/F)FR_o]$$

where:

$$R_d = 2.5 \; F = 3 \; P = 25 \; L = \tfrac{1}{3} \; D = 4 \; R_t = 5 \; U = 6\tfrac{2}{3} \; Q = 0$$
$$D = 0.075 \; P_w = 0.2 \; R_o = 1.5 \; A = 9$$

Therefore:

$$C_t = [(2.5)(25)(4)(\tfrac{1}{3})(3)] + \left[5(9 - [0 + 0.075]) \left(\frac{\frac{20}{3}}{3}\right) \right.$$
$$\left. + (5)(25)(4)(\tfrac{1}{3})(0.19) \right] + \left[(2.5)(0.075)\left(\frac{\frac{20}{3}}{3}\right)(3)(1.50) \right]$$

$$= 250.00 + 99.17 + 31.67 + 1.87 = \$385.62$$

$$C_d = \$250.00$$
$$C_v = 130.84$$
$$C_c = 1.87$$
$$C_t = 382.71$$

Table 19–6

Day	Period	Did a truck arrive?	Truck in dock at end of period	Percent left to unload at end of period	Size of queue at end of period
		Data from logbook		Calculated data	
1	1	No	No	None	None
	2	No	No	None	None
	3	No	No	None	None
	4	No	No	None	None
	5	No	No	None	None
	6	No	No	None	None
	7	No	No	None	None
	8	No	No	None	None
	9	Yes	Yes	0.925	None
	10	No	Yes	0.775	None
	11	No	Yes	0.625	None
	12	No	Yes	0.475	None
	13	No	Yes	0.325	None
	14	No	Yes	0.175	None
	15	No	Yes	0.025	None
	16	No	No	None	None
	17	Yes	Yes	0.925	None
	18	No	Yes	0.775	None
	19	No	Yes	0.625	None
	20	No	Yes	0.475	None
	21	No	Yes	0.325	None
	22	No	Yes	0.175	None
	23	No	No	0.025	None
	24	No	No	None	None
	25	Yes	Yes	0.925	None
2	26	No	Yes	0.775	None
	27	Yes	Yes	0.625	1†
	28	Yes	Yes	0.475	2†
	29	No	Yes	0.325	2
	30	No	Yes	0.175	2
	31	No	Yes	0.025	2
	32	No	Yes	0.875	1*
	33	No	Yes	0.725	1
	34	No	Yes	0.575	1
	35	No	Yes	0.425	1
	36	No	Yes	0.275	1
	37	No	Yes	0.125	1
	38	No	Yes	0.975	None*
	39	No	Yes	0.825	None
	40	No	Yes	0.675	None
	41	No	Yes	0.525	None
	42	No	Yes	0.375	None
	43	No	Yes	0.225	None
	44	No	Yes	0.075	None
	45	No	No	None	None
	46	No	No	None	None
	47	No	No	None	None
	48	No	No	None	None
	49	No	No	None	None
	50	No	No	None	None

* Indicates movement from queue to dock. During this period average queue size is larger.

† Movement into queue. Average queue size is ½ truck less.

Table 19–6 (continued)

Data from logbook			Calculated data		
Day	Period	Did a truck arrive?	Truck in dock at end of period	Percent left to unload at end of period	Size of queue at end of period
3	51	Yes	Yes	0.925	None
	52	No	Yes	0.775	None
	53	No	Yes	0.625	None
	54	No	Yes	0.475	None
	55	No	Yes	0.325	None
	56	No	Yes	0.175	None
	57	No	Yes	0.025	None
	58	No	No	None	None
	59	No	No	None	None
	60	No	No	None	None
	61	No	No	None	None
	62	No	No	None	None
	63	No	No	None	None
	64	No	No	None	None
	65	No	No	None	None
	66	No	No	None	None
	67	No	No	None	None
	68	No	No	None	None
	69	No	No	None	None
	70	No	No	None	None
	71	No	No	None	None
	72	No	No	None	None
	73	No	No	None	None
	74	No	No	None	None
	75	No	No	None	None
4	76	No	No	None	None
	77	No	No	None	None
	78	No	No	None	None
	79	No	No	None	None
	80	No	No	None	None
	81	Yes	Yes	0.925	None
	82	No	Yes	0.775	None
	83	No	Yes	0.625	None
	84	No	Yes	0.475	None
	85	No	Yes	0.325	None
	86	No	Yes	0.175	None
	87	Yes	Yes	0.025	None
	88	No	Yes	0.875	None
	89	No	Yes	0.725	None
	90	Yes	Yes	0.575	1†
	91	No	Yes	0.425	1
	92	No	Yes	0.275	1
	93	No	Yes	0.125	1
	94	No	Yes	0.975	None*
	95	No	Yes	0.825	None
	96	No	Yes	0.675	None
	97	No	Yes	0.525	None
	98	No	Yes	0.375	None
	99	No	Yes	0.225	None
	100	No	Yes	0.075	None

* Indicates movement from queue to dock. During this period average queue size is larger.

† Movement into queue. Average queue size is ½ truck less.

Accordingly, adding a dock worker saves $46.78.

This elementary planning model will allow the manager to test the desirability of alternatives. He can also test the impact of exogenous factors such as an increase in truck arrivals.

Calculations in using overtime

Let us investigate a policy of using up to one hour of overtime at the end of each day.

The only impact of the overtime policy is a reduction in the average size of the queue from 0.625 to 0.445; the increased cost of this overtime may be compared to the savings from the reduced waiting time. Using equation 5 in the original system, $C_w = \$104.17$. In this system, $C_w = 74.16$. Therefore the overtime policy saves $\$104.17 - \$74.16 = \$30.01$ in waiting costs. It cost $(2)(2.50)(1.50)(4) = \$30.00$, thus saving $0.01. This saving seems very slight. However, the condition which prevailed for the 100 periods is sufficiently below normal to change this figure substantially. This condition will be discussed further after we have discussed all of the alternatives. Because of space limitations, the table showing queue size by period for the overtime alternative is not presented. It is left as an exercise for the reader to verify these findings.

Using the driver to help unload

Using the driver to help unload requires more information on the environment. If he is employed by someone else, it may be impossible to use him to help unload. If he is employed by the company, union regulations may prevent him from assisting. If there is no impediment to using him, one may ask why he was not used before. For the moment, let us assume that we may use him while his truck is in the dock, but that we must compensate him at the normal rate of pay in addition to his normal pay. This results in a system identical to that which occurred when an additional employee was added, except that the idle-time costs of the additional employee are avoided. Hence, looking at Table 19–6, the student can verify that the dock was idle 40½ periods, or 40.5 percent of the time. Another way to verify the idle time is to remember that 8.925 trucks were unloaded, each taking 133.33 minutes, for a total of 1,190 minutes. Since the facility was open 2,000 minutes, it was idle 810 minutes, or 41.5 percent of the time. Both figures check. We may now reduce the cost found for the additional employee by the number of idle hours times the $2.50 rate per hour saved by using the truck driver instead of an additional employee. Thus:

$$(810/60)(2.50) = 13.5(2.50) = \$33.75$$

Since the total cost for an additional employee was $382.71, the total cost when using the driver is:

$$382.71 - 33.75 = \$348.96$$

Improving unloading methods

Let us assume that the addition of mechanical equipment, use of pallets (i.e., platforms on which a number of boxes are placed and removed as a unit), and more efficient stacking methods can reduce unloading time by 50 percent. This results in calculated data the same as in Table 19–6 (page 381). However, the cost of the above-mentioned changes must be identified so that we can evaluate their desirability. The reader should recognize that this alternative and the remaining one (expansion to the trucks) are quite different from the previous alternatives because they are of a much more permanent nature.

In this instance, we need more information on the environment, since we propose a change in loading methods as well as unloading methods. The first question is: Can we obtain a change in loading methods? If so, it is necessary to recognize the costs and/or savings in the loading process. Even if the loading organization is not directly related, it may be desirable to recognize the impact on it.

However, a more crucial problem is the permanency of the commitment in making an investment of this nature. We must evaluate this over its life cycle. This evaluation necessitates a projection of the use of the facility over the life cycle. Management must supply its plans which might affect the use of the facility, such as use projections (including labor costs), maintenance and wear data (including costs), scrap value, and other necessary information to evaluate the alternative. In comparing this alternative with the remaining ones, they all should be compared as to the same time period.

The MAPI methodology for decisions about equipment purchases can be found in almost any basic private finance book. We shall not discuss this methodology here. Consequently, we shall not be able to compare this alternative with the others.

Expansion of facilities

The reader will recall that the pure alternative of expansion to two facilities meant no additional employees. Expansion to two docks also requires a permanent investment and requires an even longer life cycle than improvement of facilities. As the system now stands, this expansion (using two employees) cannot change waiting time unless the employee in the idle dock does not help the employee in the full dock. In this case the waiting time is longer. We shall not compute the desirability of this alternative.

Summary of findings

The findings are:

$$C_p = \$429.59 = \text{Cost of present}$$
$$C_o = 429.58 = \text{Cost of overtime}$$
$$C_a = 382.71 = \text{Cost of additional employee}$$
$$C_d = 348.96 = \text{Cost of using truck driver}$$

Clearly, the cost of using the truck driver is the best alternative under the assumptions made. Obviously, this alternative will be more difficult to implement than the others. Aside from the difficulties of selling the idea to the drivers, we have assumed that there will not be side effects on the system. It could be that greater driver fatigue could increase travel time and increase the accident rate. If this is so, it should be considered.

It should be obvious that the cost data for the additional employee are more reliable than the data for the use of truck drivers.

Accuracy of findings

Earlier, we said that the long-term probability of arrival was 0.1, but that it was 0.09 for the 100 periods used in the analysis. The length of the analysis was far too short to produce reliable findings. The differential between the present cost and cost using either the driver or an additional employee will increase with reliable findings. The reader can appreciate the effect by assuming that a truck arrives at the 101st period and every 10th period thereafter. In this case the queue is always one, and the truck must wait 10 periods before being serviced. If we added an employee at this point, we would soon eliminate the queue.

Mixed alternatives

So far, we have only looked at pure strategies. However, we could try some combination of alternatives.

Additional considerations

This form of planning model is particularly desirable because it allows the decision maker to investigate alternatives which would be prohibitively costly in real life. Further, a well-structured planning model can be used repeatedly to investigate modifications of existing facilities.

Facilities-planning models are usually called simulations because they simulate (represent) an entity in the real world. They have been highly successful in planning a wide variety of facilities, including airports, high-ways, and industrial plants. In fact, any facility which is used repetitively and in which there is an interaction between man and the facility can conceptually be modeled for planning purposes.

Frequently, the logbook records are not the basis for determining whether a truck has arrived. If a probability distribution of truck arrivals can be obtained, then a Monte Carlo technique can be used to determine arrivals. Monte Carlo techniques will be discussed in the next chapter.

DISCUSSION TOPICS AND PROBLEMS

1. Discuss the difference between decision theory (as evidenced by the payoff matrix) and systems analysis.

2. Assume that the arrival information found in Table 19–5 applies to early arrivals at the supermarket (i.e., arrivals during the first five-hour period) discussed in problem 4 of Chapter 14. The period is 30 seconds long. Assume that five counters are available, and recognize labor costs as the only facilities costs. Overtime costs are 1.5 times normal costs.

a) Clear the que at overtime, and compare costs for three and four checkout counters.

b) As an alternative to opening the fourth checkout counter, the manager could hire a person to assist the checkout personnel by bagging the groceries. Assume that a bagger reduces average service time to nine minutes and costs $2 per hour. Discuss the validity of this assumption. What are the costs for three checkout counters and a bagger? What are the costs for two checkout counters and a bagger?

3. Defend the lease-or-buy example as an illustration of systems analysis.

4. The following table shows the median annual income (in 1949) for American males 15 years and over, by years of schooling:

Years of school completed	15–19 years old	20–24 years old	25–29 years old	30–34 years old	35–44 years old	45–54 years old	55–64 years old	65–74 years old	75 years old and over
Male, total......	$444	$1,376	$2,090	$2,363	$2,324	$2,152	$1,718	$ 887	$ 546
None.........	$367	$ 706	$ 840	$ 964	$1,034	$ 977	$ 852	$ 526	$ 393
Elementary:									
1 to 4 years...	393	847	1,130	1,249	1,278	1,217	989	604	423
5 to 7 years...	438	1,143	1,535	1,731	1,818	1,793	1,474	839	523
8 years.......	487	1,386	1,925	2,123	2,248	2,287	1,948	1,099	680
High school:									
1 to 3 years...	455	1,623	2,289	2,591	2,750	2,750	2,361	1,396	828
4 years.......	515	1,800	2,703	3,151	3,369	3,518	3,161	1,954	1,052
College:									
1 to 3 years...	168	1,139	2,590	3,512	3,865	3,913	3,443	2,203	1,296
4 years or more	0	1,200	2,921	4,203	5,029	5,364	4,864	3,526	1,868

a) Compare the expected median income for life of the high school graduate with the individual completing four years of college. (Use four years or more as representative of four years of college.) Assume a discount rate of 8 percent.

b) Assume that an education costs $2,500 per year. Is it economically justified? (Assume a discount rate of 8 percent.)

5. Five years ago, the Beta Company leased a warehouse for 10 years. The lease payments are $5,000 annually. Appreciation in building costs have pushed the cost of comparable space to $7,000 annually. You are seeking this space and offer to sublease for five years from the Beta Company at $7,000 per year. The Beta Company in turn offers to transfer its lease for a lump-sum payment of $7,500. You know you can find equivalent space elsewhere at $8,000. You demand returns of at least 10 percent.

a) Should you accept the offer of the Beta Company? How valid is your conclusion?

b) The Beta Company offers you two alternative lease agreements for its two forklift trucks. Under agreement 1, you pay the Beta Company $800 per year per truck, and the Beta Company handles all repairs. Under agreement 2, you pay $500 per year, and you handle all repairs. You expect repair costs per truck of $200 in each of the next three years, and $400 in the fourth and fifth years. Compare these two alternatives.

c) You have investigated the purchase costs of forklift trucks. The following table shows the expenditures for two new trucks of the type the Beta Company is offering to lease (Beta's are two years old). These trucks can be resold at the end of five years for $500 each.

Year	Outlay per truck
0	$3,000
1	50
2	50
3	200
4	200
5	200

Should you lease or buy the trucks from the Beta Company?

d) One of your analysts points out that you have not considered downtime (i.e., the time the equipment is inoperative). Downtime costs are $50 per day of downtime. The following table shows age and expected number of additional days of downtime when Beta Company handles repairs.

Age (years)	Downtime per year (days)
1	1
2	1
3	4
4	4
5	4
6	8
7	8

What is the best alternative, considering downtime?

6. The Dame Company has decided to surface a vacant lot next to one of its retail outlets, to serve as a parking lot for customers. Managment is considering the following bids, involving two different qualities of surfacing for a parking area of 10,000 square yards:

Bid *A.* A surface which costs $5.55 per square yard to install. This surface has a probable useful life of 10 years and will require annual maintenance in each year except the last year, at an estimated cost of 2 cents per square yard.

Bid *B.* A surface which costs $3 per square yard to install. This surface will have to be replaced at the end of five years. The annual maintenance cost on this surface is estimated at 10 cents per square yard for each year but the last year of its service.

Instructions:

Prepare a computation showing which bid should be accepted by the company. You may assume that the cost of capital is 10 percent, that the annual maintenance expenditures are incurred at the end of each year, and that prices are not expected to change during the next 10 years. On the basis of your analysis, make a recommendation to the management of the Dame Company.

SELECTED REFERENCES

Dearden, John, and McFarlan, F. Warren. *Management Information Systems: Text and Cases.* Homewood, Ill.: Richard D. Irwin, Inc., 1966.

Donald, A. G. *Management Information and Systems.* New York: Pergamon Press, Inc., 1967.

Johnson, Richard A.; Kast, Fremont E.; and Rosenzweig, James. *The Theory and Management of Systems.* New York: McGraw-Hill Book Co., Inc., 1967.

McDonough, Adrian M., and Garrett, Leonard. *Management Systems: Working Concepts and Practices.* Homewood, Ill.: Richard D. Irwin, Inc., 1965.

McMillan, Claude, and Gonzalez, Richard F. *Systems Analysis: A Computer Approach to Decision Models.* Rev. ed. Homewood Ill.: Richard D. Irwin, Inc., 1968.

Optner, Stanford L. *Systems Analysis for Business and Industrial Problem Solving.* Englewood Cliffs, N.J.: Prentice-Hall, Inc., 1965.

Optner, Stanford L. *Systems Analysis for Business Management.* 2d ed. Englewood Cliffs. N.J.: Prentice-Hall, Inc., 1968.

Shuchman, Abe. *Scientific Decision Making in Business.* New York: Holt, Rinehart & Winston, Inc., 1963.

20

Simulation

I. INTRODUCTION TO SIMULATION

The term *simulation* has found wide usage in quantitative literature. It has a technical meaning and one or more popular meanings. In popular usage the term sometimes refers to the assumption of the appearance of something without having its reality. For instance, electric light may be termed simulated sunlight. It possesses many of the properties of sunlight, but is not actually sunlight. *Simulation* is also a term that has been used to describe management games. The relationship between management games and simulation will be discussed later. For the purposes of this text, *simulation* refers to the construction and manipulation of an operating model, that model being a physical or symbolic representation of all or some aspects of an environment or process of interest to the constructor. Its purpose is to manipulate the operating model in order either to provide information about the environment or to assist in making the decision. The reader will recall the discussion in Chapter 7 about accounting models, functional models, and operating models. In that chapter, we said that an operating model is a model for which the parameter values have been specified, and thus manipulation upon the model is possible. The best way to identify the variety of uses to which simulation has been put is to discuss briefly some of the simulations that may be of interest to the reader.

In Chapter 14, we discussed some of the elementary queuing models. Simulation may be used to simulate or represent the behavior of those who enter the queuing system and the consequent impact on queue length and other variables of interest. One may wish to look not only at the queue size but also at the impact on queue size if, for example, the service is speeded up, or if the number of service facilities is increased.

Joseph Wright Forrester, in his widely read work, *Industrial Dynamics*, has modeled a production and distribution system, including factory, factory warehouse, distributors, retailers, and customers.[1] Using this model, he has investigated the impact on inventory size of various inventory and purchasing policies. His findings show that the more removed the inventory is from the customer, the wider the fluctuation in the size of the inventory, given fluctuations in demand. If the system is representative of the real world, certain modifications in inventory and purchasing policies may be considered in order to reduce the fluctuations in inventory as well as to reduce the average inventory size.

Charles P. Bonini, in his model of information and decision systems in the firm, has simulated various aspects of a firm.[2] The elements simulated include certain methods for (1) developing sales forecasts, (2) developing budgets, (3) controlling sales forecasts, (4) controlling budgets, and (5) controlling personnel. He identifies the impact of certain policies on sales, profits, and other performance variables in the firm. Consequently, modifications in policies can be studied in terms of their impact on performance variables for the firm.

G. P. E. Clarkson, in a study of the behavior of a trust investment officer in a bank, has been able successfully to predict the trust investment action that the investment officer would take for a given trust.[3] He develops this model of behavior as a means of understanding the thought processes of the trust investment officer. The purpose of the model is not to assist the trust investment officer in making better trust investments, but simply to understand how the trust investment officer goes about making his investments. If the model can explain the process used to make trust investments, it may be used as a basis for improving those investments.

Other models have been developed to simulate the production system of a firm in order to use that model to modify and improve the production system.

II. MONTE CARLO TECHNIQUE

The Monte Carlo technique is a technique usually associated with simulation which allows one to generate events or outcomes. In the dock facilities analysis the basic event was the arrival of a truck at the dock. Rather than take the event from a nonexistent or inaccurate logbook, the inci-

---

[1] Jay Wright Forrester, *Industrial Dynamics* (Cambridge: Massachusetts Institute of Technology Press, 1961).

[2] Charles P. Bonini, *Simulation of Information and Decision Systems in the Firm* (Englewood Cliffs, N.J.: Prentice-Hall, Inc., 1963).

[3] G. P. E. Clarkson, *Portfolio Selection: A Simulation of Trust Investment* (Englewood Cliffs, N.J.: Prentice-Hall, Inc., 1962).

dence of arrival might have been derived from the Monte Carlo techniques.[4]

Let us illustrate the Monte Carlo technique with the problem of an electric company with four new generators. In order to develop the optimal maintenance policy, the company needs information on life expectancy and failure of each generator. Fortunately, the units are made up of some combination of three components the company has used extensively; thus the company has failure data.

Table 20–1

Component X		Component Y		Component Z	
w_1	$P(w_1)$	w_2	$P(w_2)$	w_3	$P(w_3)$
0	Zero	0	Zero	0	Zero
4	Zero	4	0.2	4	0.1
8	0.1	8	0.3	8	0.3
12	0.3	12	0.5	12	0.3
16	0.4	16	Zero	16	0.3
20	0.2	20	Zero	20	Zero

The three components X, Y, and Z, are combined in the following ways to form the four generators:

Generator 1:   Components X and Y
Generator 2:   Components Y and Z
Generator 3:   Components Z and X
Generator 4:   Components X, Y, and Z

In a generator the failure of any component is statistically independent of the failure of any other component. When any component fails to operate, the entire unit must be shut down, and the entire unit is overhauled. This is so because the marginal cost of repairing the additional components is more than offset by subsequent savings.

Data on failure rates by component are shown in Table 20–1. The w stands for the number of weeks that elapse between the time maintenance is performed and failure occurs, and $P(w)$ is the probability that w weeks will elapse between the time maintenance is performed and failure occurs. The reader will notice that failure takes place only at the end of 4, 8, 12, 16, or 20 weeks. The purpose of the Monte Carlo technique is to predict when failures take place, and from that figure to predict average life for each generator.

Since the failure of any component is statistically independent of the failure of any other component in the generator, failure of the generator

---

[4] As a matter of fact, the arrivals in Tables 19–5 and 19–6 (pages 375 and 381) were generated with the Monte Carlo technique.

is dependent upon which component fails first. As an example, assume that we conduct an experiment with generator *YZ*. This experiment consists of separating the components and running them until each fails. Table 20–2 shows 10 replications of this experiment. If we are to believe this table, the generator will fail, on the average, in 7.6 weeks. This is found by recognizing that the total life of the generator for the 10 replications is 76 weeks (total of column 3), for an average of 7.6 weeks. Obviously, a great deal of time must elapse before this experiment could be conducted, and it would be quite costly. The Monte Carlo technique provides a means of conducting this experiment using either a table of random numbers or a random number generator.

Table 20–2

Week in which component Y failed	Week in which component Z failed	Failure of generator (earliest component to fail)
12	12	12
4	16	4
8	8	8
12	16	12
4	12	4
12	8	8
12	4	4
12	16	12
4	8	4
8	12	8
88	112	76

A random number generator can be imagined by assuming that we have a large urn containing 100 balls numbered from 00 to 99. When the numbers are mixed in the urn and a number is drawn at random, each number has an equal chance of being drawn. If we let each ball represent the event "failure in w weeks," we may draw a series of balls to represent the events of interest. For example, for component *Y* the balls shown in Table 20–3 represent the events. This representation stems from the fact that 20 percent of the failures occur in week 4, and the 20 numbers (00–19) are 20 percent of the balls in the bowl. Now assume that we draw

Table 20–3

Balls	Event—failure of component Y in week:
00–19	4
20–49	8
50–99	12

Table 20–4

Number on ball	Event—failure of component Y in week:
88	12
16	4
43	8
55	12
15	4
67	12
79	12
70	12
09	4
31	8

a ball, record the number found on the ball, replace it in the urn, and thoroughly mix the balls and repeat this procedure 10 times. Table 20–4 will show the number found on the ball and the week in which component Y fails. The reader should note that the last column of this table is identical to (and indeed the source of) the first column of Table 20–2. In

Table 20–5

Balls	Event—failure of component Z in week:
00–09	4
10–39	8
40–69	12
70–99	16

similar fashion, we may represent failure of component Z, remembering that the balls represent the events as shown in Table 20–5.

Table 20–6 will show the number found on the ball and the week in which component Z fails. The reader should note that the last column

Table 20–6

Number on ball	Event—failure of component Z in week:
61	12
88	16
22	8
91	16
51	12
19	8
6	4
92	16
13	8
40	12

of this table is identical to (and the source of) the second column of Table 20–2. The Monte Carlo technique is simply the process of generating events or outcomes using random numbers, and Table 20–2 (with Tables 20–4 and 20–6 as a source of input) summarizes the findings.

Obviously, the elaborate use of an urn is impractical when the number of events becomes unduly large. However, a more significant drawback in the use of an urn is the possibility of the selection not being completely random. Many things could affect the randomness of the draw. The process of mixing could be incomplete, and one could draw only from a particular section of the urn. Thus, some numbers may have a better chance of being drawn than others. The random numbers are normally taken from a table of random numbers; or if a computer is used, a random number generator subprogram will provide the random numbers. The table of random numbers (Table 20–7) is the source of the random numbers used in this example.

The reader will note that each number is a five-digit number, but we used a two-digit number. In Table 20–4, we have used only the first two digits beginning with the 16th number of column 8 and moving down the column. Accordingly, the first number is 88348, and we recognize the 88; the second number is 1611, and we recognize the 16, etc. Since component Z is parallel to Y, we move over to the corresponding line of the next column to find the random number for failure in component Z. Hence, we begin in line 16 of column 9 with the number 61211, and we recognize 61. The second number is 88599, and we recognize 88, etc.

The complete table for generator 2 is given in Table 20–8.

The reader should now be able to verify that average failure in component X is 14.8 weeks if we begin with the random number in the 16th line of column 7.

Since the total weeks until failure of component Y are 88 and we have a sample of 10 events, there are on the average 88/10 = 8.8 weeks until failure of component Y. Likewise, average calculated weeks until failure are 11.2 for component Z. Using the data from Table 20–1 on the probability of failure in week w, we may find the expected value of failure for each separate component. Consequently:

$$E_{f,\,x} = 8(0.1) + 12(0.3) + 16(0.4) + 20(0.2) = 14.8$$

where $E_{f,\,x}$ is the expected (or average) week of failure for component X. Then:

$$E_{f,\,y} = 9.2$$

and

$$E_{f,\,z} = 11.2$$

Thus the Monte Carlo sample drawn was low by 0.4 weeks for Y and Z, but perfect for X. A sample of 10 is far too few to provide any degree of reliability.

Table 20-7

TABLE OF RANDOM NUMBERS*

96268	11860	83699	38631	90045	69696	48572	05917	51905	10052
03550	59144	59468	37984	77892	89766	86489	46619	50263	91136
22188	81205	99699	84260	19693	36701	43233	62719	53117	71153
63759	61429	14043	49095	84746	22018	19014	76781	61086	90216
55006	17765	15013	77707	54317	48862	53823	52905	70754	68212
81982	45644	12600	01951	72166	52682	97598	11955	63018	23528
06344	50136	33122	31794	86423	58037	36065	32190	31367	96007
92363	99784	94169	03652	80824	33407	40837	97749	18364	72666
96038	16943	89916	55159	62184	86208	09764	20244	88388	98675
92993	10747	08985	44999	36785	65035	65933	77378	92339	96454
95083	70292	50394	61044	65591	09774	16216	63561	59751	78771
77308	60721	96057	86031	83148	34970	30892	53489	44999	18021
11913	49624	28510	27311	61586	28576	43092	69971	44220	80410
70648	47484	05095	92335	55299	27161	64486	71307	85883	69610
92771	99203	37786	81142	44271	36433	31726	74879	89348	76886
78816	20975	53043	55921	82774	62745	48338	88348	61211	88074
79934	35392	56097	87613	94627	63622	08110	16611	88599	02890
64698	83376	87524	36897	17215	74339	69856	43622	22567	11510
44212	12995	03581	37618	94851	63020	65348	55857	91742	79508
82292	00204	00579	70630	37136	50922	83387	15014	51838	81760
08692	87237	87879	01629	72184	33853	95144	67943	19345	03469
67927	76855	50702	78555	97442	78809	40575	79714	06201	34576
62167	94213	52971	85974	68067	78814	40103	70759	92129	46716
45828	45441	74220	84157	23241	49332	23646	09390	13032	51569
01164	35307	26526	80335	58090	85871	07205	31749	40571	51755
29283	31581	04359	45538	41435	61103	32428	94042	39971	63678
19868	49978	81699	84904	50163	22625	07845	71308	00859	87984
14294	93587	55960	23149	07370	65065	06580	46285	07884	83928
77410	52195	29459	23032	83242	89938	40501	27252	55565	64714
36580	06921	35675	81645	60479	71035	99380	59759	42161	93440
07780	18093	31258	78156	07871	20369	53947	08534	39433	57216
07548	08454	36674	46255	80541	52903	37366	21164	97516	66181
22023	60448	00344	44260	90570	01632	21002	24413	04671	05665
20927	37210	57797	34660	32510	71558	78228	43204	77197	79168
47802	79270	48805	59480	88092	11441	96016	76091	51823	94442
76730	86591	18978	25479	77684	88439	35112	26052	57112	91653
26439	02903	20935	76297	15290	84688	74002	09467	41111	19194
32927	83426	07848	59327	44422	53372	27823	25417	27150	21750
51484	05286	77103	47284	05578	88774	15293	50740	07932	87633
45142	96804	92834	26886	70002	96643	36008	02239	93563	66429
12760	96106	89348	76127	17058	37181	74001	43869	28377	80923
15564	38648	02147	03894	97787	35234	44302	41672	12408	90168
71051	34941	55384	70709	11646	30269	60154	28276	48153	23122
42742	08817	82579	19505	26344	94116	86230	49139	32644	36545
59474	97752	77124	79579	65448	87700	54002	81411	57988	57437
12581	18211	61713	73962	87212	55624	85675	33961	63272	17587
00278	75089	20673	37438	92361	47941	62056	94104	45502	79159
59317	31861	62559	30925	23055	70922	47195	29827	68065	95409
59220	42448	70881	33687	53575	54599	69525	76424	98778	10459
00670	32157	15877	87120	13857	23979	38922	62421	03043	19602

* By permission from David W. Miller and Martin K. Starr, *Executive Decisions and Operations Research* (Englewood Cliffs, N.J.: Prentice-Hall, Inc., 1960).

In the example used, we could have calculated the expected average life of generator 2 by direct means. However, as the number of components increases and the number of points in the probability distribution increases, direct means of calculating grow prohibitively costly. Thus the Monte Carlo technique becomes important.

Table 20–8

Component Y		Component Z		Failure in generator 2 (weakest link)
Random number	Week of failure	Random number	Week of failure	
88	12	61	12	12
16	4	88	16	4
43	8	22	8	8
55	12	91	16	12
15	4	51	12	4
67	12	19	8	8
79	12	6	4	4
70	12	92	16	12
09	4	13	8	4
31	8	40	12	8
Total	88		112	76

Let us show how we calculate the average failure of generator 2 by direct means. Let us observe that failure of generator 2 is the joint probability of failure in components Y and Z. However, in the final analysis, we only recognize the weakest link (i.e., the earliest failure). For example, one possible event is failure of component Y in week 4 and failure of component Z in week 4. Since these events occur under a condition of statistical independence, the probability of this joint event is:

$$(0.2)(0.1) = 0.02$$

Hence, by listing all possible events and their probability, we may establish the probability of failure of generator 2. This information is presented in Table 20–9. We may now find the individual probability of failure in

Table 20–9

Week in which Y and Z fail		Probability of Y failing $P(w_2)$	Probability of Z failing $P(w_3)$	Week of earliest failure	Joint probability
Y	Z				
4	4	0.1	0.2	4	0.02
8	4	0.3	0.2	4	0.06
12	4	0.3	0.2	4	0.06
16	4	0.3	0.2	4	0.06
4	8	0.1	0.3	4	0.03
8	8	0.3	0.3	8	0.09
12	8	0.3	0.3	8	0.09
16	8	0.3	0.3	8	0.09
4	12	0.1	0.5	4	0.05
8	12	0.3	0.5	8	0.15
12	12	0.3	0.5	12	0.15
16	12	0.3	0.5	12	0.15
					1.00

week 4, 8, or 12, summing all of the joint events in which the earliest failure was in week 4, 8, or 12. This is shown in Table 20–10. Therefore the expected failure is:

$$4(0.28) + 8(0.42) + 12(0.3) = 8.08$$

which is higher than the 7.6 arrived at by the Monte Carlo technique. As indicated earlier, the sample of 10 is entirely too small for reliable results.

Before completing our discussion of the Monte Carlo technique, we should briefly discuss the use and interpretation of the random number table. It should be noted that not only is each number random, but also each digit is random. This means that each digit in a number has an equal chance of being zero through nine. It further means that in the example

Table 20–10

Week in which generator failed	Probability of failure
4	0.28
8	0.42
12	0.30
	1.00

we could equally as well use the last two digits, or the second and third digits, etc., instead of the first two. However, we should always begin randomnly within the table. If we always begin in row 1 of column 1, we shall probably introduce a bias in all of our findings.

The arrivals in the dock facilities model of the previous chapter were drawn by Monte Carlo techniques, using the first two digits of item 16 of column 2. In this case the numbers 00–09 represent an arrival, and 10–99 represent no arrival.

III. MANAGEMENT GAMES AND MODEL BUILDING[5]

War games have been used as a teaching device by the military for well over 100 years.[6] More recently, business games have been developed for teaching and research in business administration. It has been only 11 years since the first fully developed business games were introduced.[7]

---

[5] Much of this section is drawn from the author's article, "A Computerized, Multipurpose Management Game Applied to Retailing," *Journal of Retailing*, Vol. 41, No. 4 (Winter 1965–1966).

[6] See, for example, C. A. L. Totten, *Strategies: American Games of War* (New York: D. Appleton & Co., 1880 and 1895).

[7] This was "top management decision simulation," developed by the American Management Association and reported in Franc M. Ricciardi *et al.*, *Top Management Decision Simulation: The AMA Approach*, Elizabeth Marting (ed.) (New York: American Management Association, Inc., 1957).

Since that time, the number of games developed and being developed is amazingly large. Well over 100 different games are reported in two authoritative books on the subject: Paul S. Greenlaw, Lowell W. Herron, and Richard H. Rawdon, *Business Simulation;* and Joel M. Kibbee, Clifford J. Craft, and Burt Nanus, *Management Games.*[8]

Games may be of any degree of complexity. As complexity is added, the time necessary to learn the game and evolve a satisfactory competence in operating the simulated firm increases. Conversely, the direct relationship between a given action and the results of that action becomes more masked. However, the more complex the game, the greater the appreciation for the multitude of factors that affect the results of a certain decision. Also, the appreciation for the lag effect of a decision increases, and this in turn increases the appreciation of the need for long-run planning.

A one-page game

The best introduction to management games is to play one. The following is a very simple version of a game that can be played with paper and pencil between two players (or two teams could be formed). This game is fun as well as being competitive and educational.

Assume that you are the proprietor of a novelty stand at the Washington Senators ball park. Your only product is a miniature Senator. Your only competitor stations himself at the opposite end of the stands from you. Both of you have an agreement with the Senators that you will pay them $10 each game for the privilege of selling that product in their park, plus $5 for rent of the booth. The only remaining stipulation is that you submit your price for that game to the management in secret. As alternative employment to selling, you are offered the job of taking tickets at $10 per game. The miniature Senator costs you $2, and all unsold units may be returned for a full refund.

Step 1. Set your price in secret, one game at a time.
Step 2. Match your price and your competitor's price with the noncompetitive price index shown in Table 20–11 (e.g., a price of $4 will yield a noncompetitive price index of 1.2).
Step 3. Compute the competitive price index for your store by the following formula:

$$CI_1 = I_1 + 4\left(\frac{2I_1}{I_1 + I_2} - 1\right)$$

where CI_1 is the competitive price index for stand 1, I_1 is the noncompetitive price index for stand 1, and I_2 refers to stand 2.[9]

---

[8] Paul S. Greenlaw, Lowell W. Herron, and Richard H. Rawdon, *Business Simulation* (Englewood Cliffs, N.J.: Prentice-Hall, Inc., 1962); Joel M. Kibbee, Clifford J. Craft, and Burt Nanus, *Management Games* (New York: Reinhold Publishing Corp., 1961).

[9] Stand 2 computes *CI* by using I_2 instead of I_1.

Table 20–11

Price	Noncompetitive price index
$2.00	1.6
2.50	1.5
3.00	1.4
3.50	1.3
4.00	1.2
4.50	1.1
5.00	1.0
5.50	0.9
6.00	0.8
6.50	0.7
7.00	0.6
7.50	0.5
8.00	0.4
8.50	0.3
9.00	0.2
9.50	0.1

Table 20–12

Game	Potential or base demand
1	50
2	45
3	30
4	30
5	40
6	35
7	30
8	25
9	20
10	30

Step 4. Multiply the competitive price index by the potential for that game found in Table 20–12 to get total unit sales (drop partial units).

Step 5. Complete the income statement.

The income statement contains only four lines:

1. Total dollar sales (total units sold times price)
2. Less fixed expenses $25 (includes $10 opportunity loss because you did not sell tickets)
3. Less variable expenses (total units sold times $2)
4. Equals net income before taxes

You might arrange these items as in Table 20–13.

For example, assume that stand 1 sets a price of $3, and stand 2 sets a price of $4. Then the results could be as shown in Table 20–14.

Now, verify for yourself that if stand 2 had set a price of $5 instead of $4, stand 1 would have made a profit of $78 and stand 2 a profit of $23.

Table 20–13

	Game 1	Game 2	Game 3	Game 4	Game 5	Game 6	Game 7	Game 8	Game 9
1. Total sales									
2. Fixed expenses									
3. Variable expenses									
4. Net profit									

Table 20–14

Stand 1

Step 1. 1.4

Step 2. $1.4 + 4\left(\dfrac{2(1.4)}{1.4 + 1.2} - 1\right)$

Step 3. 1.708(50) = 85

Step 4. Total sales = 85($3)........$255
Fixed costs................ 25
Variable costs 85($2)........ 170
Net profit.............$ 60

Stand 2

Step 1. 1.2

Step 2. $1.2 + 4\left(\dfrac{2(1.2)}{1.4 + 1.2} - 1\right)$

Step 3. 0.892(50) = 44

Step 4. Total sales = 44($4).......$176
Fixed costs................ 25
Variable costs 44($2)........ 88
Net profit.............$ 63

Lessons to be derived from this simple game

If you played this game either as one person or as a team member, you probably experienced the intense emotional involvement most game players undergo in the attempt to beat their competition. This emotional involvement probably forced you to try to figure out what your competitor would do. Further, you may have wondered how the market (i.e., both teams acting together) reacted to price changes. Were you able to figure out that the best price for both of you to charge was $6 (i.e., total profit for both stands was the highest at this price)? You may have experienced the case where you did not change your price but your competitor raised his; and as a consequence, you did better. You may have noticed the example where stand 2 made a higher profit when he charged a higher price. At this point, you can begin to see complexity, despite the simplicity of the game.

Obviously, this is the simplest game that can be devised.

Changing influential variables in this game

Try changing the influential variables and see what happens. For example, change the 4 to 2 in:

$$CI_1 = I_1 + 4\left(\frac{2I_1}{I_1 + I_2} - 1\right)$$

Now, verify that for the conditions stated in the example, sales would have been 77 for stand 1 and 52 for stand 2, as opposed to 85 and 44, respectively. This change makes the demand much less sensitive to different competitive prices.

Figure 20–1

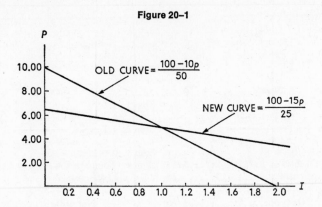

The noncompetitive price index is an index of the quantity demanded from a traditional demand curve. The equation to determine the index used in the game is:

$$I_i = \frac{100 - 10p}{50}$$

where p is the price. The expression in the numerator is the true demand curve. The graph in Figure 20–1 will show a market demand curve that is more price-sensitive.

Thus, taking points off the new curve, we have the results shown in Table 20–15.

Again applying the conditions stated in the example, you can verify that profit for stand 1 is $115, and for stand 2, $79. This change makes the game much more sensitive to price changes and consequently much more sensitive to competitive price differences.

This exercise in changing influential variables begins to show you that with any specific item in any specific industry, this formula can be manipulated to reflect any degree of the following four combinations:

1. Industry demand highly elastic, competitive price differences of slight influence
2. Industry demand highly elastic, competitive price differences of great influence
3. Industry demand highly inelastic, competitive price differences of slight influence
4. Industry demand highly inelastic, competitive price differences of great influence

Further, by changing the 4 in the CI_1 formula to 0, the competitive aspect can be dropped. Also, changes can be made in the potential demand.

Table 20–15

Price	Noncompetitive price index
$3.00	2.2
3.50	1.9
4.00	1.6
4.50	1.3
5.00	1.0
5.50	0.7
6.00	0.4
6.50	0.1

Adding factors in order to formulate a complex game

It can be observed that CI_1 was an index number that centered around one. When it was greater than one, sales were above the potential; and when it was lower than one, sales were below the potential.

Since this was an index number for behavior in setting price, one could develop an index number for behavior on something else, such as advertising. Once the index number for advertising is known, one can multiply it by the total unit sales to get total unit sales considering both advertising and price. On the other hand, one could come up with some number of units to be added to, or subtracted from, total unit sales (considering only price) to get total unit sales considering both price and advertising. Consequently, you can begin to see how we add demand factors in order to reproduce an actual market environment. The preceding factors represent changes in the demand side of the game. On the other side of the coin, changes can be made in costs.

This game also serves a useful purpose to distinguish between an accounting, functional, or operational model. It also allows us to focus on constants and variables.

In abstract or function form, we have the following system:

$$\pi_i = R_i - C_i$$

where R_i is the revenue of the ith firm, C_i is the costs of the ith firm, and π_i is the profit of the ith firm.

This relationship is an accounting relationship because it exists by definition. However, we may go on to identify R_i and C_i as follows:

$$C_i = S_i c_i + F_i$$

where c_i is the variable unit cost of the product sold by the ith firm, F_i is the fixed costs of the ith firm, and S_i is the unit sales for the ith firm; and

$$R_i = S_i p_i$$

where p_i is the price charged by the ith firm. Thus π_i may be expressed:

$$\pi_i = S_i p_i - S_i c_i - F_i$$

One might also introduce time by identifying the ith firm in the jth period, using two subscripts. Accordingly, π_{ij} is the profit of the ith firm in the jth period. Because of the added complexity, we shall omit reference to the period and implicitly understand that periods may vary. Continuing with the model:

$$S_i = CI_i(BD)$$

where CI_i is the competitive price index for the ith firm and BD is base demand.

We continue to define:

$$CI_i = I_i + \alpha \left(\frac{nI_i}{\sum_{i=1}^{n} I_i} - 1 \right)$$

where I_i is the noncompetitive price index for the ith firm, α is the price-sensitivity factor, and n is the number of firms in the market.

We continue further to identify I_i:

$$I = \frac{a - bp_i}{d}$$

Hence the complete *functional* model is:

$$\pi_i = \left[\frac{a - bp_i}{d} + \alpha \left(\frac{n\,\dfrac{a - bp_i}{d}}{\sum_{i-1}^{n} \dfrac{a - bp_i}{d}} - 1 \right) \right] BDp_i$$

$$- \left[\frac{a - bp_i}{d} + \alpha \left(\frac{\dfrac{n(a - bp_i)}{d}}{\sum_{i-1}^{n} \dfrac{a - bp_i}{d}} - 1 \right) \right] BDC_i - F_i$$

In the game, all symbols except p_i were supplied. This is, then, clearly an *operating* model. However, the model could as well have been used to look at the change in profit for our firm when α is changed and the p_i values are given. Consequently, α, which in the one-page game was a constant, now becomes a variable. This illustrates the statement made in Chapter 7 that a constant is constant *during the argument*.

V. ADVANTAGES AND OTHER USES OF SIMULATION

Simulation is a tool which owes its usefulness to the computer. The computational speed of the computer has made the use of simulation possible and effective where it would not otherwise have been. Further, simulation can be carried on without a high degree of mathematical sophistication. One advantage of simulation is that it shifts attention from methods of obtaining a solution to realistic portrayal of the system. This reduces the tendency to structure a model in terms of a known solution method.

The text contains many references and examples of complete enumeration methods which are ways of evaluating each alternative. Thus, in Chapter 1, five truck-routing alternatives were tested. This is, in fact, manipulation of an operating model and hence a form of simulation. Many of the network models proceed by manipulation of an operating model.

Some of the most useful simulations are of the "continuing use" variety. One may have a simulation of an assembly operation so that the effect of proposed modifications can quickly be checked out. If the modification is of the nature of a shift of production workers from one task to another, or a speedup of materials coming in, or a similar change, the simulation may be capable of providing information on the change merely by changing some input values. On the other hand, an extensive modification may require the development of a new model. The dock facilities model shown in the last chapter is of this type.

VI. SIMULATION OF THE MARKET ENVIRONMENT

The more the businessman knows about his environment, both internal and external, the better he can control it to conform to his objectives. A good deal of literature exists on the subject of optimizing profit (or any organizational goals), given the sales forecast. These optimizing rules utilize only a knowledge of the internal environment. However, the most basic decisions are the pricing decision, the promotion decision,[10] and the innovation decision. It is the impact of these decisions which influences the external environment and consequently the sales forecast.

---

[10] *Promotion* is here defined as any expenditure necessary directly to enhance or maintain sales. Thus, it includes salesman's salaries, advertising, and other expenditures.

The firm's environments

The purpose of this analysis is to discuss a simulation methodology which reproduces both the external and the internal environments of the firm. Once this is accomplished, we may develop quantitative, operational decision rules for the business enterprise.

The model should include forecast behavior of other companies and thus allow the firm to try any combination of actions until it finds the best combination.

Internal environment. In order to simulate a firm in an industry, there are essentially three environments which must be simulated or for which the interrelationships must be known. One of these environments is the cost or internal environment. A knowledge of the cost environment will tell us the total cost attached to a set of decisions, given the quantity or quantities sold. Work in this area has been undertaken frequently, and such a subsimulation need not be explored further here.

Of course, simulation of the cost environment still is not a procedure which is completely perfected, but errors of not more than 2 percent to 5 percent are possible (i.e., the error between a prediction of costs and actual costs). Accurate cost prediction does not assure management that its internal operations are optimal, but this is not the present problem. We are concerned with optimizing market behavior and, as a consequence, with any internal operations affected by this behavior. In other words, internal optimizing stems from taking the forecast sales and planning production, inventories, and work force accordingly. Another factor which will affect these decisions will be the forecast error stemming from our ability to forecast sales.

Competitive environment. A second environment is the competitive environment, which simulates the responses of competitors to (1) firm actions and (2) economic conditions.

Customer environment. The third environment is the customer environment, i.e., what reactions consumers will have to the various alternatives offered them by the decisions of the firms. Thus the demand curve or schedule of traditional economics portrays the behavior of consumers under different price conditions when other things are equal. This environment is conditioned by the combined actions of all firms as well as stimuli outside the control of the firm (e.g., changes in income, the season, etc.)

The process of simulating a firm in an industry

Conceptual framework. Fortunately, each of the three environments can be derived independently of one another. Then, for any given point in time, the first step toward optimizing the firm's goals is to predict a competitor's behavior. This requires first a general model to evaluate competitors' behavior, which then can be reused by feeding in the competitor's behavior from the last period to ascertain any change in his behavior pattern (as a practical matter, a semiannual or annual updating may be preferable). Given the competitor's behavior, each of the alternative market[11] behaviors of the firm can be mapped into the model (along with the competitor's behavior) to derive the predicted sales. Then the sales can be mapped into the model of the firm to determine the net profit, and that alternative market behavior of the firm which maximizes net profit is the optimal behavior. As indicated earlier, the sales prediction is used as the basis for determining nonmarket behavior, i.e., production, raw material purchases, plant expansion, equipment replacement, and financial decisions.

The above discussion presents a procedure which will maximize net profit per period but may not maximize long-run profit. In order to maximize long-run profit, we would have to determine the outcome for each alternative course of market behavior for this period, coupled with each alternative for each period in the future. The result would conceptually look like a probability tree and would soon be overpowering in size. For example, if we were talking about a single product firm and we admitted only six different prices as alternatives and only three different promotion expenditures, and three different media mixes, then the possible alternative market behaviors for the initial period are 56, and for six periods there are approximately 550 million possible combinations of market behaviors. Even for a high-speed digital computer, locating the profit-maximizing path would be a major undertaking. In addition, it would be highly hazardous to assume that the behavior pattern for your competitors would not change over an extended period of time. Therefore the model's predictive ability decreases with time. The only apparent solution to these opposing problems is to consider a period of time longer than one period, but not an extended period of time. Since, in the above example, a period of time of three periods represents 175,000 possible combinations of market behavior, two periods (which is the minimum period necessary to gauge the effect of competitors' reactions) seems most appropriate.

Up to this point in time, we have proposed an enumeration method of locating the optimal behavior path. There may be some better method of locating the path. Experimentation with different systems and different path location rules may result in some improved methods which will allow a close approximation to the optimal behavior path.

Another question which can be raised is the interrelatedness of the firm's market behavior and its nonmarket behavior. Since it is here assumed that the market behavior decision precedes the nonmarket behavior

---

[11] *Market behavior* here refers to pricing, promotion, and innovation. Innovation is a technical change or new product recognized by the consumer as *clearly* doing a better job of fulfilling a need or needs.

decision, the latter is merely adaptive and does not become a problem. However, the status of nonmarket variables (i.e., inventories, work force, etc.) determines the desirability of the market behavior. For example, at a given point in time and with a given set of assumed competitors' behaviors, the profit-maximizing market behavior for the firm may be different, depending upon the size of finished goods inventories. Thus the essential interrelatedness of the market behavior and nonmarket behavior is preserved, but is not a problem in the simulation.

Definitional problems

Since this simulation is to take place in the real world, we must wrestle with the problems of defining an industry, a product, and even a firm. From the theoretical standpoint, defining an industry is not difficult because we merely exclude those products a firm may be producing which do not belong in the industry.

An industry is normally defined from the consumer standpoint; hence an industry is a group of sellers of close substitutes who supply a common group of buyers. According to this definition, a large number of firms, perhaps the majority, are engaged in production in a number of industries.

Promotion expenditures are any expenditures designed expressly to maintain or increase a firm's customers; i.e., this must be the motivation behind the expenditure. Consequently, expenditures on product design are to pinpoint the customer group and are not promotion expenditures.

Price itself is not simple to define. Nondirect price is here defined as any concession to a customer or group of customers which directly affects his cost of acquiring the product. The most notable of these concessions are producer absorption of delivery costs, quantity discounts, financial discounts, special services such as costless installations, etc. When the industry standard includes delivery, this becomes a nonpromotion expenditure; i.e., promotion should be an item of competition and thus differentiable between firms.

VII. SIMULATION OF MARKET BEHAVIOR IN A MANAGEMENT GAME

Reported below is the model for a simulation of market behavior in a management game. Actual histories of play were analyzed to produce the model. The model could have been used to play the game in competition with student players. The results show that this model, if computerized, would have performed as well as the average student team. However, the complexity of the game environment allows superior teams to triumph.

The game used as the basis of this simulation is MANSYM.[12] The ver-

---

[12] Robert E. Schellenberger, *MANSYM* (Wayne, Penn.: M.D.I. Publications, second edition, 1969).

sion simulated included three teams or firms per industry. Each firm produces one product basically similar to the product of the other firms. Decisions are submitted bimonthly. Thus, period 1 refers to the January–February period, period 2 refers to the March–April period, etc. In general, sales were higher in periods 2–5. Market decisions included only the price of the product and the promotion expenditure. The industry contains three firms.

Prediction models and rules

The basic approach is to develop a model which will (1) predict the price and promotion of other firms; (2) try a price and promotion decision for your firm; (3) given all price and promotion decisions, predict industry sales; (4) given industry sales and each firm's price and promotion, predict sales for your firm; and (5) given sales, price, and promotion, determine profits. With a model of this nature, the firm merely tries numerous combinations of price and promotion, and decides actually to use the combination which yields the highest profit. The heart of the system comes in steps 1, 3, and 4. The following pages present the final model (without discussing the methodology used to develop it) for (1) the prediction of price and promotion of all firms; (2) the prediction of industry sales, given the price and promotion of all firms; and (3) the predicted sales for each firm, given market behavior and industry sales.

The price prediction model

The following set of price-estimating rules evolved:

Case 1. If profits in the previous period were one-third or more of industry profits, and the period for which the price decision is being made is periods 2–5:

$$P = \tilde{P}_h$$

where P is the predicted price for the firm, $\tilde{P}_h$ is the average price in periods 2–5, $\tilde{P}_L$ is the average price in periods 1 and 6, and P_{j-1} is the price charged by the competitor with the highest price in the previous period.

Case 2. If profits in the previous period were one-third or more of total industry profits, and the period for which the price decision is made is period 1 or period 6:

$$P = \tilde{P}_L$$

Case 3. If profits in the previous period were less than one-third of total industry profits, if your price last time was higher than either of your competitors', and if the period for which the price decision is being made is periods 2–5, then your price is dependent upon the following additional factor.

If the difference between your price and that of the competitor with the highest price is greater than 75 cents:

$$P = P_{j-1} - \$0.75$$

If the difference between your price and that of the competitor with the highest price is less than or equal to 75 cents:

$$P = P_{j-1}$$

Case 4. If profits in the previous period were less than one-third of total industry profits, if the period for which the price decision is being made is periods 2–5, and if your price last time was *not* higher than both of your competitors' prices:

$$P = \tilde{P}_h - \$0.25$$

Case 5. If profits in the previous period were less than one-third of the total industry profits, if the period for which the price decision is being made is period 1 or period 6, and if your price last time was higher than either of your competitors' prices, then your price is dependent upon the following additional factor.

If the price of your competitor with the highest price in the previous period is greater than $\tilde{P}_L$:

$$P = \tilde{P}_L$$

If the price of your competitor with the highest price in the previous period is less than or equal to $\tilde{P}_L$:

$$P = P_{j-1}$$

Case 6. If profits in the previous period were less than one-third of total industry profits, if the period for which the price decision is being made is period 1 or period 6, and if your price last time was *not* higher than both of your competitors' prices:

$$P = \tilde{P}_L$$

It should be pointed out that $\tilde{P}_h$ and $\tilde{P}_L$ are reevaluated each period on the basis of the actual price charged. Thus, for example, at the start of the second year of actual play, we have two observations upon which to determine $\tilde{P}_L$; but after that period, we have three observations upon which to determine $\tilde{P}_L$. As a consequence, the model is dynamic, in that the average price will follow some long-run movement. Accordingly, if the pressures of increasing raw material prices force prices up in the long run, this pressure would be recognized. However, it would be more fully recognized by a weighting procedure which would weight more recent observations heavier. It will be seen later that the errors wrought by not weighting are much more pronounced with reference to promotion.

The simulation did not attempt to validate the resulting rules of price behavior. However, for the first four periods of the actual simulation, these rules resulted in a mean of zero between the actual prices and the estimated prices. Consequently, the rules of price behavior appear to be valid enough for our purposes.

The promotion expenditure prediction model

Case 1. If the period for which the promotion expenditure decision is being made is period 1 or period 6:

$$PR = PR_L$$

where PR_L is the average promotion expenditure in periods 1 and 6.

PR_h is the average promotion expenditure in periods 2–5, and PR is the promotion expenditure.

Case 2. If the period for which the promotion expenditure decision is being made is periods 2–5:

$$PR = PR_h$$

Using past data, it was found that the average error (considering the overall mean) for the high sales periods is 12.3 percent, and the average error for the low sales periods is 19.3 percent.

Industry sales prediction model

The industry sales prediction model is:

$$IS_j = [27,166.5(21 - \tilde{p}) + 0.3(PE - 150,000) + 98,000](SI)T^j$$

and $\tilde{p}$ is computed as follows:

If $SP > 2.00$, then $\tilde{p} = \bar{s} - [-0.3746 + 0.28177 \ (SP)]$.
If $2.00 < SP < 0.5$, then $\tilde{p} = \bar{s} - [-0.054 + 0.096423 \ (SP)]$.
If $SP < 0.5$, then $\tilde{p} = \bar{s}$.

The symbols are defined in Figure 20–2.

Firm sales prediction model

Sales for the firm are:

$$FS_i = (IS_j)(\tfrac{1}{3} - [-0.0628438(\tilde{p} - p_i)])$$

The symbols are defined in Figure 20–2.

Figure 20–2

Glossary of Symbols

IS_j = Industry sales in period j

PE = Industry promotion expenditure

SI = Seasonal index

T^j = Secular trend index

$\tilde{p}$ = Weighted average industry price

$\bar{s}$ = Simple average industry price

SP = Spread between high price and low price

FS_j = Sales of the firm in period j

P_i = ith firms' price

The results of the simulation

Complete information on results is only available for all firms in three industries for periods 1–4. It is difficult to evaluate predictions unless we have some standard against which we may test the prediction. Inasmuch as the players submitted sales forecasts, we can at least compare our predictions with those of the firm. The findings are summarized in Table 20–16.

Line 1 shows that total sales for the 36 observations predicted by the firm and by our model are virtually identical, and both of these are within 1 percent of actual sales. However, lines 2 and 3 indicate that the pattern of prediction varies. In general, the model overpredicts during periods

Table 20–16

Periods	Actual sales (total for 36 observations)	Firm's estimated sales	Our estimated sales
1–4................	2,006,450	1,979,510	1,979,676
1 and 2...........	845,185	888,310	772,793
3 and 4...........	1,161,265	1,091,200	1,206,883

Table 20–17

Period	Firm's estimates		Our estimates	
	Number of high estimates	Number of low estimates	Number of high estimates	Number of low estimates
1............4		4	0	9
2............3		6	5	4
3............3		6	6	3
4............4		4	6	3

3 and 4, and underpredicts during periods 1 and 2, whereas the firms do just the opposite. If we look at the sign of the error by periods, we see a pattern emerging. The information is presented in Table 20–17. It appears evident that the seasonal index developed in the industry sales prediction model for period 1 is understated, thus inducing considerable error. In fact, in terms of magnitude, the underestimate of sales in period 1 totaled 81,287 units. However, in order to draw any conclusion, we should have the results of periods 5 and 6.

DISCUSSION TOPICS AND PROBLEMS

1. Find the answer to part (*a*) of Question 4 of Chapter 14, using a Monte Carlo approach at one-minute intervals. Ignore the possibility of multiple arrivals in any given time interval. Make your own decision about the sample size, but indicate how you made your decision. In order to compare the costs of various numbers of checkout counters, clear the ending queue at overtime (1.5 times normal).

2. Suppose the store manager for the supermarket of Question 4 of Chapter 14 had subsequently obtained the following probability distribution of customers arriving per minute:

Customers arriving	Probability
0	0.743
1	0.200
2	0.040
3	0.015
4	0.002

Plot this distribution, with the number of customers arriving per minute on the X-axis and the probability of arrival on the Y-axis. This is known as a Poisson distribution. What are its characteristics? Verify the probability of arrival which you used in Question 1 above. Rerun the analysis of Question 1 and compare your results. What can you say about the impact of ignoring multiple arrivals?

3. Are management games true simulations? Support your answer.

4. Suggest two situations where simulation for management could be used but has not (to your knowledge) been used. Provide enough detail to demonstrate that its use is feasible. Also, be sure to indicate how it would be used for decision making.

5. What is the relationship between the computer and simulation?

6. It has been said that the fact that sophistication in simulations is not dependent upon mathematical training is both a major advantage and a major disadvantage of simulation. Discuss.

7. The following is the probability distribution of time necessary to process one unit:

Minutes required	Probability
1	0.3
2	0.4
3	0.3

Start at the top of the left-hand column of the table of random numbers and move down the columns, and apply a Monte Carlo procedure to run a sample of 25 units through the system.

a) Assume that one unit enters the system every two minutes. Find the average waiting size.

b) Assume that two processors are available and they are fed by a single line (i.e., when the processor is free, it takes the first item in line). Further, assume that one unit enters the system every minute. Find the average waiting size.

c) Under conditions of part (*a*) above, assume that each item must go through a second process with the following distribution of time necessary for processing:

Minutes required	Probability
2	0.3
3	0.4
4	0.3

Assuming that the time necessary for the second process is independent of the time necessary for the first process, find the total waiting time. In a separate analysis assume the time necessary to complete both steps is always four minutes. Thus when the first step takes one minute, the second takes three minutes. Ignore the distribution of times shown under part (*c*) and find average waiting time.

d) If the relationship between the first and second process had been the following:

First process	Second process	Total time
1 minute	1 minutes	2 minutes
2 minutes	2 minutes	4 minutes
3 minutes	3 minutes	6 minutes

how would the queue for this condition compare with the queue for the previous conditions?

8. A professional football coach is trying to decide on the optimum number of running backs to have on his squad. He believes that in order to produce a championship team, he must have a minimum of four running backs in excellent health for every game. In case of a minor injury the player must be removed from the game and cannot play in the next game. A major injury puts the back out of action for the rest of the season. The season is 12 games. Through his many years of experience, the coach has witnessed the following maximums: 1 major injury per season and 11 minor injuries per season. The probability of a major injury per game is 0.05. The probability distribution of minor injuries per game is:

Number of injuries	Probability
0	0.2
1	0.5
2	0.22
3	0.05
4	0.025
5	0.005

These injuries have happened in a completely random manner, with no predictable pattern from season to season. The coach also discovered that after the season begins, he can not pick up any decent running backs.

He therefore asks you what number of running backs he should start out with each season in order to have himself covered in this department. However, you must bear in mind that since he can only have 40 players on his roster each year, he cannot afford to have more than the minimum necessary number of backs. In view of this, he says he is willing to accept a 2 percent chance of having three or less good backs available. If time permits, answer the coach's question. If not, design the simulation model and simulate two games.

9. You operate a downtown restaurant which has space for 48 patrons (12 tables). During the lunch hour, restaurant capacity is severely strained. In fact, lines are the rule. Once the lines form, their length is dependent upon the speed at which you and your competitors process the patrons' orders. The probability distribution of the time a group of customers will take after receiving their food are as follows:

Time in minutes	Probability
9	0.25
13	0.25
17	0.25
21	0.25

Each waitress can take an order in five minutes, and customers order immediately upon being seated. The time required to deliver the order is dependent upon what is ordered. The following distribution of order delivery times holds for each waitress:

Time in minutes	Probability
4	0.3
5	0.4
6	0.3

Assume that the kitchen takes five minutes to process each order. Assume that eating time and order delivery time are independent. Under the present competitive conditions, the distribution of arrivals per nine-minute interval (always in groups) between 11:45 and 12:30 is as follows:

Number of groups arriving	Probability
0	0.02
1	0.08
2	0.20
3	0.50
4	0.15
5	0.04
6	0.01
7	Zero

The distribution of arrivals per interval from 12:30 to 1:15 is as follows:

Number of groups arriving	Probability
0	0.15
1	0.60
2	0.15
3	0.08
4	0.02
5	Zero

Assume that no customers are in the store prior to 11:45 and none arrive after 1:15. Further, assume that customers will wait in line only if the line has 16 or less customers, and that customers arrive in groups of four. Thus, all seats may be occupied at all times. Assume arrivals occur midway in the period.

a) Assume that each group of customers takes 15 minutes to eat and 15 minutes for servicing (i.e., 5 minutes for ordering, 5 minutes for processing, and 5 minutes for delivering the order. Test the desirability of three, four, five, or six waitresses. (*Hint:* Divide the restaurant into waitress-service areas.)

b) If you have the time and/or facilities, use the probability distributions on eating and servicing times, and find the number of waitresses required.

c) Do you agree that the owner should be maximizing the number of customers serviced?

SELECTED REFERENCES

Balderston, Frederick E., and Hoggatt, Austin C. *Simulation of Market Proccesses.* Berkeley: Institute of Business and Economic Research, University of California, 1962.

Bonini, Charles P. *Simulation of Information and Decision Systems in the Firm.* Englewood Cliffs, N.J.: Prentice-Hall, Inc., 1963.

Clarkson, Geoffrey P. E. *Portfolio Selection: A Simulation of Trust Investment.* Englewood Cliffs, N.J.: Prentice-Hall, Inc., 1962.

Feigenbaum, E., and Feldman, J. *Computers and Thought.* New York: McGraw-Hill Book Co., Inc., 1963.

Forrester, Jay Wright. *Industrial Dynamics.* Cambridge: Massachusetts Institute of Technology Press, 1961.

Guetzkow, Harold (ed.). *Simulation in Social Science: Readings.* Englewood Cliffs, N.J.: Prentice-Hall, Inc., 1962.

Hoggatt, Austin C., and Balderston, Frederick E. *Symposium on Simulation Models: Methodology and Applications to the Behavioral Sciences.* Cincinnati: South-Western Publishing Co., 1963.

Orcutt, G. H.; Greenberger, Martin; Korbel, John; and Rivlin, Alice M. *Microanalyis of Socioeconomic Systems: A Simulation Study.* New York: Harper & Bros., 1961.

Schellenberger, Robert E. *Development of a Computerized, Multipurpose Retail Management Game.* Chapel Hill: Graduate School of Business, University of North Carolina, 1965.

SECTION SIX

Validity

21. Validity

21

Validity

I. INTRODUCTION

Phase 3 of managerial analysis is concerned with determining and maintaining validity. The essence of this phase is to evaluate the model and the data in order to give the decision maker a basis for deciding the degree of faith he can have in the course of action recommended by the analyst. Three kinds of validity must be recognized: (1) technical validity, (2) operational validity, and (3) continuing validity. Technical validity requires the identification of all divergences in model assumptions from reality as well as the identification of the validity of the data. Rarely will one be able to find an analysis in which the model perfectly fits reality and the data are entirely valid. Thus the analyst must raise the question of the meaningfulness of these divergences. Operational validity deals with the question of the importance of the divergences which are identified under technical validity. Finally, we must assure the manager that the model will continue to be operationally valid. This is called continuing validity and requires an analysis of the provisions for the application to be modified in light of new circumstances.

II. TECHNICAL VALIDITY

Technical validity refers to a reasonably identifiable set of criteria against which any application of managerial analysis may be compared. It is termed *technical* because the analysis of technical validity does not include a judgment about the importance of the divergence from some ideal. Judging the importance of the divergence is the subject of operational validity.

The four primary components of technical validity are (1) model validity, (2) data validity, (3) logical validity, and (4) predictive validity.

Each is judged on the basis of subcriteria. The four primary components will now be discussed and illustrated. These illustrations will be centered around the inventory and linear programming models.

Model validity

Model validity refers to the correspondence of the model to the real world. As indicated in Chapter 7 on models and systems, the best possible model is one which exactly reproduces what we perceive to exist. The validity of the model must be judged by comparing each assumption to the real world. Consequently, the starting point for judging technical validity is to identify all assumptions. Very little has been written on the process of identifying assumptions. The process of developing a model involves implicit or explicit assumptions throughout the course of the model development. Certain hypothesized relationships between variables are implicitly or explicitly tested during the course of model development. Obviously, the good model developer will keep track of these assumptions for use at this juncture. The model assumptions must agree with the manager's perception of the real world, and not the analyst's.[1]

Throughout this text, we have attempted to identify the assumptions that operate for all of the models presented. Despite this overt attempt, it is highly unlikely that all of the assumptions will have been stated. This is partly true because in transferring the model to a particular environment, there are some assumptions which are made so that the model is applicable to that environment and could therefore not be anticipated in the text.

Assumptions can frequently be spotted after the fact by looking at the entire process step by step. At one time, many of the advertising agencies were offering a media-mix model which used linear programming presumably to identify the best mix of media that an organization could use in order to maximize the effectiveness of its advertising. One of the applications sought to aim the message at an audience possessing certain desirable characteristics. One of the hidden assumptions of that model would have drawn the erroneous conclusion that it was equally desirable to advance the message to a group of individuals possessing an IQ of 80 and another group possessing an IQ of 120 when the ideal audience was to

---

[1] It should be noted that some people claim that one of the greatest benefits of managerial analysis is its ability to improve the decision maker's perceptions about the real world. On the other hand, more than one analyst has resigned because the decision maker did not share his perception about the real world. However, the analyst may attempt to improve the decision maker's perception by persuasion, *not by fiat*. The burden of failure to change perception must rest with the analyst's lack of evidence or ability properly to convey that evidence. Management can only be held at fault when it grants the analyst no audience to communicate his perceptions of the real world.

possess an IQ of 100. Such oversights are not entirely uncommon. At the introductory level, one cannot dwell at length on the procedures for identifying assumptions, but can only emphasize the necessity of being fairly familiar with the model assumptions.

Assumptions may be clearly expressed or implied. Implied assumptions are frequently spotted by looking at results or outcomes. The following pages should serve to illustrate this point.

Even the most capable analyst makes liberal use of all or parts of existing models of common processes. Many of these models or their component parts are used because they seem capable of predicting the outcome of a given action. Consequently, all managerial analysts must be capable of extracting the assumptions from an existing model. Model validity can be investigated by looking at the mathematical assumptions, the content assumptions, and the causal assumptions.

Mathematical assumptions.   Some assumptions exist because of the mathematical nature of the model. The linear nature of the linear programming model is so important that it is mentioned in the title.

In fact, the assumption of linearity is one of the most common assumptions. This assumption says that (within the relevant range) the slope of the equation is constant throughout. One of the first assumptions to be recognized should be the mathematical form of the model.

The economic order quantity model offers a useful example to use throughout our discussion of validity. The EOQ model is:

$$TC = \frac{D}{Z} C_1 + \frac{Z}{2} C_2 P$$

D = Annual demand
Z = Order quantity
C_1 = Order cost per order
C_2 = Cost of carrying \$1 in inventory per year
P = Value of item carried in inventory

In the EOQ model the order quantity is the independent variable, and total cost is the dependent variable. The order cost element is nonlinear, and the carrying cost element is linear, as shown in Figure 21–1.

Another mathematical assumption which occurs because the ordering-cost term and the carrying-cost term are added but not multiplied is that ordering costs do not influence carrying costs, and vice versa; i.e., each of the terms are independent of one another. In this model, such an assumption seems entirely correct. The same assumption is made in the linear programming model. For example, one of the constraint equations from Chapter 15 is:

$$4X_1 + 2X_2 \leq 32$$

Figure 21–1

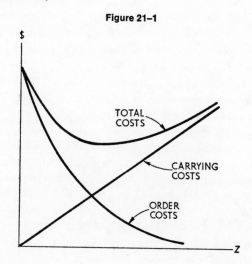

This depicts the limited amount of processing time available in department 1 and the fact that it takes four hours to process good 1 and two hours to process good 2. This equation implies that the amount of processing time is independent of the number of different goods processed. If the manager believes that production is higher the more sustained the work on a single product, we might find that a third term is necessary to reflect this relationship.

A reasonable third term might be $\dfrac{-X_1X_2}{8}$, giving the equation this form:

$$4X_1 + 2X_2 \leq -\frac{X_1X_2}{8} + 32$$

The third term acts to reduce available capacity when both X_1 and X_2 are being produced. Table 21–1 shows selected mixes of products when all available time is used and before the penalty effect of this term takes

Table 21–1

Units of X_1	Units of X_2
8	0
7	2
6	4
5	6
4	8
3	10
2	12
1	14
0	16

effect—i.e. for $4X_1 + 2X_2 = 32$. Imposing the penalty term $\dfrac{X_1 X_2}{8}$ on either extreme, its value is zero. Thus, no penalty is incurred in producing all one good. If two goods are produced, this term assumes that it is more desirable to produce one at a high level and the other at a low level. Table 21–2 shows the penalty.

Although this term cannot be accommodated by the linear programming model, it does illustrate a means of recognizing dependency between the indicated variables. Hence the second type of mathematical assumption to recognize is the relationship between independent variables.

Another frequent mathematical assumption is that the relationships are continuous in the relevant range. This means that a change in the

Table 21–2

X_1	X_2	*Penalty*
8	0	0
7	2	$1\frac{3}{4}$
6	4	3
5	6	$3\frac{3}{4}$
4	8	4
3	10	$3\frac{3}{4}$
2	12	2
1	14	$1\frac{3}{4}$
0	16	0

independent variable (no matter how small) is always accompanied by a change in the dependent variable. It also means that such a change is possible and has meaning. Thus the solution to the linear programming model may indicate the production of partial units. The EOQ model may indicate ordering partial units. Partial units have no real meaning. However, partial units may in some instances be ignored without causing harm. If you are ordering or producing nails, ignoring the partial unit will not affect the solution. However, if you are ordering or producing battleships, the partial unit could be a real problem.

Content assumptions. The second type of model assumption deals with the content of the terms and content of variables within the terms. For the EOQ model, we shall discuss both the carrying-cost and the order cost terms. This model assumes that inventory costs are of three types: (1) those dependent upon the number of units in inventory, (2) those dependent upon the number of orders, and (3) those dependent upon annual demand. Carrying costs are the same per unit in inventory. Order costs are the same per order. Fixed costs are those costs which are the same regardless of the number of orders or inventory size and are thus either dependent upon annual demand or fixed regardless of demand. The EOQ model ignores those costs which do not vary, as indicated above. For example, quantity discounts cannot be handled in the EOQ model.

Another asumption is that each increment of labor or capital released can immediately be used elsewhere at its actual cost. Thus, each dollar released from inventory can be immediately reinvested elsewhere because carrying costs are dependent upon the average inventory size. This also implies that the warehouse space released when inventory is used can immediately be put to alternative use. Such an assumption seems invalid. However, warehousing costs are apt to be dependent upon the space used when the order is first received, i.e., maximum inventory size. If this is the case, a simple doubling of the warehousing portion of the carrying cost per dollar of inventory per year will correct this error because maximum inventory size is twice average inventory.

Another assumption that affects the validity is that the EOQ for one good is independent of the EOQ of all goods. Further, the model implies that ordering costs and carrying costs for each good are independent of carrying costs or order costs of other goods. In the inventory chapter (Chapter 13), when we discussed joint order preparation, we demonstrated the fallacy of this assumption.

The EOQ model also assumes that the time the purchasing clerk uses to prepare an order can be employed in other productive activity. Accordingly, the direct labor cost of preparing an order is clearly included in the order cost. However, we have not discussed whether some or all of the overhead costs are included.

The size of the warehouse and the size of the purchasing department are both strongly influenced by the number of orders and average aggregate size of inventory. When it comes to placing one more order, the out-of-pocket costs of physically placing the order are probably negligible. But the annual costs of operating the purchasing department are very real. The purchasing department's contribution to the order costs is not easy to identify. How do we identify the technically correct order costs?

In the EOQ model, as in most other similar models, only truly fixed costs are ignored. Therefore, when identifying order preparation costs, one procedure is to try to identify all order preparation activities and the costs attached to each. Then the average cost is found for each order or each class of order. Obviously, a wide variety of approaches may be taken. This problem is discussed here because the proper content of the cost terms is a part of the model assumptions. However, how close the actual data meet the model asumptions is part of the subject of data validity.

Causal assumptions.   The ideal model contains only true causal variables. Often, we do not know what causes a given event to occur, but we can identify some other event which, by its movement, allows us to predict movement in the given event. The primary example is the use of time to predict growth rates. For example, we may predict growth in sales of a given product as a function of time. Obviously, the consumption of a certain product is not dependent upon the passage of time. However, if time will provide good estimates, we shall probably use the prediction equation developed by time series analysis.

Data validity

The topic of data validity was covered quite thoroughly in Chapter 6. The reader will probably find it desirable to review pages 76–80 of that chapter.

Briefly, the three criteria for data validity are:

1. Accuracy, which is the ability correctly to measure and identify the data
2. Impartiality, which is the assurance that the data are correctly measured and recorded
3. Representativeness, which is the assurance that the universe from which the data are drawn is properly identified and that the sample was random

That chapter also pointed out the necessity of assuring that data which are to be compared are actually comparable. However, with the possible exception of the question of comparability, all of these criteria deal with the validity of raw data. The analyst will also need to look at the validity of the information when it has been structured and the relationships have been specified. It is entirely possible that valid raw data are incorrectly structured, resulting in an incorrect solution. Before discussing the question of the validity of structured data, let us look at some specific examples of problems with raw data.

Validity of raw data. Earlier, we talked about identifying the order preparation component of ordering costs. As we have indicated, there is a direct cost component which is conceptually easy to identify. An order must be authorized by the appropriate official and typed up by a clerk. All of the labor costs of handling the order and the materials used are readily identified. However, even direct labor costs have data pitfalls. Some officials are paid a given salary regardless of the hours they work. This would imply that each additional increment of time is costless. On the other hand, even an executive must sleep, and his time is limited. Thus, each increment of order preparation time may keep him from some other activity. A further confusing factor is that it is not only the hourly wage rate that must be recognized as direct labor cost, but also the cost of fringe benefits. But fringe benefits are not necessarily proportional to the hourly rate.

This discussion points out that direct cost data almost always fail any test of technical validity. However, direct cost data are considered relatively accurate. The crucial consideration is how actual costs change with changes in the number of orders and inventory size. Obviously, a reduction in the number of orders by one will have almost no impact on order preparation costs, but a sizable reduction in the number of orders will decrease costs. Hence the accuracy of the estimated order preparation costs depends upon the magnitude of the change engendered by the model.

Obviously, these data come from accounting records, and the analyst must understand how they were figured and whether they are accurate for his purposes.

Validity of structured data. Structured data are raw data upon which some manipulation has been performed. Basically, each step of the manipulation should be reviewed to assure that it is correct. If the structuring involves the use of statistics, a statistician should be consulted.

As indicated earlier, investigation of the validity of structured data may involve questioning data comparability. Whenever data are aggregated, they are structured. The final values of the carrying costs and order costs are aggregations of the components. Identifying the validity of structured data is so dependent upon the circumstances surrounding the application that it is difficult to generalize about this topic.

Logical validity

The components of validity represent a series of questions to be answered in order to make reasonably sure that the recommended course of action has been completely scrutinized. Many of the points raised have no clear answer. Consequently, the analyst is tempted to skip lightly over this phase. It is not easy to evaluate logical validity because no clear methodology exists to conduct such an evaluation.

Logical validity is concerned with the assurance of a logical progression from model construction to solution. The most identifiable component of logical validity is the correctness of the solution procedure. That is, were the mathematical manipulations correct and accurate?

The remaining component of logical validity deals with the logical flow of the model. It is also difficult to identify a methodology for checking the logical flow. One element which can be checked is the logic of mixing the elements in the model. As indicated earlier, mixing an equal number of IQ's of 80 and IQ's of 120 does not yield IQ's of 100. Another question is: Are the outcomes which have been predicted consistent with expected or known outcomes?

The methodology for checking outcomes is known as sensitivity analysis and is the subject of a later section of this chapter. By comparing the outcomes of the model with actual outcomes, we obtain some indication of the predictive ability of the model for conditions which have occurred in the past. At this stage, our primary purpose is to identify errors which signal the obvious omission of a relevant variable.

Predictive validity

Predictive validity deals with prediction errors. In logical validity, we looked at major errors which suggested the omission of important causal variables. In predictive validity, we are looking at all errors between the actual outcome and the predicted outcome for any of the relationships within the model. We also look at errors between actual and expected outcomes for the final model. The reader will recall that a prediction model is used as an input to the final model used for managerial analysis. Thus a prediction model demonstrates relationships between variables. In some cases the prediction model may be synonymous with the final model. But in many cases the prediction model is only an element in the final model. For example, each coefficient in the linear programming model must be extracted from company records via a prediction model.

Predictive validity in prediction models. If one is developing a model requiring economic inputs, such as a forecast of sales of bricks, one develops a model which identifies brick sales as a dependent variable and other factors (such as housing starts) as the independent variable(s). The analyst then proceeds to identify the relationship between the dependent variable and the independent variables. The reader will recall that this is normally accomplished via regression analysis.

Regression analysis uses the deviations between the actual and expected outcome as an integral part of the analysis. It minimizes the squared error and identifies the predictive ability of the regression equation by the regression coefficient (r^2). Predictive validity is then concerned with identifying the divergences between the actual outcome and the outcome expected from the prediction model.

As pointed out in the chapter on regression analysis (Chapter 9), minimizing the squared error is not the only basis for identifying the error. For example, absolute error could be used as the criterion for the best fit. However, we are not concerned here with the best fit, but with evaluation of the fit. The ratio of the *variation accounted for* to the *total variation* seems like a logical basis for measuring the goodness of the prediction equation.

Predictive validity in the final model. It should be remembered that both prediction equations and the final model must be evaluated. The comments thus far have been most appropriate for evaluating prediction models. The reader will recall from the example in Chapter 1 that vehicle operating costs for each route were figured from a regression equation. However, the final model can actually be set up as a linear programming problem with the costs as coefficients. Thus the original cost prediction equation must be evaluated as a means of evaluating the final model. In other words, predicting equations are used as inputs to the final model.

The final model may also be evaluated by looking at the errors between actual and predicted outcomes, if such exist. It should be remembered that the economic order model is the total cost equation and has nothing to do with the solution which identifies the economic order quantity. Therefore, verification of the total cost equation requires that we identify predicted costs for actual inventory levels. However, this becomes rather difficult because carrying costs are being accumulated at all points in time and order costs are not readily associated with any particular order. However, one partial alternative is to look at the total system and attempt to identify whether in given periods of time this kind of system will at least account for all of the costs that must be accounted for, even if it cannot account for them on an item-by-item basis. Thus the company must account in total for all of the inventory costs for all of the goods, even if it cannot identify error terms for each good.

The point of this section is to recognize the fact that when and where comparisons can be made between actual and expected outcomes of either the predicting equations or the final model, such comparisons should be made.

It should also be recognized that another element of predictive ability deals with the ability to predict into the future. In fact, the reason for using past information is because of its ability to predict future events. Accordingly, the question of ability to predict into the future is one that should be considered either at this junction or when we are evaluating continuing validity (i.e., validity at future points in time). Consequently, the question of our ability to predict into the future will be explored in more depth at that point in time. Predicting past events will be called *passive prediction*. Predicting future events will be called *futuristic prediction*.

III. OPERATIONAL VALIDITY

Operational validity deals with the importance of the divergences found under technical validity. Virtually no model can meet all the criteria for being technically valid. However, the real question is how important is the divergence. Unfortunately, that question is not easily answered. However, a number of subquestions or considerations, when taken together, will generally provide enough information to decide to accept or reject the analysis and its conclusion.

It should be recognized that this phase of managerial analysis requires meaningful interaction with the decision maker. Obviously, the result of this interaction will be to assure that the basic assumptions and trial outcomes are consistent with the decision maker's expectations. However, it is not at all uncommon for the decision maker to modify his expectations of the outcome on the basis of a fruitful exchange with the analyst. Further, interaction at this juncture may result in a modification of the model so that the outcome is consistent with the decision maker's expectations. It should be remembered that the term *outcome* applies only to the output of the model, not to the recommended decision. For example, in the EOQ model the outcome is the total costs when the inventory is of a given size. The economic order quantity may be a complete surprise to the decision maker.

Degree of improvement

Probably the first consideration in assessing operational validity should be the degree of improvement generated by the new system over a reasonable period of time. The degree of improvement is the ratio of the new

Table 21–3

Economic order quantity	Total costs (old system)	Total costs (new system)	Carrying costs	Savings	Ratio
1,095.........	$13,040	$3,500	0.16	$ 9,548	0.268
980.........	16,240	3,920	0.20	12,320	0.241
894.........	19,440	4,296	0.24	15,144	0.221

criteria to the old. For example, in the EOQ model used in this text, the new cost is $3,919, and the old cost was $16,240. Thus the ratio is:

$$\frac{3,919}{16,240} = 0.241$$

Since the new cost is 24 percent of the old (a reduction of 76 percent), the improvement is so great that it outshadows any of the questions raised by technical validity. Since the costs of an existing system are generally easier to identify than the costs of a new system, small savings must be viewed skeptically. Here the savings are generated by a drastic reduction in carrying costs. If carrying costs are crucial to the validity of the savings, one could conduct sensitivity analysis by identifying the possible extremes the carrying costs could assume and then looking at the effect on total costs. Hence, if carrying costs range from 0.16 to 0.24, EOQ ranges from approximately 1,095 to 894, and the total cost ranges from $3,500 to $4,300.[2] This can be compared to the total cost without EOQ. Under these circumstances, Table 21–3 depicts the situation. Hence, carrying costs have an impact on both the dollar amount and the percentage of savings; the higher the carrying costs, the higher the percentage of sav-

---

[2] The student will recall that $D = 24,000$, $p = 20$, $C_1 = 80$, and $C_2 = 0.20$; and that:

$$Z = \sqrt{\frac{2DC_1}{C_2 p}}$$

ings. However, in all cases the savings are so great as to negate any other questions of validity.

Testing error extremes

Probably the second most important question of operational validity involves a manipulation of the model by modifying parameter values so that they operate at their extremes and then ascertaining the effect of the operation of these parameter values at the extremes. One of the effects may be that the decision is different in kind rather than simply in magnitude. An example is when the linear programming model results in different variables being in the solution vector than under the original solution. If there is a difference in kind, then the solution is sensitive to the extreme values the parameters may assume.

Table 21–4

Order costs	Carrying costs	Economic order quantity	Number of orders	Total costs
$80	$0.20	980	24.5	$3,920
80	0.16	1,095	21.92	3,500
50	0.16	866	27.7	2,770
50	0.20	777	30.97	3,097

It should be remembered that a testing of all possible extreme values of the parameters may result in an unwieldy number of tests. Accordingly, the analyst must identify those combinations of extremes which could reasonably occur and ignore those combinations of extremes which could not reasonably occur. Using the economic order formula as an example, let us assume that order costs fall between $50 and $80, and that the carrying cost is 0.16 to 0.20. Then, checking all of the extremes results in Table 21–4.

One way of identifying the potential error involved is to find out what the total costs would be, testing the extreme values for one of the parameters and holding the other constant. Thus, in this example, we could ascertain what the actual cost would be if we had figured the economic order quantity at an order cost of $80 and a carrying cost of 20 cents when the order cost was in fact $50. Since we placed 24.5 orders with an order cost of $80, the actual cost of placing the orders will be 24.5 times $50, rather than 24.5 times $80. That gives us a total of $1,225. However, since inventory size is 980 units and carrying cost is still 20 cents, the carrying-cost side of the equation will then result in a carrying cost of

$1,960, for a total of $3,185. Since the total cost would have been $3,097 if we had in fact known what the order cost was, the differential cost of our ignorance is $3,185 minus $3,097, or $88. Table 21–5 will make all of the comparisons and indicate the value of having this information. It can be seen that the costliest error occurs when order costs are assumed to be $50 when they are in fact $80. The second most costly error occurs when the reverse is true. However, this is at least in part due to the fact that the percentage variation in the ordering costs is larger than the percentage variation in carrying costs.

The results of this analysis may be used to evaluate the desirability of spending more to obtain information on these costs. The point of the

Table 21–5

Assumed parameters	Actual parameters	Total cost under assumed conditions	Total cost if actual parameters has been assumed	Total costs under actual conditions	Difference in cost
$80 and $0.20	$80 and $0.16	$3,920	$3,500	$3,528	$ 28
50 and 0.20	50 and 0.16	3,500	2,770	2,792	22
80 and 0.20	50 and 0.20	2,770	3,097	3,185	88
50 and 0.16	80 and 0.16	3,097	3,500	3,765	265
80 and 0.16	80 and 0.20	3,528	3,920	3,944	24
80 and 0.16	50 and 0.16	3,528	2,770	2,848	78
50 and 0.20	80 and 0.20	3,097	3,920	4,032	112
50 and 0.16	50 and 0.20	2,770	3,097	3,117	20

discussion has been to indicate that we may utilize the information on the possible extremes to identify the impact of potential errors on the decision made.

We may also test the error extremes by looking at errors in model assumptions. For example, we previously discussed errors in the linear programming model when we did not include interaction effects between the variables. When the interaction affects are recognized, we have the equation:

$$4X_1 + 2X_2 \leq -\frac{X_1 X_2}{8} + 32$$

The penalty term can be ignored and then imposed later. Earlier, without the penalty term, the optimal answer indicated that we should produce $6\frac{2}{3}$ units of X_1 and $2\frac{2}{3}$ of X_2. If this optimum is considered in this equation, we find that we have 2.23 less units of capacity available in that department. Since we calculated the value of added capacity, the impact of this interaction term is 2.23 times the per unit value of added capacity. In other words, including this term would reduce profit by this amount.

Also, we have an operational problem because production cannot be met and erroneous modifications in production may further reduce profits.

Effect of actions near the optimum

The sensitivity of the criteria to actions near the optimum yields information on how important it is to be near the optimum. In the EOQ model, we may look at two extreme examples. In the first example, assume that a bulky and rapidly deteriorating item is purchased. In this instance, setup costs are $500, and carrying costs are 0.5; the item is worth $20, and 10,000 items are used annually. Thus the EOQ is:

$$\sqrt{\frac{2(10,000)500}{0.5(20)}} = 1,000$$

The second item is readily purchased and small relative to its value. In this instance, setup costs are $50, and carrying costs are 0.2; the value of the item is $5, and 10,000 items are used annually. Hence the EOQ is:

$$\sqrt{\frac{2(10,000)50}{0.2(5)}} = 1,000$$

If we purchase 800 units instead of 1,000, TC for the first item is:

$$6,250 + 4,000 = \$10,250$$

and TC for the second item is:

$$625 + 400 = \$1025$$

If we purchase 1,000 units, total costs are $10,000 and $1,000, respectively. The percentage error is the same in both instances (2.5 percent). However, the error in actual dollars is 10 times as great for the first as for the second.

A 20 percent deviation in order quantity has resulted in only a 2.5 percent deviation in total costs. Therefore the decision maker has much more freedom to modify actions than if a 2.5 percent deviation in the decision variable resulted in a 20 percent error in the criterion. As a starting point, the analyst might provide the decision maker the 5 percent range for the decision variable. Consequently, in the second example above, we know that TC equals $1,000 at the minimum and a 5 percent error means that TC equals $1,050. The TC equation may be expressed:

$$1,050 = \frac{10,000}{Z}(50) + \frac{Z}{2}(0.2)(5)$$

$$1,050 = \frac{500,000}{Z} + \tfrac{1}{2}Z$$

Multiplying by Z gives:

$$1,050Z = 500,000 + \tfrac{1}{2}Z2$$
$$\tfrac{1}{2}Z^2 - 1,050Z + 500,000 = 0$$

Using the quadratic equation:

$$Z = -\frac{-1,050 \pm \sqrt{1,102,500 - 1,000,000}}{1}$$
$$= 1,050 \pm \sqrt{102,500}$$
$$= 1,050 \pm 320.0$$

Thus in the 5 percent range Z goes from 730 to 1,370. Let us verify that both $Z = 730$ and $Z = 1,370$ yield a TC of $1050:

$$TC = \frac{10,000}{730}(50) + \frac{730}{2}(0.2)(5)$$
$$= 13.7(50) + 365$$
$$= 685 + 365$$
$$= \$1,050$$

and

$$TC = \frac{10,000}{1,370}(50) + \frac{1,370}{2}(0.2)(5)$$
$$= 7.3(50) + 685$$
$$= 365 + 685$$
$$= \$1,050$$

The reader will note that the deviation is 270 units below the optimum and 370 units above the optimum. This can be seen by looking at the slope of the total cost equation in Figure 21–2. The values at selected points are shown in Table 21–6. The reader can see that the total cost equation declines more rapidly from the left than it increases to the right.

Two extreme possibilities of the importance of actions near the optimum can be depicted in Figure 21–3. Deviations from the minimum in curve *B* have a marked effect on the value of the criterion, whereas deviations from the minimum in curve *A* have a slighter effect on the value of the criterion.

Effects of segmentation

The effects of segmentation or discontinuities can be quite marked. Earlier, we cited the example of the partial unit in the EOQ or linear programming model. Another example occurs when considering equipment purchases and/or labor savings. For example, assume that a geographically dispersed retail chain is considering the purchase of a piece of equipment for each of its stores. This piece of equipment has been

Figure 21–2

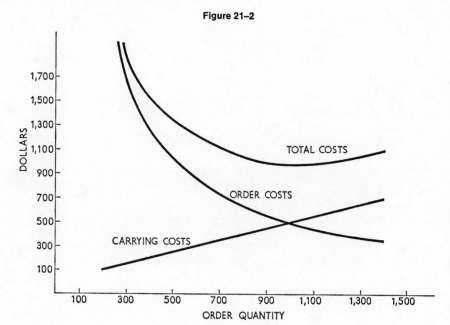

justified on the basis of its laborsaving ability. It saves one hour per week of each clerk's time. The number of clerks per store ranges from 10 to 40, with a total of 400 clerks. Assume that each clerk's direct cost is $2 per hour. The analyst concludes that as long as weekly allocated equipment costs are less than $800, the equipment should be purchased. This assumes that each hour of time released can be put to productive use. Further, clerks are idle an average of 30 percent of the time, but this fact

Table 21–6

Order quantity	Order costs	Carrying costs	Total costs
200............	$2,500.00	$100	$2,600.00
300............	1,666.67	150	1,816.67
400............	1,250.00	200	1,450.00
500............	1,000.00	250	1,250.00
600............	833.33	300	1,133.33
700............	714.25	350	1,064.25
800............	625.00	400	1,025.00
900............	555.55	450	1,005.55
1,000............	500.00	500	1,000.00
1,100............	454.55	550	1,004.55
1,200............	416.65	600	1,016.65
1,300............	384.50	650	1,034.50
1,400............	357.15	700	1,057.15

was not considered for the analysis. The analysis used to justify the equipment purchase has assumed that the new machine can be credited with saving one hour per week (at $2 per hour) for each clerk. If the number of clerks can be reduced so that these payroll costs can in fact be eliminated, the analysis is correct, and the idle time is not a consideration.

It seems unlikely that a store with 10 clerks can reduce its payroll by 10 hours because this is one quarter of a clerk. Even a store with 40 clerks may find it difficult to reduce its payroll by one clerk because the savings are spread over 40 clerks. On the other hand, if the saving in time occurs at times when the clerk is very busy, the improvement in customer serv-

Figure 21–3

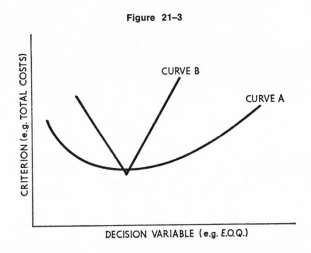

ice may more than offset the cost of the new equipment. In this instance the actual saving could be from nothing to more than that reported. Obviously, resolving this question is very important to the analysis. The actual saving can be expressed by multiplying the possible saving by a coefficient; that is:

$$S_a = a\, S_p$$

where:

S_a = Actual savings
S_p = Potential savings
a = Savings coefficient

The savings coefficient may be used in two ways. The decision maker may estimate the savings coefficient and a reasonable deviation (in both directions). Given this, he may test the results with these estimated values. Quite separately, one may identify the indifference point between purchasing and not purchasing. For example, if the machine costs are $500 per week and the potential saving is $800 per week (all in labor), we need to find S_a equals $500. Inserting this information in the above equation, we have:

$$500 = a\ 800$$
$$a = 500/800 = 0.625$$

This means that the indifference point occurs when actual savings are 62.5 percent of the potential savings.

Subjective methods

One way of dealing with the importance which each of the factors contributing to validity has is to rate each one on a scale of 1 to 10. Then

Table 21–7

Factor	Scale score	Weight	Score times weight
F_1	6	1.0	16.0
F_2	8	1.5	12.0
F_3	10	1.5	15.0
F_4	10	2.0	20.0
F_5	8	2.0	16.0
F_6	9	2.0	18.0
			87.0

each factor can in turn be weighted according to its importance, so that the total weights are 10. Thus a validity scale from 0 to 100 results. For example, assume that there are six factors: F_1, F_2, F_3, F_4, F_5, and F_6, and that each is weighted as follows:

$$W_1 = 1$$
$$W_2 = 1.5$$
$$W_3 = 1.5$$
$$W_4 = 2.0$$
$$W_5 = 2.0$$
$$W_6 = 2.0$$

Table 21–7 shows sample scale evaluations and the total of the validity scale.

This analysis receives an 87 validity score. The decision maker now has a basis of comparing different analyses and establishing his own cut-off score, i.e., that score below which he will reject the analysis. It should be remembered that as a general rule it is unwise to compare subjective scales between individuals unless a good degree of consistency has been demonstrated on earlier scales. It is also possible to obtain an average for a group of individuals as long as the cutoff score was established for that group of individuals. Therefore the validity score on the above analysis may have been 87, 83, 90, and 88 for four individuals. This yields an average of 87. In this approach, it is wise to set both a cutoff score and a cutoff range. Here the low score was 83, and the high score was 90, yielding a difference of seven points. This would appear to constitute relative agreement among the evaluators. If the difference were wide, it would be wise to investigate the consistency of each of the factors. If one or two items account for the difference, they should be reinvestigated. If the difference is spread over all items, it is probably attributable to a consistent and acceptable pattern of differences. An additional advantage of this scale is that it forces the use of a checklist and indicates where the weakness lies.

Implementation validity

The final component of operational validity is concerned with assuring that the expected outcomes occur when the system is in fact operating. For example, the linear programming model may dictate a change in product mix which can readily be accomplished with the resources at hand. However, the production employees may artificially restrict production because they do not like the new product mix. Implementation validity asks the question: Will the real world respond as the model indicates? Generally, the response error is the result of errors in predicting human responses. This kind of response error generally refers to changes in controllable behavior rather than physiological changes. For example, the chapter on linear programming (Chapter 15) raises the question of fatigue at the higher production levels. This is a physiological question and is not of concern here. Aversion to change and relinquishment of control is a very real threat when objective decision criteria are being substituted for subjective criteria.

IV. CONTINUING VALIDITY

Continuing validity evaluates the provisions for updating parameters and relationships. Obviously, those analyses which are concerned with a unique decision need not be concerned with continuing validity. However, models of common processes frequently deal with repetitive decisions. The EOQ is a repetitive decision, as is the production mix generated by a linear programming model. The provisions for updating require that the model and the solution have the possibility of being updated and a source of information which allows it to be updated. The possibility of updating requires that the model be written with abstract notation, with parameter values added later. Thus the linear programming model is written:

Maximize: $Z = C_1X_1 + \ldots + C_mX_m + 0_{m+1}X_{m+1} + \ldots + 0_{m+n}X_{m+n}$

Subject to: $A_{11}X_1 + \ldots + A_{1(m+n)} X_{m+n} = b_1$

$$\ldots\ldots\ldots\ldots\ldots\ldots\ldots\ldots\ldots\ldots\ldots\ldots$$

$$A_{m1}X + \ldots + A_{m(m+n)} X_{m(m+n)} = b_m$$

When analysis is required, A_{ij}, b_i, and C_i are given values. In fact, frequently used models of common processes may be computerized. Accordingly, the analyst will call for the particular computer program and add to it the size of m and n as well as values for A_{ij}, b_i, and C_i.

The possibility for updating is called flexibility. When all parameters are abstract, we have technical flexibility. When the form of the equations may be changed, we have form flexibility.

In the models used in this book, a modification of the form of equations may render the solution procedure useless. Since the number of possible forms is large, form flexibility is generally unwieldly and not used.

The last ingredient in continuing validity is an assurance that the system which provides this information is operating, so that it can notify the appropriate individual or machine when parameter values change.

Since most large companies have extensive computerized financial systems, the reader can easily visualize that changes in the value of items (p) can readily be incorporated in the EOQ model. However, the changes which affect ordering costs and carrying costs are much more subtle and require a considerable amount of manipulation to reidentify. When a warehouse employee receives a wage increase, warehousing costs go up, and so do carrying costs. Obviously, the impact of such an increase is negligible. Thus, one problem is identifying when a change in costs should be reflected in new values for C_1 and C_2. Since this model is relatively insensitive to errors, changes are appropriate only when major factors have affected costs, or via a periodic updating (e.g., once a year).

Many companies are moving toward a central system for maintaining appropriate and current information. These systems are called *information systems* or *planning and control systems*.[3]

V. CHOICE OF NEW PROJECTS AND REANALYSIS OF OLD PROJECTS

The degree of sophistication used in managerial analysis should be dependent upon the benefit to be derived by increased sophistication. Gen-

---

[3] For a discussion of the analytical components of such a system, see Robert E. Schellenberger and R. Sprague, contributing authors in Martin Rubin (ed.), *Data Processing Handbook* (Silver Spring, Md.: Data Processing Publications, Inc., 1969), chap. xxv.

Figure 21–4

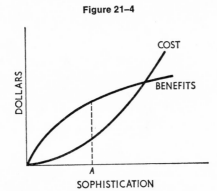

erally, the marginal effectiveness or benefit of the analysis declines as the sophistication increases. This can be depicted in the graph in Figure 21–4. As sophistication increases, the cost increases at an increasing rate, but benefits increase at a decreasing rate. Point *A* shows the point where marginal benefits equal marginal costs, and is the optimum degree of sophistication.

In a similar vein, E. Leonard Arnoff has suggested the graph in Figure 21–5. This shows that as effort increases, the effectiveness does not increase proportionately. It also shows that effectiveness is limited.

New projects must be chosen on the basis of the potential benefits to be generated. In other words, analytical efforts must be evaluated. The first question is: What are the costs of the present system? Obviously, this places a limit on the benefits. Next a preliminary study (sometimes called a feasibility study) attempts to identify a basic approach and a subjective estimate of gross benefits. Finally, an estimate of the cost of the analysis is made, which is subtracted from the benefits. Then all possible projects are listed in order of the benefits. Management is then in a posi-

Figure 21–5

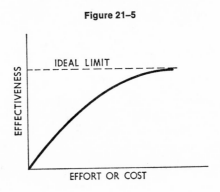

tion to authorize those projects it can afford to fund and those which generate the greatest returns (either tangible or intangible).

Sometimes, it becomes important to consider improving an analysis. In this case, as with new projects, the net benefit of reanalysis must be estimated. We have already discussed the value of added information which may be used as a basis for deciding the desirability of improving the analysis.

VI. SENSITIVITY ANALYSIS

Throughout this text, we have made frequent reference to sensitivity analysis. Sensitivity analysis, when used to test validity, attempts to determine the impact of errors in input information and errors in model assumptions. This concept is simple and has been illustrated frequently in this and previous chapters.

Sensitivity analysis can also be used as an integral part of systems analysis by allowing the analyst to alter a model systematically to look at the impact of that alteration on the criteria. In this case, we are asking: What is the impact or sensitivity of feasible changes in the system? For example, a retail store may wish to know how many brands of clothing to carry. If the model is appropriately constructed, the analyst may test the sensitivity of profit to an increase in the number of brands carried. Sensitivity analysis may be necessary because the nature of the relationships in the environment are too complex to identify with a single equation. The reader will recall that the definition of simulation was the construction and manipulation of an operating model. Obviously, this form of sensitivity analysis fits that definition.

Rather than develop principles, this chapter will examine primarily the sensitivity of various models or components. However, a few general concepts should be investigated.

The rate of change near an extremum

If the model can be expressed as a single continuous function with one dependent variable and one independent variable, divergences near the optimum are always insensitive (i.e., a slight divergence in the independent variable results in a smaller divergence in the dependent variable). This is so because as we approach a maximum, the function is increasing at a decreasing rate; conversely, as we approach a minimum, the function is decreasing at a decreasing rate. This is illustrated by looking at the slope of tangents as they approach the extrema on Figures 21–6 and 21–7. The second tangent in Figure 21–6 has a smaller slope than the first, thus illustrating that the function is increasing at a decreasing rate. The sec-

Figure 21–6

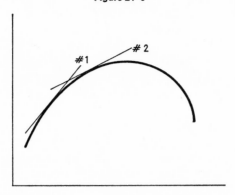

ond tangent in Figure 21–7 has a smaller negative slope, thus illustrating that the function is decreasing at a decreasing rate.

However, this general behavior pattern need only exist very close to the optimum. This can be partially understood by looking at the slope of the tangents in Figure 21–8. The slope of tangent 1 is 3/2, which means that a two-unit change in the independent variable is accompanied by a three-unit change in the dependent variable. This is a condition of sensitivity. However, at tangent 2 a one-unit change in the independent variable is accompanied by a one-unit change in the dependent variable. This is a condition of indifference. However, from that point to the minimum is a condition of insensitivity. The insensitive range continues to tangent 3, where a one-unit change in the independent variable is accompanied by a one-unit change in the dependent variable. This is the range X_1 to X_2. Now, consider Figure 21–9, where the insensitive range (X_1 to X_2) is very small.

Figure 21–7

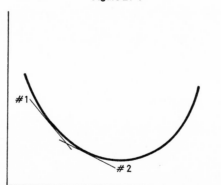

Figure 21–8

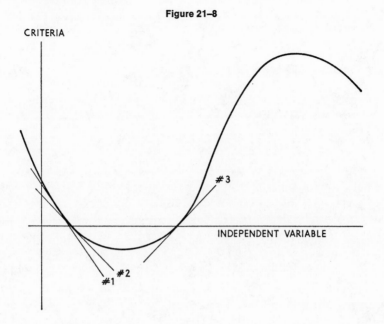

Figure 21–9

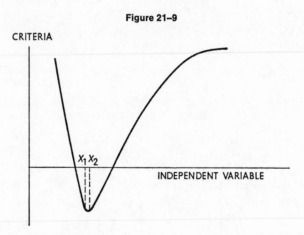

Multiple independent variables

If there are multiple independent variables, one may look at the change in the dependent variable accompanied by a change in one independent variable while the other independent variables are held constant. In this instance the previous comments about sensitivity of functions of one independent variable hold. However, slight variations in more than one variable are more apt to have a marked effect on the dependent variable.

The problem here is to decide what combined changes should be investigated.

Discontinuities and sensitivity

In Chapter 10, we discussed the cost function for purchasing an item on which a quantity discount applied for all purchases over 200,000 units. That function was:

$$\text{If } P \leq 200{,}000, \text{ then } C = 0.4P.$$
$$\text{If } P > 200{,}000, \text{ then } C = 0.36P.$$

P is purchases in units, and C is purchase cost. It was shown that purchasing 200,000 units instead of 200,001 units increases costs by almost $8,000. This is a classic example of the marked impact which deviations from the optimum can have if the optimum occurs in the vicinity of the discontinuities. Thus, sensitivity analysis should investigate the impact in the vicinity of discontinuities.

Sensitivity analysis and the EOQ model

We have already discussed numerous questions of validity with respect to the EOQ model. Here, we shall address ourselves to some additional considerations which can be investigated by sensitivity analysis. Let us look at the impact of joint errors in C_1 and C_2:

$$\text{EOQ} = \sqrt{\frac{2C_1D}{C_2P}}$$

This may be reexpressed:

$$\text{EOQ} = \sqrt{\frac{C_1}{C_2}}\sqrt{\frac{2D}{P}}$$

It can readily be seen that as long as the ratio between C_1 and C_2 remains constant, the EOQ remains constant. If, for example, order costs vary from $75 to $50 ($C_1$ is $75, and C_1^1 is $50) and carrying costs vary from 0.24 to 0.16 (C_2 is 0.24, and C_2^1 is 0.16):

$$\frac{C_1}{C_2} = \frac{C_1^1}{C_2^1} = \frac{75}{0.24} = \frac{50}{0.16}$$

because:

$$\frac{75}{0.24} = 312.5$$

and

$$\frac{50}{0.16} = 312.5$$

Table 21–8

	Assumed parameters C_1	C_2	Assumed economic order quantity	Total cost under actual conditions	Difference
1. Errors in opposite direction	$80	0.16	1,095	$3,394.00	$42.00
	50	0.20	777	3,412.00	60.00
2. Errors in same direction	80	0.20	980	3,356.50	4.50
	50	0.16	866	3,359.30	7.30

This shows the impact when the errors in C_1 and C_2 are proportionately equal. In other words, the impact on EOQ is nonexistent when:

$$\frac{C_1}{C_2} = \frac{C_1^1}{C_2^1}$$

where:

$$C_1 = \text{Original order cost}$$
$$C_1^1 = \text{Modified order cost}$$
$$C_2 = \text{Original carrying cost}$$
$$C_2^1 = \text{Modified carrying cost}$$

The effects of errors in C_1 and C_2 which are of the same direction (but not proportionate) as well as errors when the direction is opposite may be investigated by using the technique discussed earlier under the section of this chapter on testing error extremes (pages 430–31). Table 21–8 shows the results of this analysis, assuming actual C_1 is 65 and actual C_2 is 0.18, $D = 24,000$, and $P = 20$. In this case, EOQ is 931, and TC is $3,352.00. The sensitivity analysis lends further support to the contention that the EOQ model is quite insensitive to errors within a reasonable range. However, these data also indicate that the magnitude of errors is greater when errors in C_1 and C_2 are in the opposite direction.

Table 21–9

	Original data		Present-value	Present value	
Year	Buy	Lease	factor	Buy	Lease
0	$4,000	......	1.000	$4,000.00	....
1	1,000	$2,520	0.909	909.00	$2,290.68
2	1,000	2,646	0.826	826.00	2,185.60
3	1,600	2,777	0.751	1,201.60	2,085.52
4	2,300	2,916	0.683	1,570.90	1,991.62
				$8,507.50	$8,553.42

Sensitivity in present-value analysis

In the lease-or-buy problem in Chapter 19 (reproduced as Table 21–9), we used a discount rate of 10 percent. One purpose in using sensitivity analysis is to identify the point of indifference between the "lease" and the "buy" alternatives. Let us investigate (in Table 21–10) the desirability

Table 21–10

	Original data		Present-value factor	Present value	
Year	Buy	Lease		Buy	Lease
0........$4,000		......	1.000	$4,000.00	....
1......... 1,000		$2,520	0.893	893.00	$2,250.00
2......... 1,000		2,648	0.797	797.00	2,108.86
3......... 1,600		2,777	0.712	1,139.20	1,977.22
4......... 2,300		2,916	0.636	1,462.80	1,854.58
				$8,292.00	$8,191.02

of the "lease" alternative at a discount rate of 12 percent. This changes our decision from one of "buy" at a discount rate of 10 percent to "lease" at 12 percent. If we are limited to discount rates which can be investigated by Table 19–2, we can only say that the point of indifference is between 10 percent and 12 percent.

DISCUSSION TOPICS AND PROBLEMS

1. Discuss the role of assumptions in managerial analysis models, using one of the models in the text to illustrate this role.

2. The owner of a small chain of ladies' ready-to-wear shops is contemplating hiring an MBA (master of business administration). This employee would apply managerial analysis to the company.

a) Give the owner at least three specific examples of models of common processes which could be applied to his operations; i.e., explain the general model and the elements which characterize this model. Be sure to discuss the limitations of these techniques.

b) Explain to the owner what managerial analysis is all about.

c) Give the owner some indication of the dollar value of managerial analysis to his organization and some method of evaluating the potential contribution of managerial analysis to his organization.

d) Would you recommend that the owner proceed with his plan? Defend any answer you suggest.

3. The members of your managerial analysis team have come to you with a breakthrough which they are urging you to adopt. List and discuss each of the questions you would ask them.

4. Discuss the validity of the linear programming example in Chapter 15.

5. It has been said that expenditures on mangerial analysis are always directly related to the size of the organization. Comment.

6. Comment on the technical and operational validity of the revision of a prior probabilities model.

7. What are the assumptions of the EOQ model? (Ignore any measurement assumptions; i.e., assume that all elements can be measured.)

8. Discuss the validity of the four parameter values (C_1, C_2, p, and D) used in any application of the EOQ Model.

9. Discuss the validity of the model assumptions if the EOQ model is applied to all items in a normal grocery store.

SELECTED REFERENCES[4]

Books

Ackoff, Russell L., and Sasieni, Maurice W. *Fundamentals of Operations Research*. New York: John Wiley & Sons, Inc., 1968.

Churchman, C. West; Ackoff, Russell L.; and Arnoff, E. Leonard. *Introduction to Operations Research*. New York: John Wiley & Sons, Inc., 1957.

Connors, Michael M., and Teichroew, Daniel. *Optimal Control of Dynamic Operations Research Models*. Scranton: International Textbook Co., 1967.

Hillier, Frederick S., and Lieberman, Gerald J. *Introduction to Operations Research*. San Francisco: Holden-Day, Inc., 1967.

McDonough, Adrian M. *Information Economics and Management Systems*. New York: McGraw-Hill Book Co., 1963.

Miller, David W., and Starr, Martin K. *Executive Decisions and Operations Research*. Englewood Cliffs, N.J.: Prentice-Hall, Inc., 1960.

Miller, David W., and Starr, Martin K. *The Structure of Human Decisions*. Englewood Cliffs, N.J.: Prentice-Hall, Inc., 1967.

Articles

Clough, David J. "Operations Research—A Critical Look: Special Techniques That They Use and the Tests of Validity That Should Be Applied to Their Results," *Business Quarterly*, Vol. XXVII (Spring, 1962), pp. 33–37.

---

[4] Most of the structure of the material on validity is original. Since small bits of material were extracted from various sources and some from journals, this list includes selected journal references. This is not to imply that journal references were not consulted for other chapters, but that the essence of the material could be found by consulting the appropriate books.

Conway, R. W. "Some Tactical Problems in Digital Simulation," *Management Science*, Vol. X, No. 1 (October, 1963), pp. 47–61.

Mayne, J. W. "Accuracy, Precision, and Reliableness in Operational Research," *Operations Research*, Vol. XI (November, 1963), p. 909–1006.

Miller, D. K. "Reliability Analysis: A Management Method for Today's Businessmen," *Heating, Piping, & Air Conditioning*, Vol. XXXIX (July, 1967), pp. 123–26.

Woods, D. H. "Improving Estimates That Involve Uncertainty," *Harvard Business Review*, Vol. 44 (July–August, 1966), p. 91.

Epilogue

Epilogue

The Epilogue brings us to a time for reflecting upon the real essence of what has been presented and learned. It is a time for sober reflection on what has not been presented.

The book has looked rather critically at the economic order quantity model and the linear programming model. It has looked less critically at other models, but has attempted to provide the reader with a basis for a thorough look at the remaining models. The criticism leveled should not act as a deterrent to the use of the models. They are tremendously useful, but the manager must know their limitations. Since the list of models finding wide application is bound to expand, it will undergo alteration. At the same time, the frequency of use of models in the real world is rapidly expanding.

The book has not attempted to discuss more sophisticated models of common processes. This is true because the tools necessary for the use of more complicated models involve higher mathematics. In addition, many of the more sophisticated techniques cannot be handled with paper and pencil. The electronic computer is essential to many of these techniques. In fact, linear programming and simulation are topics requiring a computer for their conduct. The author views the computer as a tool necessary for the effective conduct of managerial analysis in the same sense as statistics or mathematics are necessary for managerial analysis. Since the computer, more than statistics and mathematics, is a facilitating tool, it is not discussed. At the same time, the author believes that the future analyst or manager cannot expect to function effectively without an adequate background in the use of the computer.

Further, the system which the managerial analyst is trying to model includes unpredictable human beings. An understanding of the human side of the organization is as essential a tool as the other tools. From the observation of this author, the behavioral scientist has been relatively unsuccessful in translating his knowledge of human behavior and its impact on the environment into operational terms. Admittedly, behavioral systems may be most complex. However, one often gets the feeling that the behavioral scientist has little desire to make his findings operational because of their probabilistic nature.

The section on models of complex systems may not properly convey the vast possibilities and scope of the topics presented. It is in these mod-

451

els that advancement of immediate significance to mankind is possible. The federal government has supported massive studies utilizing simulation and systems analysis. Unfortunately, the tremendous size of the system and the massive mechanics involved in these applications have overshadowed penetrating questions of validity. Further, the state of the art still limits the portrayal of dependencies between variables. However, the author believes that the models of complex processes will drastically improve both from the standpoint of evaluation techniques and from the standpoint of portraying dependencies between variables. Obviously, the mere process of recognizing all relevant variables and some elementary interrelationships has been a major advance in managerial analysis for complex systems.

This book has said very little of the place of the managerial analyst in the structure of the organization. We have pointed out that it is essential that there be three sources of projects: (1) the continuous monitor system containing performance standards, (2) requests by managers, and (3) projects initiated by the analyst. The appropriate place in the organization structure is a position which allows the analyst to carry out his charge properly. Since he can only function effectively with proper entry to managers and information sources throughout the firm, his position must be of sufficient importance to assure this entry.

This book has said very little about the source of data for managerial analysis. Many relationships cannot be ascertained because of the unavailability of data. Many organizations are moving toward total information systems. It is up to the managerial analyst to identify essential information which should be gathered in order to improve past, present, and future analysis. Further, he will want to see that the information system provides updated parameter values to operational models so that the decisions can be modified as necessary.

Also, a word should be said about the frequently cited team approach to operations analysis. Russell L. Ackoff and Patrick Rivett claim that one of the essential ingredients in operations research is the team approach.[1] This is justified by citing the difficulty any one individual has in removing himself from the biases his training and experience give him. An example of this bias is shown in the case of the slow elevator. Tenants were complaining about waiting for the elevator. The mathematicians and engineers investigated numerous ways to speed up service but could not find a solution. A psychologist viewed the problem differently and suggested that mirrors be installed so that the women could primp while waiting and the men could watch the women. Although this may illustrate the viewpoint of various analysts, it does not pinpoint the underlying char-

---

[1] Russell L. Ackoff and Patrick Rivett, *A Manager's Guide to Operations Research* (New York: John Wiley & Sons, Inc., 1963).

acteristic necessary for conducting managerial analysis, which is the ability to identify the system, model it, and derive a solution. Admittedly, the more balance on an analytical team, the better it can identify the system, model that system, and derive a solution. Thus the team approach is a useful and highly desirable means to the end.

This author believes that a good analytical group will include a balanced team. It becomes difficult to identify the ideal or even minimum members of such a team. However, two requisites seem universally necessary. One requisite is the ability to model. Obviously, this requires some mathematical preparation but more importantly the ability to translate the real world into the abstract world of mathematics. Hence, it is not the degree of mathematical training but what can be done with it that counts. The better the training, the more a capable person can do with it. The second requisite is the ability to understand the user's needs, problems, and viewpoint. Some companies feel that an undergraduate engineer with an MBA and training in management science or operations research comes closest to this set of characteristics. Some feel that a managerially oriented industrial engineering program provides these characteristics. There are some operations research programs which attempt to provide this set of characteristics. Obviously, some mathematicians have the first characteristic, and they obtain the second because of the nature of their personalities. Given these characteristics, the team is usually expanded to include members trained in the tool specialties and analytical specialties.

Finally, the Epilogue should review the scope of managerial analysis. We have said that managerial analysis assists the manager in making decisions as long as (1) the analysis recognizes organizational goals; (2) the analysis recognizes relationships between relevant variables; (3) the recommended course of action is explicit, verifiable, and independently reproducible; and (4) the recommended course of action uses an adaptation of the scientific method. One can add that the decision in question must be material. A restaurant owner does not need an analyst to decide what kind and quality of toilet paper to purchase, although a large chain may find the question material.

One real problem is to decide what constitutes a decision. When a top-level manager sets policy, does that constitute a decision? If so, can it be assisted by managerial analysis? When a top-level manager sets up a committee to study a problem, is that a decision? Forming a committee merely prolongs execution on the operational problem and cannot be considered a decision in this context. Setting policy, on the other hand, does not prolong execution, although execution is not possible without further decision making. In the case of policy the guidelines constitute a boundary within which the decision must be made. Whether the policy decision was assisted by managerial analysis depends on whether the previously stated characteristics are present.

Frequently, the student of business administration is asked to conduct case analysis. This often consists of a series of statements and data about a company's market performance. The data often contain market performance information about competitors. In question is the decision whether changes are necessary in the line of products carried by the firm. From the data at hand, it is impossible to construct a totally acceptable representation of the situation facing the company. Here the analysis obviously must recognize organizational goals. It should recognize relationships between relevant variables. Indeed, the essence of this approach is to hypothesize relationships. The frustrating part of the analysis is the lack of obvious or direct support for hypothesized relationships. Given the hypothesized but unsupportable relationships, the recommended course of action can be explicit, verifiable, and independently reproducible. As long as the analyst follows the tenets of the scientific method, he can meet the fourth characteristic. Unfortunately, all too infrequently the recommendation is made without any attempt to identify relationships, and thus the recommendation is not verifiable and independently reproducible. The point is that even policy decisions can be attacked by the managerial analyst, although the validity of his hypothesized relationships may seriously affect the usefulness of his recommendations. From a practical standpoint, the managerial analyst will want to avoid analytical efforts which string together a series of unsupported or poorly supported relationships.

Index

Index

This book has been set in 10 and 9 point Janson leaded 2 points. Section and chapter titles are 16 point Helvetica Medium. Section numbers are 12 point Helvetica Bold. Chapter numbers are 18 point Helvetica Medium. The size of the type page is 27 by 45½ picas.